Concepts in
Biology

Concepts in
Biology

Eldon D. Enger
Andrew H. Gibson
J. Richard Kormelink
Frederick C. Ross
Rodney J. Smith

Delta College
*University Center,
Michigan*

Wm. C. Brown Company Publishers wcb
Dubuque, Iowa

Copyright © 1976 by Wm. C. Brown Company Publishers

Library of Congress Catalog Card Number: 75–17422

ISBN 0–697–04540–4

Fifth Printing, 1978

Printed in the United States of America

Contents

1

The More You Know, the More You Can Do   1

Biological Questions—food production / genetic diseases / penicillin resistance / chemicals and farming. *Organization of the book*—an informed populace / from chemistry to evolution.

2

What Is Biology?   9

The Difference Between Science and Nonscience—astronomer vs. astrologer / constructing rules / scientists testing rules. *Different Kinds of Science*—defining science / applied and theoretical science. *Characteristics of Living Things*—defining death? / the structure of living things / metabolism / responsiveness / evolution / reproduction. *What Is Biology?*—practical vs. theoretical. *The Value of Biological Study*—food production / improved health. *Biological Problems*—forest fires may be good / introduction of exotics. *The Future of Biology*—population control / genetic diseases / ecology.

3

The Simple Stuff of Life   27

Basic Structures—elements. *The Atom and Its Structure*—atomic number / isotopes / mass number / radioactive isotopes. *Molecular Structure*—compounds / chemical bonds / covalent bonds / ions / ionic bonds / hydrogen bonds. *Acids and Bases*—acids / hydrogen ions / bases / hydroxyl ion / pH numbers. *Chemical Reactions*—changing chemical bonds / energy changes / reversibility of reactions / dehydration synthesis / hydrolysis. *Energy*—first law of thermodynamics / kinds of energy / energy conversion / second law of thermodynamics / states of matter / molecular motion.

4

Some Not So Simple Stuff of Life   43

The Chemistry of Life—inorganic materials / organic materials. *Carbon Is the Central Atom*—long carbon chains / carbon forms 4 bonds / the double bond / macromolecules / variety of organic molecules / chemical formula / structural formula. *Common Organic Molecules*—carbohydrates / simple and complex sugars / lipids / proteins / nucleic acids.

Contents

Preface

The origin of this book is deeply rooted in our concern for the learning of students enrolled in college biology courses. Since a textbook is likely to be one of the more important aids to student learning, we have long felt that it should be written for the student. To this end, we have attempted to write a book that students will be able to use—one that will be interesting to them. Many examples and analogies are used to help put some complicated ideas into plain language. Our purpose in writing this book is two-fold. We think it is very important that students have fun while learning about some of the *concepts in biology,* and we hope to stimulate a continuing interest in biology.

Many individuals have knowingly or unknowingly helped us write this text. First of all, we acknowledge our wives and families for their understanding while we spent so much more time with each other, than with them. Secondly, we acknowledge the thousands of students in our classes, who over the years have given us feedback concerning the material and its relevancy. They were the best possible source of criticism. We acknowledge the work of John H. Standing, Delaware Valley College; Michael J. Timmons, Moraine Valley Community College; Albert J. Gennan, San Diego Mesa College; Gil Desha, Tarrant County Junior College; Robert P. Ouellett, Massasoit Community College; Ernest L. Rhamstine, Valencia Community College; Rhoda Love, formerly of Lane Community College; Don Misumi, Los Angeles Trade-Technical College who critically reviewed each chapter and gave so many valuable suggestions. The artistic quality of many of the illustrations are due to the excellent work of our biological illustrator Margaret Brudon. Special mention is made of Ray Deveaux, whose knowledge and experience in editing science textbooks made this project possible. And finally we thank Marilyn Plowdrey, who typed the entire manuscript, and Mary Meier who gave us the hundred-and-one assistances that only a secretary can.

To the Student

A number of things that are a part of the construction of the text are designed to make understanding biological principles easier. At the beginning of each chapter (except chapter one) is a section entitled *purpose*. This section gives you some hints about how the chapter fits in with the other parts of the book. It is a signpost that directs you to where you are going and lets you know why you are going there. If you pay careful attention to the purpose, you can tell when you have attained your goal, and you will be able to gain some insight into why this goal was set.

Each chapter is subdivided into topics separated by topical headings. These subdivisions are not chosen by chance, but are logical chunks of material. These subdivisions should make learning more manageable for you.

As is the case with most science classes, you are likely to find biological vocabulary a hurdle that is difficult to jump. To prevent you from becoming unduly discouraged as you approach this "foreign language," the first time an important term is used in the text it is printed in **boldface.** The terms printed in this manner should become a flag for you. Each of these *new terms* is defined for you at least three times in the text: first, in the narrative when the term becomes a functional part of biological thought; second, in the chapter glossary at the end of the chapter in which it first appears; and third, in the total glossary at the end of the book. As you review a chapter, you should mentally define each of the new terms for yourself. If you are unsure of the meaning of these terms, you can check yourself against the definitions in the book.

There are a number of illustrations throughout the text. These illustrations should do more than just attract your attention. Each has been chosen carefully to help you understand a point or to help you tie a point to something you already know. Use these illustrations and their captions to help you learn and understand the ideas presented.

Each chapter ends with a summary. As you finish your study of a chapter, read the summary sentence-by-sentence. Make sure that there is no new information in the summary. If something is new to you, it is because you have not thoroughly digested part of the chapter.

Finally, at the end of the chapter we have presented a thought-provoking situation. This allows you to use your newfound knowledge, and to place all of your previous experience to bear on the situation. Most often, there is no one right answer. It is a device that can stimulate you to think something through, and to raise points for discussion. One of the most valuable aspects of an introductory biology course is not the tidbits of factual information that you gather, but the new way in which you see yourself and your environment. We hope these thought stimulators will give you practice in using biological information and allow you to apply basic biological concepts to real life situations.

Following each thought-provoking situation, there are a series of review questions. These questions can be used in a variety of ways: you might use them to help channel your attention as you study a chapter, or as a review to tell you when you are well prepared for a test over the chapter material. Each of these questions is directly answered in the chapter narrative or in the illustrations.

Concepts in
Biology

Purpose This chapter is intended to be a general introduction to the significance of biology to your everyday life. It also presents some questions that you will be better able to consider after you have completed the course. The general philosophy and organization of the book are also presented.

The More You Know, the More You Can Do

Will you have enough food to eat twenty years from now? What are the chances that you will have a genetically abnormal child? When will a cure for cancer be developed? Will the current increase in ecological awareness continue? Is it safe to pick and eat an apple?

These questions are being raised more frequently today than ever before. Like the many other pertinent questions being asked, they are based on biological principles. There are no easy answers. There are, however, informed ways of looking at problems and arriving at solutions (fig. 1.1). Because you are a living thing, you are involved in these problems and may be a part of their solution.

Food for Thought

Let's go back and take a closer look at some of these questions. Will you have enough food to eat twenty years from now? Your first reaction to this question may be, how much is enough (fig. 1.2)? Do we eat to live, or do we live to eat! A diet consisting of three thousand calories per day may support your bodily

Fig. 1.1 *One Problem and Its Solution.* The solution to this problem is easier if you know that donkeys like carrots.

PROBLEM

ANALYSIS OF THE PROBLEM

SOLUTION OF THE PROBLEM

Fig. 1.2 *Soil Management.*
These two photos illustrate how differences in farming practices can alter the landscape. The wind erosion shown on the top was a result of poor farming practices and drought. (Courtesy of USDA—Soil Conservation Service.)

functions, but if it's the same food day after day, will it satisfy your psychological need to eat? Different cultures have different food habits. A good meal is beef to Americans, caterpillars to Australian aboriginals, rice and fish to Chinese, and blubber to Eskimos. Food that is acceptable to a family in Chicago may be quite different from that of an Australian aboriginal family, and yet the food value may be very similar. Twenty years from now, there will be more people and consequently less food per person. We cannot expect food production to increase as it has in the past. If the number of hungry increase enough, will they demand food from those who have more? Will there be anyone who can afford to share what he has?

Chapter 1

Diabetes, sickle-cell anemia, and farsightedness are all abnormalities that originate in the genetic information systems of living cells. Some of these abnormalities just create inconveniences, forcing you to watch your diet or wear glasses. Others may cause extreme discomfort or early death. While some of these problems are routinely treated by doctors, others are more serious and can merely be diagnosed (fig. 1.3). Perhaps the only absolute advice a doctor can give is not to have any children, since they will probably inherit the same problem.

Penicillin, the wonder drug of World War II, has been used to combat many diseases. Its use became so commonplace that whenever you coughed, you ran to the doctor for a shot. When first used, penicillin was very effective in killing many disease-causing bacteria. Because some bacteria have become tolerant to penicillin and are no longer affected by this drug, penicillin is not the wonder drug we once thought it was.

At the turn of the century about 50 percent of all Americans lived on farms. When a family was having apple pie, the tree in the backyard was the

Fig. 1.3 *Doctor-Patient Interaction.* Doctors are able to advise patients on how some diseases may be controlled. (Courtesy of the American Medical Association.)

source of the apples. Since a family could eat only a limited number of pies and the tree had hundreds of apples, only the best were used. Now only about 2 percent of the people in the United States are farmers. They grow apples and other foods for the rest of the population. They cannot afford to have pests damage the apples on their trees because people will not buy them. So with the use of chemical sprays to control pests, the apple supply increases and the cost of the fruit decreases (fig. 1.4). But the spray is consumed by anyone who eats the apples. In a world where people are clamoring for more food, can we afford not to spray our crops even though these chemicals may cause us harm in the long run?

What's Behind It All?

Everyone should be aware that such problems exist. Your future is closely tied to how these and other biological problems are solved. As an informed citizen in a democracy, you can have a great deal to say about the solutions to these problems. In a democracy it is assumed that the public is informed enough to make intelligent decisions. This is why an understanding of biological concepts is so important for any individual regardless of his vocation. *Concepts in Biology* was written with this philosophy in mind. The concepts covered in this book were selected to help you become more aware of how biology influences nearly every aspect of your life.

Most learning follows a certain pattern. You began to learn to communicate ideas a long time ago. Progressively, you learned to make basic sounds, form words, speak in sentences, and communicate abstract ideas. Learning includes a number of such steps, all of which have been built upon previous steps to provide the foundation for future learning. You constantly expand and build your knowledge on the more basic information. The same thing is true of biology. There are certain underlying ideas that you must understand before you can see the whole picture. These ideas need to be approached in an orderly fashion. In biology, the most basic ideas deal with chemical activities, and you will need to make this your first step. Chemistry is presented in chapters three and four. Just as you had to make sounds before you could make conversation, a knowledge of chemistry is necessary before you can really understand the biological concepts presented later in this book (fig. 1.5). Speech was worth the effort; hopefully, you will also find the understanding of chemistry to be worth this first step.

Once you have gained the knowledge of chemical activity, you will be ready to take the next step in which you will be introduced to cells and some of the important things they do. Because organisms are composed of cells, it is logical to study the structure and function of cells before studying organisms and how they interact with each other.

The characteristics of cells and organisms are determined by the chemical code system found in the cells. Any change in this code system could result in differences that separate one kind of organism from another. An under-

Fig. 1.4 *Crop Dusting.* The application of pesticides by airplane is possible in some situations. (Courtesy of Shell Chemical Company.)

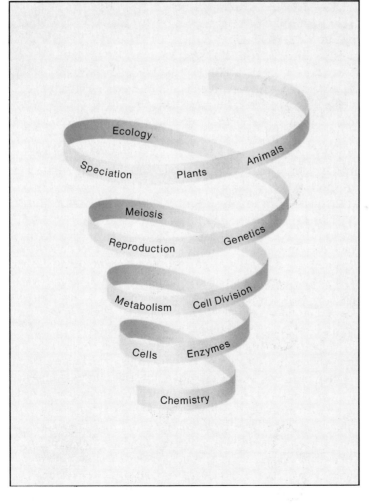

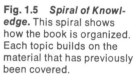

Fig. 1.5 *Spiral of Knowledge.* This spiral shows how the book is organized. Each topic builds on the material that has previously been covered.

Ecology

Speciation   Plants   Animals

Meiosis

Reproduction   Genetics

Metabolism   Cell Division

Cells   Enzymes

Chemistry

Fig. 1.6 *Interactions Between Populations.* Living systems are very complex and interrelated. The grass population influences the population of deer, and they in turn influence the cougar population.

standing of individual organisms is necessary, since individuals of the same kind make up a population. One of the fascinating characteristics of a population is how the group reacts with other populations. For example, a population of deer interacts with plant populations by feeding upon them. The deer are in turn eaten by cougars (fig. 1.6). The study of such interactions leads us to the field of ecology.

This book and its organization progress from the basic to the complex: from chemical structure to cells, organisms, populations, communities, ecosystems, and finally to the evolution of various kinds of organisms. Each segment of the book is built on the foundation of the preceding chapters. You may wish to reshuffle the chapters slightly in your study. For instance, chapter five, "The Origin and Evolution of Cells," may be covered before or after chapter six, "Cell History, Structure, and Function." However, the material covered in chapter ten, "Information Systems," and eleven, "Mitosis," assumes some knowledge of cellular structure covered in chapter six. Many questions are raised throughout the text and at the end of each chapter. Answers to these questions can be arrived at by relying on the material presented within the chapters.

In addition, at the end of each chapter we have presented a situation that requires some thought. Generally, these questions will help you tie the "big picture" together. Use all the knowledge you have gained from the instructor, laboratory, text, and your own experiences to help you organize your thoughts concerning these questions.

The problems raised at the beginning of this chapter are points of vital concern to your future life. They really do not have a single right answer or best solution. Each question involves a certain amount of compromise between what society wants and what your biological self must have. Each of the questions is so complex that few individuals can see the "whole picture." They are questions that need input from various points of view, considerable thought, compromise, and active work on the part of many persons in order for acceptable solutions to be reached. Furthermore, what we may consider to be an acceptable solution to a problem today may be totally unacceptable in the future as we gain more knowledge and are better able to understand the nature of living things.

Purpose The first chapter presented a number of broad questions that the rest of this book may help you to answer. The answers themselves are not easy, and there may be a number of different answers for each of the questions asked. This chapter will begin laying the groundwork to help you answer these questions. It will introduce you to a scientist's view of the world and begin to describe what living things are and how they differ from nonliving things.

What Is Biology?

2

Science and Nonscience

You probably have some idea that **biology** has something to do with plants and animals. You probably also recognize it as a **science** of some kind. Most textbooks would define biology as the science that deals with the study of **life.** This appears to be a very nice little definition until you begin to think about what the words *science* and *life* mean.

Science is the study or collection of knowledge in an orderly fashion. The information (fact) is collected and the scientist uses certain rules to help him place these facts into a framework that makes sense. Rules, laws, and principles are developed as scientists begin to see patterns or relationships among a number of isolated facts. Some of the rules are very old while others are being constructed today. It is the method of collecting information and the way in which it is organized that makes something a science. In some cases, the same knowledge may be used in both scientific and nonscientific areas of study. Probably one of the best examples of this is the difference between **astronomy,** which is a science, and **astrology,** which is not a science. These studies make use of some of the same information. Both astronomers and astrologers observe the sun, moon, and stars, and chart their positions, movements, and interactions. The astronomer makes measurements and other observations, and organizes all of this information according to physical laws, such as the law of gravity. In other words, he simply observes what is happening and uses various physical laws to organize the information, so that it makes sense as a collection of information. Science seeks to simplify millions of bits of information by the use of a few basic rules or laws. The laws and rules are continually tested by the addition of new bits of information. If the new information can fit into the framework constructed, it is really a reinforcement of the framework.

The astrologer looks at the same sun, moon, and stars and also develops rules about how these celestial bodies relate to one another. However, these rules cannot be tested for accuracy. As a matter of fact, an astrologer is usually not very interested in having his rules challenged or tested and usually writes them so that they cannot be tested. An astrologer's basic rule is that the various celestial bodies control the progress of human events. No information can be collected that consistently supports this basic rule.

Just because scientists say something is true does not necessarily make it true. Everyone makes mistakes, and quite often as new information is gathered, old rules, which once seemed to be valid, must be changed or discarded. For example, at one time people were sure that the sun went around the earth. Their observations showed the sun rising in the east and traveling across the sky to set in the west. Since people could not feel the earth moving, it seemed perfectly logical that the sun must travel around the earth. Once people understood that the earth actually rotated on its axis, they began to understand that the rising and setting of the sun could be explained in other ways. A completely new concept of the relationship between the sun and the earth developed (fig. 2.1).

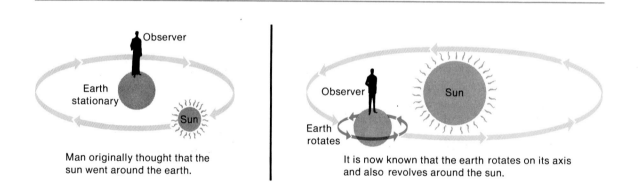

Man originally thought that the sun went around the earth.

It is now known that the earth rotates on its axis and also revolves around the sun.

Fig. 2.1 *Knowledge Changes.* Man's understanding of the relationship between the earth and the sun has changed considerably as more information has been gained.

This kind of study seems rather primitive to us today, since man has actually travelled through space, to the moon, and back again. At one time, this change in thinking was a very important step in understanding the universe and how the various parts were related to one another. This was the necessary background information that was built upon by many generations of astronomers and space scientists, and that finally led to space travel.

So the difference between science and nonscience is not always clear. The differences are often based on the assumptions and methods used to gather and organize information and most importantly, the testing of assumptions. The difference between a scientist and a nonscientist is based on the fact that a scientist continually tests his principles and rules, whereas a nonscientist may not feel that this is important (fig. 2.2).

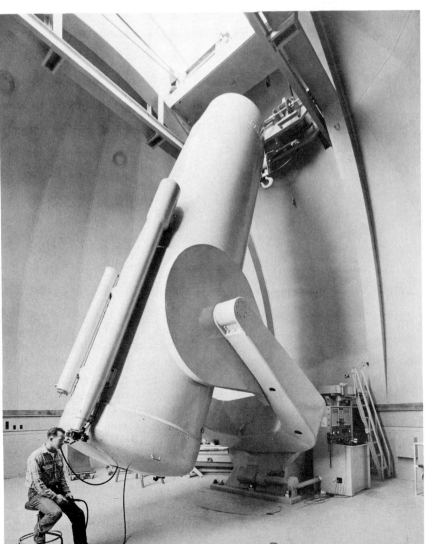

What Kinds of Sciences Are There?

Now that you have some idea of the difference between science and non-science, let's explore some of the various areas of science. We don't have any trouble identifying chemistry, physics, biology, and astronomy as sciences; but what about economics, sociology, anthropology, history, philosophy, and literature. All of these fields may make use of certain laws that are derived in a logical way, but they also have some components that cannot be scientific. Some things are beyond science and cannot be approached from a scientific point of view. Just because a field of study is not a science doesn't mean that it lacks value. Those fields of study dependent primarily on human emotion, such as art, literature, theology, and philosophy are rarely thought of as being sciences. Studies such as physics, chemistry, geology, and biology are almost always considered to be sciences. Other areas of study are in a middle ground, where scientific approaches may be used to some extent. Music is a good example of this. What is "good" music is certainly unrelated to science, but the study of how a guitar or horn makes a sound is certainly based on the scientific laws of physics. Any serious student of music will study sound waves and how they are produced by vibrating strings. Table 2.1 illustrates several fields of study and how they are generally classified.

Table 2.1 *Science and Nonscience*
What is science? This table shows some traditional fields of study and how they are generally classified.

Definitely science		Definitely not science
Geology	History Psychology	Astrology
Chemistry	Music	Theology
Physics	Economics	Literature
Biology	Sociology	
Astronomy	Political science	
Geography	Anthropology	

We can also divide science into theoretical and applied fields of study. A farmer is an applied scientist. He uses scientific principles to get the best yields from his farm. A doctor is an applied scientist, too, because his primary interest is to keep people healthy through the use of scientific knowledge. The theoretical scientist does not have in mind any specific use for the new knowledge he gains. He is interested in obtaining new information and seeing how it fits the "old laws," and he will write "new laws" if they are necessary.

Fig. 2.3 *Knowledge Accumulates.* Copernicus and space exploration are related to one another. Copernicus was one of the first people to develop the theory that the earth goes around the sun. The scientists who designed the spacecraft made use of this and many other theories in a practical way to help them design the spacecraft. (Rocket photograph courtesy of NASA.)

Are the practical and theoretical scientists related in any way? They certainly are, since applied scientists almost always make use of the theories provided by the theoretical scientists. For example, the design and manufacture of the various kinds of space vehicles over the last few years is applied science, but it could not have been made possible without the prior knowledge of the law of gravity (fig. 2.3).

Louis Pasteur was interested in the theoretical problem of whether life could be generated from nonliving material. Much of his theoretical work led to very practical applications. His theory that there were very small organisms that caused diseases and decay led to the development of vaccinations against certain diseases and the preservation of foods by pasteurization (fig. 2.4).

Fig. 2.4 *Louis Pasteur and Pasteurized Milk.* Louis Pasteur performed many experiments while he studied the question of the origin of life. This led directly to food preservation methods. (Photo of Pasteur courtesy of The Bettmann Archive.)

What Is Life?

At the beginning of this chapter, biology was defined as the science that deals with the study of living things. But what is life? You would think that a biology textbook could be able to answer this question very easily. However, this question is more than just a theoretical one, since it has become necessary in recent years to construct some legal definitions of what life is, and when it begins and ends. The legal definition of death is important, since it may help determine whether or not a person will receive life insurance benefits or if body parts may be used in transplants. In the case of heart transplants, the person donating the heart may be "dead" but his heart certainly isn't, because it can be removed from the "dead" person while the heart still has "life." The heart will remain alive for some time inside the recipient. In other words, there are different kinds of death. There is death that the whole living unit experiences and death that each cell within the living unit experiences. A person actually "dies" before every cell has died. Death, then, is the absence of life; but that still doesn't tell us what life is. At this point we won't try to define life, but will list some of the basic characteristics of living things. Once you understand some of the characteristics that living things show, it may help you to understand what life is.

Characteristics of Living Things

Living things are structurally different from matter that was never alive. This is true at a chemical level, and you will learn that these chemicals are organized into larger structural units. In chapter four you will see that the chemistry of living things is different from the chemistry of nonliving things. Chapter six will talk about the basic structural unit of life. This basic structure, called the cell, is found only in things that are alive or were alive at one time. A cell is a basic unit used to build larger organisms. The cells are basically similar in all kinds of living organisms and may be specialized for particular jobs. Things that were never alive do not show a cellular structure.

A second characteristic that life exhibits is a need for a constant supply of energy, which can be used for such activities as movement, growth, and getting food. The energy is used through a complex series of chemical changes commonly called **metabolism.** For example, a green plant may receive sunlight energy, which is converted into the energy in sugar molecules, which can then be converted to additional parts of the plant as it grows.

A third characteristic that living things show is an ability to respond to changes in their surroundings. This is easily seen when animals respond to changes in light intensity, sound, touch, and other kinds of changes. It is not quite as easy to see this in plants, but they also respond to changes. You are aware that certain trees in northern climates lose their leaves in the fall of the year. This usually happens at about the time that the first few frosts occur. However, if you take those same trees and move them to an area where there is no frost, they will probably still lose their leaves because they will still react to the change in the length of day. In other words, they can detect that the days are getting shorter.

A fourth characteristic that living things possess is the ability to change slowly over millions of years so that they are still able to cope with their surroundings, which have also undergone change. This slow change is called **evolution** and it is covered in detail in later chapters.

Finally, living things show the ability to manufacture more individuals like themselves. In many ways **reproduction** is one of the most important characteristics of life because it is the only way that new living beings are created today. The process of reproduction is so important that plants and animals use much of their energy in this process. The production of seeds by a plant or the care and feeding of young by parents requires large amounts of energy.

Table 2.2 summarizes these characteristics of life. Much of the rest of the book will expand on these characteristics of life. Perhaps at the end of this book you will be able to write a definition of what life is.

Table 2.2 *Characteristics of Life*
Living and nonliving things differ in a number of ways. Some of these differences are shown here.

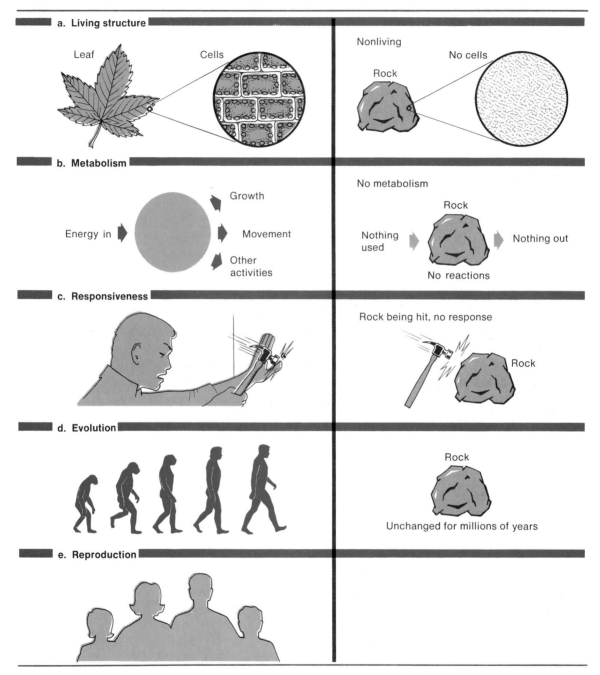

a. **Living structure**

Leaf   Cells

Nonliving   No cells

Rock

b. **Metabolism**

Energy in   Growth   Movement   Other activities

No metabolism

Rock

Nothing used   Nothing out

No reactions

c. **Responsiveness**

Rock being hit, no response

Rock

d. **Evolution**

Rock

Unchanged for millions of years

e. **Reproduction**

The metric system will be used throughout this book. This table lists the common metric units and their English equivalents.

	Basic Measure	Units	Value	English Equivalent
Length	meter (m)			39.4 inches
		kilometer (km)	1000 m	0.621 miles
		centimeter (cm)	.01 m	0.394 inches
		millimeter (mm)	.001 m	0.0394 inches
		micrometer (μm)	.000001 m	
Mass	gram (g)			0.035 ounces
		kilogram (kg)	1000 g	2.2 pounds
		milligram (mg)	.001 g	
		microgram (μgm)	.000001 g	
Volume	liter (l)			1.06 quarts
		milliliter (ml)	.001 l	

Now What Is Biology?

The science of biology is a broad one. It draws on chemistry and physics for its foundation and applies these basic physical laws to living things. Because there are millions of kinds of living things, there is a very large number of special study areas in biology. Practical biology—like medicine, agriculture, plant breeding, and dentistry—is balanced by more theoretical biology—evolutionary biology, molecular genetics, and just plain fun biology like insect-collecting and bird-watching. Biology then is a science that deals with living things and how they interact with all of the things around them (fig. 2.5).

What Good Is Biology?

Much of our current standard of living we owe to biological advances in two areas, food production and disease control. Plant and animal breeders have been able to develop plants and animals that provide better sources of food than the original variety. Probably one of the best examples of this is the various changes that have occurred in corn. Corn is a grass that produces its seeds on a cob. The original corn plant had very small ears, which were perhaps only three or four centimeters long.

Through selective breeding, varieties of corn with much larger ears and more seeds per cob have been produced. This has increased the yield greatly. In addition, the same basic plant has been adapted to produce other kinds of corn, like sweet corn and popcorn. Corn isn't an isolated example. Improve-

Fig. 2.5 *Biological Activities.* All of these activities are being carried out by biologists (Courtesy of Robert Fleming, Photographer.)

19

ments in yield have been brought about in wheat, oats, rice, and other cereal grains. The improvements in the plants along with changed farming practices (also brought about because of biological experimentation) have led to greatly increased production of food (fig. 2.6 *a*).

Animal breeders have also had some great successes. The pig, chicken, and cow of today are much different animals than were available even one-hundred years ago. Chickens lay more eggs, dairy cows give more milk, and beef cattle grow faster (fig. 2.6 *b*). All of these improvements raise our standard of living. One interesting change involves the kinds of hogs that are raised. At one time, farmers wanted pigs that were fat. The fat could be made into lard, soap, or a variety of other useful products. As the demand for the fat products of pigs began to decline, animal breeders began to develop pigs

Fig. 2.6 *Food Production Increases.* Both of these graphs illustrate a steady increase in the yield. A large part of this increase is the result of changing farming practices and selective breeding programs.

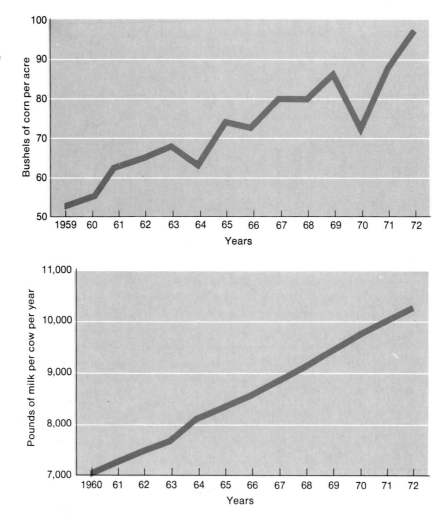

that gave a high yield of meat and relatively little fat. Today, plant and animal breeders can just about make plants and animals to specifications.

Much of the improvement in food production has resulted from the control of those plants and animals that compete with the organisms we use as food. The control of insects and fungi that weaken plants and reduce yields is as important as the invention of new varieties of plants. Since these pests are also alive, various biological studies have been involved in developing an understanding of these pests.

In the area of health and disease control, there has been fantastic progress. Many diseases such as polio, whooping cough, measles, smallpox, and others can be easily controlled by vaccinations or "shots." Unfortunately, the vaccines have worked so well that some people no longer worry about getting their shots and we are beginning to see the reappearance of some of these diseases. These various diseases have not been eliminated, and people who are not protected by vaccinations are still susceptible to these diseases.

The understanding of how the human body works has led to many kinds of treatments that can control diseases such as diabetes, high blood pressure, and even some kinds of cancer. But in the health field, these advances contribute to a major biological problem: the increasing size of the human population.

Biological Boo Boo's

Now that you have seen some progress that can be laid at the door of biologists, let's look at some of the problems that have been created by improperly used biological principles. The drive to preserve nature has in some cases

---

Box II

Edward Jenner first developed the technique of vaccination in 1795. This was the result of a twenty-six year study of two diseases, cowpox and smallpox. Cowpox was known as *vaccinae,* and it was from this word that the present terms *vaccination* and *vaccine* have evolved. Jenner observed that milkmaids rarely became sick with smallpox, but they developed pocklike sores after milking cows infected with cowpox. This led him to perform an experiment in which he transferred puslike material from the cowpock to human skin. Since the two disease organisms are so closely related, the person vaccinated with cowpox developed an immunity to the smallpox virus as well. The reaction to cowpox was minor in comparison to the more serious smallpox. Public reaction was mixed. Some people thought that the process of vaccination was a work of the devil. But many European rulers supported Jenner by encouraging their subjects to be vaccinated. Napoleon, and the Empress of Russia were very influential, and in the United States Thomas Jefferson had a number of his family vaccinated.

done more harm than good. Many of our western forests have been preserved as parks. In order to preserve the trees, fire was not allowed in these forests. The lack of fire has led to a buildup of debris that makes the situation even worse (fig. 2.7). Before man's involvement, these forests normally had been exposed to fire. The fire cleaned out the debris and helped to preserve the trees from more intense fires. The periodic natural fires also eliminated species of trees that were not desired. Man's intentions might have been good, but he should have looked at the natural situation before he started to tinker around with things. A whole generation of people have grown up with the idea that all fires in forests are bad. Didn't Smokey the Bear tell us so? We are beginning to recognize that in certain cases forest fires may do more good than harm. The original concept that all forest fires are bad is false and resulted from oversimplified thinking. Now a whole generation needs to be convinced that some forest fires may be good (fig. 2.8).

A second major biological mistake has involved the introduction of exotic (foreign) species of plants and animals for a variety of reasons. In the United States, this has had disastrous consequences in a number of cases. Both the American chestnut and the American elm have been nearly eliminated by diseases that were introduced by accident. These are probably excusable, since they were accidental introductions. However, other things have been introduced on purpose, which just shows shortsightedness or a total lack of understanding about biology. The starling and the English sparrow were both introduced into this country by people who thought that they were doing good. Both of these birds have multiplied greatly and replaced some of the birds that were native to the United States. Even with these examples before us, we still find people who try to sneak exotic plants and animals into the country without thinking about the possible consequences of their actions.

Biological Frontiers

Where do we go from here? Many problems remain to be solved. Major breakthroughs in the control of the human population are being sought. There is a continued interest in the development of more efficient methods of producing food.

One of the major areas that will receive interest in the next few years will be the relationship between genetic information and diseases, such as high blood pressure, stroke, arthritis, and cancer. There are many kinds of diseases that are caused by abnormal body chemistry. These changes are the result of hereditary characteristics. The problem of curing certain hereditary diseases is a big job. It requires a complete understanding of genetics and the introduction or subtraction of hereditary information from all of the trillions of cells of the organism.

Fig. 2.7 *Fire Hazard.* This forest has so much litter on the forest floor that a fire could get started that could destroy the whole forest. (Courtesy of USDA—Soil Conservation Service—photo by Elmer Turnage.)

Fig. 2.8 *Changing Attitudes.* Smokey the Bear campaigns resulted from oversimplified thinking. In some cases, forest fires may be valuable.

Another area that will receive more attention in the next few years is the field of ecology. The energy crisis is real; pollution is still a problem; and the majority of people still need to learn that some environmental changes may be acceptable, whereas other changes will ultimately lead to our own destruction. The task here may be divided into two segments. The first involves improved technology and a better understanding of how things work in our biological world. The second is probably the hardest and involves educating, pressuring, and reminding people that their actions determine the kind of world we will have in the next generation.

Summary The science of biology involves the study of living things and how they interact with their surroundings. Science and nonscience can be distinguished by the kinds of laws and rules that are constructed to unify the body of knowledge. If the rules are not testable or if no rules are used, it is not science. Science involves the continuous testing of rules and principles by the collection of new facts. Living things show the characteristics of (1) specific structure; (2) controlled chemical reactions that result in energy changes, growth, and movement; (3) an ability to react to changes in their surroundings; (4) an ability to produce more organisms like themselves; and (5) an ability to change slowly and permanently to fit in with slow changes of their surroundings. Biology has been responsible for some of the major, practical advances of mankind in the areas of food production and health. The incorrect use of biological principles can also lead to such severe problems as elimination of useful organisms and the destruction. of organisms we wish to preserve. The future work in biology involves many kinds of study, but two that are sure to receive attention are the relationship between heredity and disease, and a better understanding of ecological principles.

Consider This Many television commercials claim that their products have undergone strict scientific experimentation to prove them worth their purchase price. What kinds of tests must have been done in order to make their statements true, and what more do you need to know to evaluate the truth of their claims?

1. What is biology?
2. What is the difference between science and nonscience? Give examples.
3. Why is testing so important in science?
4. What is the difference between pure science and applied science? Give examples.
5. List five characteristics of living things.
6. List three advances that have occurred as a result of the study of biology.
7. List three mistakes that could have been avoided had we known more about living things.

astrology   The study of the stars and planets and how they influence human events.

astronomy   The scientific study of the structure and activities of the stars, planets, and other heavenly bodies.

biology   The study of life.

evolution   The slow change in living things so that they can cope with changes in their environment over many generations.

life   (Has never been satisfactorily defined.)

metabolism   All of the series of complex chemical reactions within a living thing.

reproduction   The ability to produce more organisms like oneself.

science   A study or collection of knowledge in an orderly fashion.

Purpose In order to understand the structure and activities of living organisms, it is necessary to know something about the materials from which they are made. In this chapter we will discuss the structure of matter, and the energy it contains. As you read this chapter, you should consciously try to build a vocabulary that will help you describe matter.

The Simple Stuff of Life

3

The Smallest Pieces

All the matter you can think of—the sidewalk, water, and air—is made up of one or more types of substances called **elements.** You already know the names of some of these elements: oxygen, iron, aluminum, silver, carbon, and gold. Elements can be divided into smaller pieces. The smallest piece of an element is an **atom.** The atom is constructed of a central region called the **nucleus,** which is surrounded by smaller parts that fly around it at certain distances (fig. 3.1). The nucleus is composed of two types of particles, **neutrons** and **protons.** The particles flying around the nucleus are called **electrons.** Neutrons have no electrical charge, protons have a positive electrical charge, and electrons have a negative charge. An atom has an equal number of protons and electrons, so the number of positive charges equals the number of negative charges. This means that atoms have no overall electrical charge.

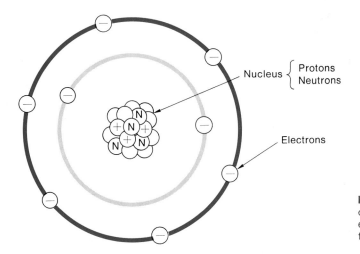

Fig. 3.1 *Oxygen Atom.* An oxygen atom is composed of eight protons, eight neutrons, and eight electrons.

The atoms of each kind of element have a specific number of protons. For example, oxygen always has eight protons, and no other element has that number. Carbon always has six protons. The **atomic number** of an element is based on the total number of protons in an atom of that element; therefore, each element has a different atomic number. Since oxygen has eight protons, its atomic number is eight. Looking at it from another point of view, since nitrogen has the atomic number seven, you can conclude that nitrogen has seven electrons because you know that the number of electrons and protons are the same (table 3.1).

Table 3.1   *Table of Protons and Electrons*

Elements		No. of Protons = (+) Atomic No.	No. of Electrons = (−)
Carbon	(C)	6	6
Nitrogen	(N)	7	7
Oxygen	(O)	8	8
Sodium	(Na)	11	11
Phosphorus	(P)	15	15
Chlorine	(Cl)	17	17
Potassium	(K)	19	19
Calcium	(Ca)	20	20

Although atoms of the same element have the same number of protons, they don't always have the same number of neutrons. In the case of oxygen, over 99 percent of the atoms will have eight neutrons, but there will be others with more or less than this number. These atoms of the same element that differ only in the number of neutrons they contain are called **isotopes.** The **mass number** of an atom is customarily used to compare different isotopes of the same element. The mass number is found by adding the number of neutrons and protons in the particular atom you are considering. Therefore, you can speak of an isotope of oxygen with a mass number of sixteen, or another isotope of oxygen with a mass number of seventeen (fig. 3.2). Can you state the number of neutrons that each of these oxygen atoms will have in its nucleus?

Since isotopes differ in their structure, you may expect that some isotopes will show characteristics that are different from the most common form of the element. For example, there are two isotopes of iodine, ^{127}I is the most common isotope and has a mass number of 127. ^{131}I differs in mass

NUCLEI

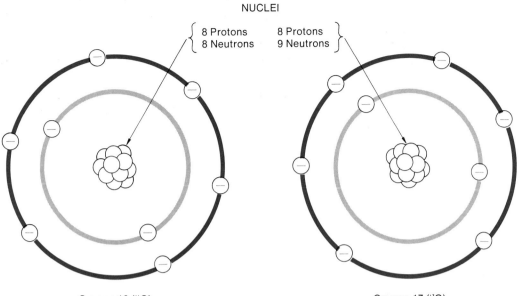

{ 8 Protons
8 Neutrons

8 Protons
9 Neutrons }

Oxygen 16 (^{16}O)   Oxygen 17 (^{17}O)

number and it is also **radioactive.** Radioactive isotopes are unstable and break down into smaller atoms. The radioactive isotope of iodine releases an amount of energy large enough to be recognized as a change on photographic film or a Geiger counter. If a doctor suspects that one of his patients has an improperly working **thyroid gland,** he may use ^{131}I to help confirm his guess. The thyroid normally collects iodine atoms from the blood, and this iodine is used in the manufacture of the body-regulating chemical **thyroxin.** If the thyroid gland is working properly to form thyroxin, the radioactive iodine will collect in the gland and its presence can be detected. If no iodine is found, this will indicate that the gland is not functioning correctly, and the doctor can take steps to help the patient.

Fig. 3.2 *Two Isotopes of Oxygen.* Note that they differ in the number of neutrons.

Big Ones from Little Ones

Many atoms can combine with each other to form **molecules.** For example, oxygen atoms combine with iron atoms to form molecules of rust. Molecules are units of matter made up of two or more atoms. When molecules are composed of atoms from different kinds of elements, these combinations are called **compounds.** Salt, water, and carbon dioxide are all compounds (fig. 3.3).

The forces that combine atoms together in molecules are called **chemical bonds.** Chemical bonds can vary in strength. Three kinds of chemical bonds are **covalent bonds, ionic bonds,** and **hydrogen bonds.** The covalent bond is formed by two atoms that share a pair of electrons. Figure 3.4 shows the

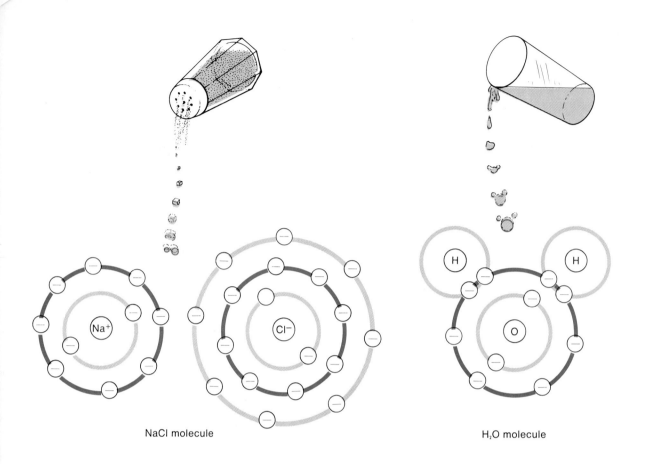

NaCl molecule   H₂O molecule

Fig. 3.3 *Some Common Inorganic Compounds.* Table salt and water are two examples of common chemical compounds.

separate diagrams of two hydrogen atoms and one oxygen atom. Figure 3.5 shows the oxygen atom sharing two electrons with each of the two hydrogen atoms. Each chemical bond should be thought of as belonging to each of the atoms involved. You could visualize atoms as people shaking hands; the people are the atoms and the handshake is the bond. Generally, this sharing of a pair of electrons is represented by a single straight line between the atoms.

An ionic bond is formed when atoms steal electrons from other atoms. An atom with an extra electron is a negatively charged particle, since it no longer has an equal number of positive and negative charges. Similarly, the atom losing an electron has lost a negative charge and, therefore, has one more positive charge than negative charge. An atom with either a negative or a positive charge is called an **ion.** The first atom described above has stolen an electron and is a negatively charged ion while the second atom has lost an electron and is now a positively charged ion. Since opposite charges attract each other, an ionic bond is formed between these oppositely charged ions. Figure 3.6 shows this relationship between a sodium ion and a chloride ion in a molecule of common table salt.

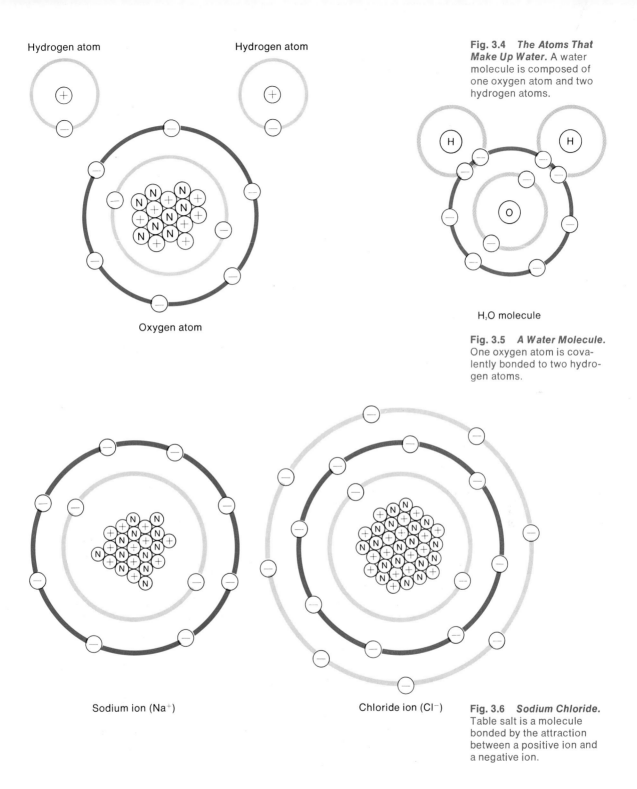

Hydrogen atom

Hydrogen atom

Oxygen atom

Fig. 3.4 *The Atoms That Make Up Water.* A water molecule is composed of one oxygen atom and two hydrogen atoms.

H_2O molecule

Fig. 3.5 *A Water Molecule.* One oxygen atom is covalently bonded to two hydrogen atoms.

Sodium ion (Na^+)

Chloride ion (Cl^-)

Fig. 3.6 *Sodium Chloride.* Table salt is a molecule bonded by the attraction between a positive ion and a negative ion.

The Simple Stuff of Life   31

Fig. 3.7 *Hydrogen Bonds.* Hydrogen bonds cause molecules to orient themselves with respect to each other. These bonds are represented by three dots (. . .).

Magnets will attract each other at opposite poles

Water molecules are also attracted to each other in a manner similar to magnets

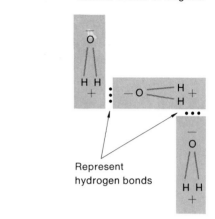

Represent hydrogen bonds

Hydrogen bonds are the weakest of the three types of bonds. This bond is similar to a weak magnetic force between some types of molecules (fig. 3.7). These bonds determine important characteristics of the materials in which they are found. Proteins and other biologically important molecules have internal hydrogen bonds, which we shall hear more about later.

Of Lemons and Limes

Acids and **bases** are another class of biologically important compounds. Their characteristics are determined by the nature of their chemical bonds. When acids are dissolved in water, **hydrogen ions** (H^+) are set free to float around. A hydrogen ion is positive because it has lost its electron, and now has only the positive charge—the proton. Compounds that behave this way are called acids. Two common examples of acids are sulfuric acid (H_2SO_4), which is used in your car's battery, and acetic acid (CH_3COOH), which is present in vinegar.

Some other compounds when dissolved in water release **hydroxyl ions** (OH^-). Each of these ions is negatively charged and consists of an oxygen atom and a hydrogen atom combined together. Some cans of drain cleaner contain the strong base caustic soda ($NaOH$). If you have read the directions on the can, you know that such a base can be as dangerous as a strong acid. Some acids and bases are actually stronger than others. The strength of an acid or a base is represented by a number called its **pH.** A pH of seven indicates that the solution is neutral and that an equal number of hydrogen and hydroxyl ions are floating around. As the pH numbers get smaller, the strength of the acid increases. Similarly, as the pH numbers increase, the strength of the base increases. Notice the pH values of the various substances

Box III

Traditionally elements are represented in a shorthand form by letters rather than writing out the complete name of the molecule (i.e., water = H_2O), which means that a molecule of water consists of two atoms of hydrogen and one atom of oxygen. These chemical symbols can be found on any Periodic Table of Elements.

THE PERIODIC SYSTEM of THE ELEMENTS

IA	IIA	IIIB	IVB	VB	VIB	VIIB		VIII		IB	IIB	IIIA	IVA	VA	VIA	VIIA	O	
1 **H** 1.008																1 **H** 1.008	2 **He** 4.003	2
3 **Li** 6.939	4 **Be** 9.012											5 **B** 10.81	6 **C** 12.01	7 **N** 14.01	8 **O** 16.00	9 **F** 19.00	10 **Ne** 20.18	2·8
11 **Na** 22.99	12 **Mg** 24.31											13 **Al** 26.98	14 **Si** 28.09	15 **P** 30.97	16 **S** 32.06	17 **Cl** 35.45	18 **Ar** 39.95	2·8·8
19 **K** 39.10	20 **Ca** 40.08	21 **Sc** 44.96	22 **Ti** 47.90	23 **V** 50.94	24 **Cr** 52.00	25 **Mn** 54.94	26 **Fe** 55.85	27 **Co** 58.93	28 **Ni** 58.71	29 **Cu** 63.54	30 **Zn** 65.37	31 **Ga** 69.72	32 **Ge** 72.59	33 **As** 74.92	34 **Se** 78.96	35 **Br** 79.91	36 **Kr** 83.80	2·8·18·8
37 **Rb** 85.47	38 **Sr** 87.62	39 **Y** 88.91	40 **Zr** 91.22	41 **Nb** 92.91	42 **Mo** 95.94	43 **Tc** (97)	44 **Ru** 101.1	45 **Rh** 102.9	46 **Pd** 106.4	47 **Ag** 107.9	48 **Cd** 112.4	49 **In** 114.8	50 **Sn** 118.7	51 **Sb** 121.8	52 **Te** 127.6	53 **I** 126.9	54 **Xe** 131.3	2·8·18·18·8
55 **Cs** 132.9	56 **Ba** 137.3	57 **La** 138.9	72 **Hf** 178.5	73 **Ta** 180.9	74 **W** 183.9	75 **Re** 186.2	76 **Os** 190.2	77 **Ir** 192.2	78 **Pt** 195.1	79 **Au** 197.0	80 **Hg** 200.6	81 **Tl** 204.4	82 **Pb** 207.2	83 **Bi** 209.0	84 **Po** (210)	85 **At** (210)	86 **Rn** (222)	2·8·18·32·18·8
87 **Fr** (223)	88 **Ra** (226)	89 **Ac** (227)																

Atomic Number (# of Protons)
6
C — Symbol
12.01 — Atomic Weight

Lanthanum Series

58 **Ce** 140.1	59 **Pr** 140.1	60 **Nd** 144.2	61 **Pm** (147)	62 **Sm** 150.4	63 **Eu** 152.0	64 **Gd** 157.3	65 **Tb** 158.9	66 **Dy** 162.5	67 **Ho** 164.9	68 **Er** 167.3	69 **Tm** 168.9	70 **Yb** 173.0	71 **Lu** 175.0	2·8·18·32·9·2

Actinium Series →

90 **Th** 232.0	91 **Pa** (231)	92 **U** 238.0	93 **Np** (237)	94 **Pu** (242)	95 **Am** (243)	96 **Cm** (247)	97 **Bk** (247)	98 **Cf** (249)	99 **Es** (254)	100 **Fm** (253)	101 **Md** (256)	102 **No** (253)	103 **Lw** (259)	2·8·18·32·?·9·2

Mass numbers of the most stable known isotopes are shown in parentheses.

Atomic weights are given to four significant figures.

1—Hydrogen (H)	9—Fluorine (F)	17—Chlorine (Cl)	47—Silver (Ag)
2—Helium (He)	10—Neon (Ne)	18—Argon (Ar)	53—Iodine (I)
3—Lithium (Li)	11—Sodium (Na)	19—Potassium (K)	79—Gold (Au)
4—Beryllium (Be)	12—Magnesium (Mg)	20—Calcium (Ca)	80—Mercury (Hg)
5—Boron (B)	13—Aluminum (Al)	26—Iron (Fe)	82—Lead (Pb)
6—Carbon (C)	14—Silicon (Si)	29—Copper (Cu)	90—Thorium (Th)
7—Nitrogen (N)	15—Phosphorus (P)	30—Zinc (Zn)	92—Uranium (U)
8—Oxygen (O)	16—Sulfur (S)	35—Bromine (Br)	

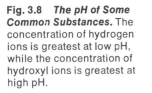

Fig. 3.8 The pH of Some Common Substances. The concentration of hydrogen ions is greatest at low pH, while the concentration of hydroxyl ions is greatest at high pH.

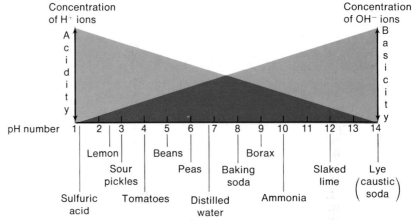

in figure 3.8. This figure shows that a strong acid, such as sulfuric acid, has a high concentration of hydrogen ions and a low concentration of hydroxyl ions. This balance between hydroxyl and hydrogen ions can be produced either by adding hydrogen ions or trapping hydroxyl ions. For this reason an acid can be a molecule that not only releases hydrogen ions, but also captures hydroxyl ions. The opposite situation is true for bases. A base can be a molecule that either releases hydroxyl ions or captures hydrogen ions and removes them from the solution.

Chemical Reactions

Strong acids and bases have a powerful ability to enter into situations in which parts of molecules are exchanged. This rearrangement of parts is called a **chemical reaction.** Perhaps when you were younger you tried stirring together a bunch of chemicals with the hope that something flashy would happen. Only certain types of reactions are possible, and it is fortunate for those of you who have tried this to find that most of your "experiments" just set there. A chemical reaction you have all seen is the burning of natural gas to produce heat and light. This reaction is shown in figure 3.9. It involves a breaking of the chemical bonds in the gases methane and oxygen, followed by the formation of new bonds in the carbon dioxide and water molecules. Since the energy found in the chemical bonds of the carbon dioxide and water molecules is less than the energy that was present in the methane and oxygen molecules, the excess energy is released in the form of heat and light. A comparable situation occurs in "fireflies" when molecules are rearranged in a chemical reaction and light energy is released; however, very little heat is produced in this case. Otherwise, they would burn their tails off. Other reactions do not release excess energy but require an input of energy to enable the reactions to occur. An example of this type occurs in photosynthesis. Sunlight energy is required by green plants to combine carbon dioxide with water to form sugar (fig. 3.10).

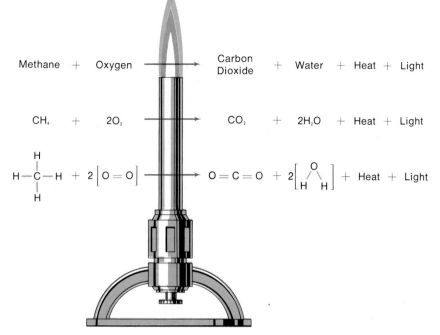

Fig. 3.9 A Chemical Reaction. Oxidation of methane is one example of a chemical reaction.

Methane + Oxygen → Carbon Dioxide + Water + Heat + Light

CH_4 + $2O_2$ → CO_2 + $2H_2O$ + Heat + Light

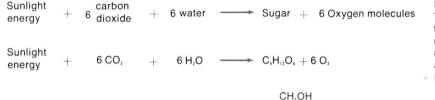

Fig. 3.10 Photosynthesis. The above summary equation does not show the many reactions that produce the result. The 6 CO_2 in the above equation means six molecules of CO_2.

Sunlight energy + 6 carbon dioxide + 6 water → Sugar + 6 Oxygen molecules

Sunlight energy + $6 CO_2$ + $6 H_2O$ → $C_6H_{12}O_6 + 6 O_2$

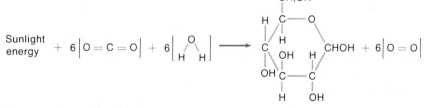

In each of these examples, certain starting molecules are changed during the chemical reaction to form new arrangements of atoms. The molecules that enter the reaction are called the **reactants,** and the newly formed molecules are called the **products** of the reaction. As the reaction takes place, the amount of reactant decreases and the amount of product increases. As long as the new products are in close contact with one another, they, too, may react to again form the original molecules. This type of back-and-forth chemical reaction results in a balance of the reactants and products (fig. 3.11). However, if any one or all of the products are removed or lost during the reaction, it will

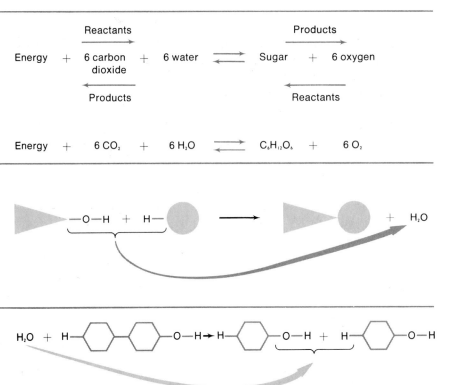

Fig. 3.11 Chemical Equilibrium. Most reactions are reversible; that is, they can proceed in either direction. The direction depends on the energy that is available and the relative amounts of materials involved.

Reactants

Energy + 6 carbon dioxide + 6 water ⇌ Sugar + 6 oxygen   Products

Products   Reactants

Energy + 6 CO$_2$ + 6 H$_2$O ⇌ C$_6$H$_{12}$O$_6$ + 6 O$_2$

Fig. 3.12 Dehydration-Synthesis Reaction. This type of reaction occurs when two molecules are bonded together. H+ is removed from one molecule and OH− is removed from the other. The H+ and OH− ions bond together to form water.

—O—H + H— → + H$_2$O

Fig. 3.13 Hydrolysis. This is the opposite of dehydration synthesis. H+ and OH− from water split a molecule into two pieces.

H$_2$O + H——O—H → H——O—H + H——O—H

continue until all of the reactants have been changed into product molecules. In photosynthesis, the reaction results in the formation of oxygen molecules that leave the leaf of the plant, therefore preventing the conversion of sugar and oxygen back to carbon dioxide and water. This results in the accumulation of sugar molecules, which are used in growth, reproduction, and other plant activities.

Let us consider two of the common types of chemical reactions that happen in living things. **Dehydration synthesis** is such a process. It results in the joining of two smaller molecules to make one larger molecule with the removal of a molecule of water. The water molecule from this dehydration-synthesis reaction was not originally present as a molecule of water. It was manufactured from a hydrogen from one of the smaller molecules and a hydroxyl group from the other molecule, as shown in figure 3.12. You can see that the H from one molecule and OH from the other molecule leave and join together to form the molecule of water.

This is the sort of reaction that happens when we gain weight around the waistline as a result of depositing molecules of fat. The opposite kind of reaction is called **hydrolysis.** In this reaction, a large molecule is split into two smaller molecules with the addition of a water molecule. This happens when we boil potatoes. We split the large starch molecules into smaller molecules (fig. 3.13).

Energy

In these reactions, matter (atoms) and energy are not created or destroyed but are converted from one form to another. This statement is known as the **First Law of Thermodynamics.** We are all familiar to some extent with the forms that **energy** can take. There is light, sound, heat, mechanical, electrical, and chemical energy; these can be converted from one form to another. You know that electrical energy can be converted by means of a television set into the light that forms a picture on the screen and the sound that comes from the speaker. In biology, we are concerned with many types of energy conversions. It is also important to know that whenever such a conversion takes place, there is always a loss of some "usable" energy. For example, in an ordinary light bulb, electrical energy is converted to usable light energy; however, some heat energy is lost as unusable energy. The idea that *whenever energy is converted from one form to another, some useful energy is lost,* is called the **Second Law of Thermodynamics** (fig. 3.14).

Fig. 3.14 *The Second Law of Thermodynamics.* When electrical energy is changed to light energy, there will be some loss of energy in the form of heat. The light bulb will be too hot for comfort.

Living systems obey the Second Law of Thermodynamics, and are therefore constantly losing some of their useful energy in the form of heat. If living things do not receive a constant supply of energy, usually in the form of chemical-bond energy, they will die. Molecules possess two kinds of energy: chemical-bond energy, which holds molecules together and is used for life processes; and energy of motion which is known as **kinetic energy.** The kinetic energy that all molecules possess causes them to move about in a random fashion. If the molecules of a substance have little kinetic energy, they will move slowly or may actually just vibrate in place. The physical state of such a collection of molecules is called a **solid.** If additional energy in the form of heat is added to this solid, the kinetic energy of the molecules will increase, changing the physical condition of the solid to a **liquid,** because the increased kinetic energy will allow the molecules to move over one another. The further addition of energy will continue this change and result in the production of a **gas,** in which the molecules are no longer even associated with one another. Even though the amount of kinetic energy of the individual molecules has increased in this situation, the total amount of chemical-bond energy remains the same in the molecules. Since the molecules of liquids and gases can move past one another, there can be a redistribution of the molecules.

Wandering Molecules

Let us consider an example of this motion. Suppose we had a crystal of purple dye at the bottom of a jar of still water (fig. 3.15). The purple color would spread slowly out into the surrounding water even if we did not disturb the contents of the jar. This can be explained by saying that the tiny molecules of the dye and the water are all individually in motion. The molecules travel in straight lines until they hit either another molecule or the jar and they then bounce off in different directions. As a result of this motion, there is a natural tendency for the molecules to scatter from an area where they are concentrated toward a neighboring area where they are

Fig. 3.15 *Diffusion.* Just as in rush hour traffic, the flow of diffusing materials goes from a region of high concentration to one of lower concentration.

less concentrated. This scattering of molecules from an area of high concentration to an area of low concentration is called **diffusion.**

Summary

All matter is composed of atoms. The atoms contain a nucleus that has neutrons and protons. The nucleus is surrounded by moving electrons. There are several different kinds of atoms called elements. These differ from one another by the number of protons and electrons they contain. Each is given an atomic number, based on the number of protons in the nucleus, and a mass number, determined by the total number of protons and neutrons. Atoms of an element that have the same atomic number but different mass numbers are called isotopes. Some isotopes fall apart releasing energy and smaller particles, and are called radioactive elements. Atoms may be combined into larger units called molecules. There are three kinds of chemical bonds that typically hold atoms together as molecules. They are covalent, ionic, and hydrogen bonds.

An ion is an atom that is electrically unbalanced. Those compounds that release hydrogen ions when dissolved in water are called acids, while those that release hydroxyl ions are called bases. A measure of the hydrogen ions in relation to the hydroxyl ions present in a solution is known as the pH of the solution. Molecules that interact and exchange parts are said to undergo chemical reactions. The changing of chemical bonds in a reaction may release energy or require the input of additional energy. Two important biological reactions are dehydration synthesis and hydrolysis. Energy can neither be created nor destroyed, but it can be converted from one form to another. When energy is converted from one form to another, some of the useful energy is lost. The amount of kinetic energy that molecules of various substances contain determines whether they will be solids, liquids, or gases. The random motion of molecules results in their equal distribution throughout the available space.

Consider This

Hydrogen peroxide (H_2O_2) is commonly found in the medicine cabinet and is used as an antiseptic. Its antiseptic properties result from the breakdown of this molecule into water and oxygen (O_2), which can destroy germs.

$$2H_2O_2 \longrightarrow 2H_2O + O_2$$

This reaction can take place right in the bottle over a period of time and results in the loss of germ-killing properties. Can you describe what is happening to the molecules of hydrogen peroxide, and to the water and oxygen? Can you describe why the bottle will finally contain nothing but water and oxygen? In your description, include diffusion, possible changes in chemical bonds, and kinetic energy.

1. How many electrons, protons, and neutrons would be in an atom of potassium (K) having a mass number of 39?
2. Diagram an atom showing the relative positions of electrons, protons, and neutrons.
3. Name three kinds of chemical bonds that hold atoms together. How do these bonds differ from one another?
4. List five different kinds of elements.
5. What does it mean if a solution has a pH number of 3, 12, 2, 7, or 9?
6. What relationship does diffusion have to molecular motion?
7. Name two kinds of energy possessed by molecules.
8. Define the term *chemical reaction* and give an example.
9. What is the difference between atom and element; molecule and compound?
10. How do acids and bases differ?

Chapter Glossary

acid A substance that gives up hydrogen ions (H^+) when dissolved in water. Acids also act as hydroxyl ion (OH^-) acceptors.

atom The smallest particle of an element that still retains all the properties of the element.

atomic number The number that is assigned to an element and is determined by the number of protons in an atom of that element.

base A substance that gives up hydroxyl ions (OH^-) when dissolved in water. Bases also act as hydrogen ion (H^+) acceptors.

chemical bond The attraction that one atom, ion, or molecule has for another atom, ion, or molecule.

chemical reaction The interaction between two or more chemicals, whereby new bonds are formed and energy is subsequently exchanged.

compound A substance made up of atoms of two or more kinds of elements chemically bonded together.

covalent bond The attraction between two atoms formed by the sharing of electrons.

dehydration synthesis A type of chemical reaction in which two molecules are combined with the loss of a molecule of water.

diffusion The net movement of molecules from an area of higher concentration to an area of lower concentration.

electron A negatively charged particle located some distance from the nucleus of an atom.

element One of the basic materials from which all substances are composed.

energy An ability to do something. Various forms include heat, light, electricity.

First Law of Thermodynamics Matter and energy cannot be created or destroyed, but can be converted into different forms.

gas Of the three states of matter, the one that is highest in kinetic energy—molecules are moving very rapidly.

hydrogen bond A weak bond formed by the attraction between a positively charged part of one molecule and a negatively charged part of a second molecule.

hydrolysis   A type of chemical reaction by which a large molecule is split into smaller molecules with the addition of water.

hydroxyl ion   A negatively charged group composed of one oxygen atom, one hydrogen atom, and one extra electron.

ion   An atom with a charge; either negative ions have gained electrons or positive ions have lost electrons. such that the electron and proton are not equal.

ionic bond   The attraction between a positive ion and a negative ion.

isotopes   Atoms of an element that have different atomic weights, due to varying numbers of neutrons.

kinetic energy   An ability to move. Electrons moving about the nucleus of an atom are exhibiting this energy of motion.

liquid   Of the three states of matter; the one that has more kinetic energy than a solid, but less than a gas—molecules are moving over one another.

mass number   A number that identifies an isotope.

molecule   A unit of matter composed of two or more atoms held together by chemical bonds.

neutron   A particle in the nucleus of an atom that does not have an electrical charge.

nucleus   The center of mass in an atom containing protons and neutrons.

pH   A number indicating the strength of acidity or basicity of a substance. The numeral 7 indicates neutrality, less than 7 is increasingly acid, and more than 7 is increasingly basic.

product   The material that results from a chemical change. Products are usually on the right in a chemical equation.

proton   A positively charged particle in the nucleus of an atom.

radioactive   Applies to an atom having an unstable nucleus that flies apart. An isotope that is likely to break apart like this is said to be a *radioactive isotope*.

reactant   The material(s) that engage in chemical changes. Reactants are usually on the left side of a chemical equation.

Second Law of Thermodynamics   The concept of the change of one form of energy to another with an associated loss of usable energy. This loss is in the form of heat.

solid   Of the three states of matter, the one that is lowest in kinetic energy—molecules are vibrating in place.

thyroid gland   A structure located in the neck of humans, responsible for producing chemical control molecules such as thyroxin. Malfunction of this gland results in slowed or accelerated metabolic activity.

thyroxin   The chemical produced by the thyroid gland. Its function is that of controlling the metabolic rate.

Purpose   The chemistry of living things is really the chemistry of the carbon atom and a few other atoms that are able to combine with carbon. In order to understand some aspects of the structure and function of living things, which will be covered later, it is important that you be exposed to some basic organic chemistry.

Some Not So Simple Stuff of Life

Organic Chemistry—The Chemistry of Life

The principles and concepts discussed in chapter three apply to all types of matter. Living systems are composed of rather complex molecules that contain carbon atoms as basic building blocks. These are called **organic molecules.** In contrast to these complex, carbon-containing molecules, most of the ones we discussed in the last chapter were **inorganic molecules.**

The original meaning of the terms inorganic and organic related to the fact that organic materials were thought either to be alive or to be produced only by living things. Inorganic materials were neither alive nor could they be produced by the aid of living things. Therefore, a very strong link exists between organic chemistry and the chemistry of living things, which is called **biological chemistry.** Modern chemistry has altered this original meaning considerably, since it is now possible to manufacture unique, organic molecules that cannot be produced by living things. Many of the materials we use daily are the result of the organic chemist's art. Nylon, aspirin, polyurethane varnish, silicones, Plexiglas, food wrap, Teflon, and insecticides are just a few of the unique molecules that have been invented by organic chemists (fig. 4.1).

Fig. 4.1 *Some Common Organic Materials Made by Man.* These items are examples of useful man-made organic compounds.

Fig. 4.2 *Natural and Synthetic Organic Compounds.* Some organic materials, such as rubber, were originally produced by plants, but they are now man-made. (Courtesy of Goodyear Tire and Rubber Company.)

In other instances, organic chemists have taken their lead from living organisms and have been able to produce organic molecules more efficiently, or in forms that are slightly altered from the original natural molecule. Some examples of these are rubber, penicillin, some of the vitamins, insulin, and alcohol (fig. 4.2).

Organic Chemistry Is Based on the Behavior of the Carbon Atom

All organic molecules, whether they are natural or man-made, have certain common characteristics. The carbon atom, which is the central atom in all organic molecules, has some unusual properties. Carbon is unique in that it can combine with other carbon atoms to form long chains.

$$—C—C—C—C—C—C—C—C—C—$$

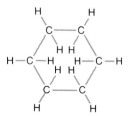

Fig. 4.3 *Ring Structure.* The ring structure shown here is formed by joining the two ends of the carbon chain.

In many cases the ends of these chains may join together to form ring structures (fig. 4.3). Only a few other atoms have this ability. What really is unusual is the fact that these bonding sites are all located at equal distances from one another. If you were to take a rubber ball and stick four nails into it so that they were equally distributed around the ball, you would have a good idea of the geometry involved (fig. 4.4).

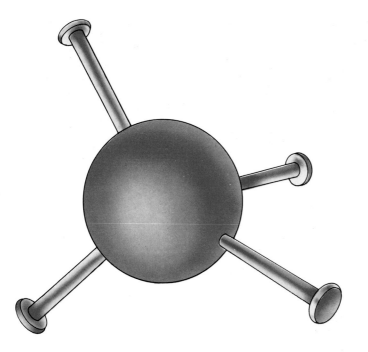

Fig. 4.4 *Bond Sites of a Carbon Atom.* The arrangement of bonding sites around the carbon atom is similar to a ball with four equally spaced nails in it.

Fig. 4.5 *Methane Molecule.* A methane molecule is composed of one carbon atom bonded with four hydrogen atoms. These bonds are formed at the bonding sites of the carbon. Note: For the sake of simplicity, all future diagrams of molecules will be two-dimensional drawings, although in reality they are three-dimensional.

Each line in this diagram represents a covalent bond between two atoms.

Carbon atoms are usually involved in **covalent bonds.** Compare carbon, which can form four covalent bonds, with nitrogen, which can form three covalent bonds; oxygen, which can form two covalent bonds, with hydrogen, which can form only one covalent bond. Since carbon has four places where it can bond, the carbon atom can have four other atoms combined with it. This is the case with the methane molecule, which has four hydrogen atoms attached to a single carbon atom. Methane is a colorless and odorless gas that is usually found in natural gas (fig. 4.5).

Some atoms may be bonded to a single carbon atom more than once. This results in a slightly different arrangement of bonds around the center of the carbon atom. Generally, this kind of covalent bond is referred to as a **double bond** (fig. 4.6). It is denoted by the two lines ($=$) between the carbon and oxygen atoms ($—C=O$). The two carbon atoms in figure 4.6 each share four bonds, and each of the four hydrogen atoms shares a single bond. Although most atoms can be involved in the structure of organic molecules, a few are most commonly found. Hydrogen (H) and oxygen (O) are almost always present. Nitrogen (N), sulfur (S), and phosphorus (P) are also very important in specific types of organic molecules.

Most organic molecules are quite large and are called **macromolecules.** The size of organic molecules is directly related to the fact that carbon atoms are able to form long chains or rings. Many organic molecules con-

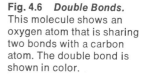

Fig. 4.6 *Double Bonds.* This molecule shows an oxygen atom that is sharing two bonds with a carbon atom. The double bond is shown in color.

tain thousands of carbon atoms, while most inorganic molecules contain ten or fewer atoms. Therefore, organic chemistry is the chemistry of large molecules. An enormous variety of organic molecules are possible because carbon is able to bond at four different sites, form long chains, and combine with a variety of other atoms. The types of atoms present in the molecule are important in determining the properties of the molecule. The three-dimensional arrangement of the atoms within the molecule is also important. Since most inorganic molecules are small and involve few atoms, there is usually only one way in which a group of atoms can be arranged to form a molecule. There is only one arrangement for a single oxygen atom and two hydrogen atoms in a molecule of water.

In a molecule of sulfuric acid there is only one arrangement for the one sulfur atom, the two hydrogen atoms, and the four oxygen atoms.

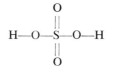

However,

both contain two carbon atoms, six hydrogen atoms, and one oxygen atom, but they are quite different in the arrangement of atoms and in the chemical properties of the molecules.

 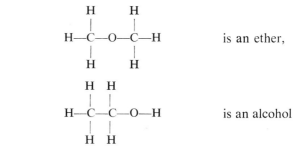

—the kind of alcohol found in beer, wine, and liquor. Since the ether and the alcohol molecules both have the same number and kinds of atoms, they are said to have the same chemical formula, which in this case is written C_2H_6O. This formula simply indicates the number of each kind of atom within the molecule. However, it is obvious that their **structural formula** is not the same. As the number of carbon atoms increases, the number of different structural arrangements increases. For example, there are at least five different structural formulas for all the molecules having the same chemical formula, $C_6H_{12}O_6$ (fig. 4.7).

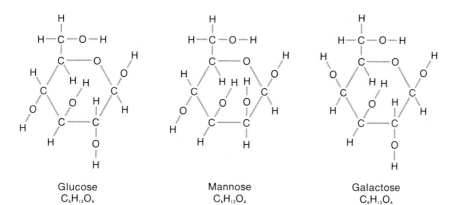

Fig. 4.7 Six Carbon Sugars. Some structural arrangements of six carbon sugars. Each of these molecules has the same number of carbon, hydrogen, and oxygen atoms; but they are arranged differently.

Glucose
$C_6H_{12}O_6$

Mannose
$C_6H_{12}O_6$

Galactose
$C_6H_{12}O_6$

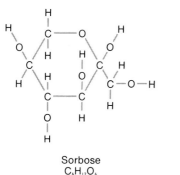

Sorbose
$C_6H_{12}O_6$

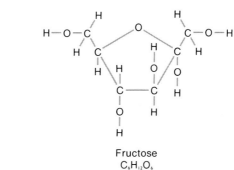

Fructose
$C_6H_{12}O_6$

Box IV

Frequently structural formulas are simplified by removing the carbons and just connecting lines at the points where the carbons would have been.

For example:

can also be used to indicate a sugar like glucose.

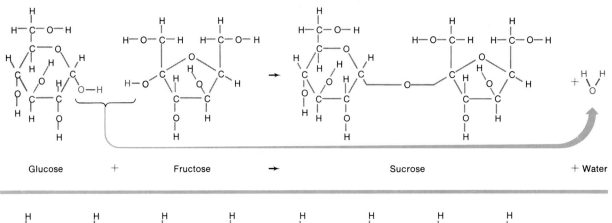

Glucose   +   Fructose   →   Sucrose   + Water

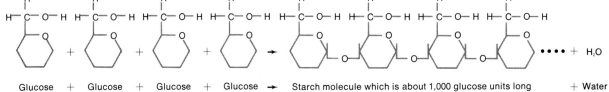

Glucose   +   Glucose   +   Glucose   +   Glucose   →   Starch molecule which is about 1,000 glucose units long   + Water

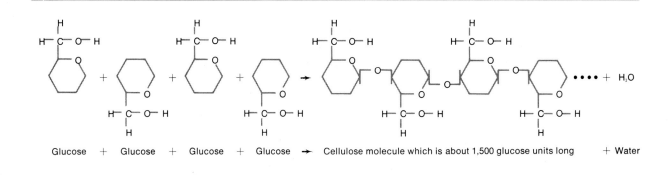

Glucose   +   Glucose   +   Glucose   +   Glucose   →   Cellulose molecule which is about 1,500 glucose units long   + Water

Fig. 4.8 *Complex Carbo-hydrates.* Many complex carbohydrates are formed by joining simple sugars together in a specific manner.

Some Common Naturally Occurring Organic Molecules

Since there is such a large number of different organic molecules, it is helpful to organize them into groups on the basis of the similarity of structure and/or the chemical properties of the molecules. All living organisms consist of cells that are made up of a large variety of molecules. We can't describe all of them, but it is important to be familiar with a few types of organic molecules that are especially common or have particular significance.

Carbohydrates

Carbohydrates contain three kinds of atoms: carbon, hydrogen, and oxygen. In general, the number of carbon and oxygen atoms are equal, while the number of hydrogen atoms is about double the number of carbon or oxygen atoms. There are a large number of different molecules that fit this basic pattern. For example, $C_6H_{12}O_6$ is a carbohydrate and five structural formulas are commonly found (fig. 4.7).

Some common carbohydrates include many kinds of sugars, corn syrup, cornstarch, and wood fiber. These different kinds of carbohydrate molecules are used in a variety of ways by cells. **Simple sugars** such as glucose, fructose, and galactose provide the chemical energy necessary to keep organisms alive. Simple sugars may also combine together by dehydration synthesis to form larger molecules. Sucrose (common table sugar) consists of a glucose and a fructose molecule hooked together. Glycogen, an energy storage molecule commonly found in animals, consists of a large number of glucose molecules hooked together. Starch, an energy storage molecule commonly found in plants, and cellulose, a component of the cell walls of plants, are also composed of glucose molecules (fig. 4.8).

Simple sugars can also be used by the cell as a component of other, more complex molecules such as **adenosine triphosphate (ATP)**. The sugar present in ATP is a five-carbon sugar known as ribose. This simple sugar molecule is located in the center of the ATP molecule and has attached to it many other types of atoms, including oxygen, hydrogen nitrogen, and phosphorus (fig. 4.9).

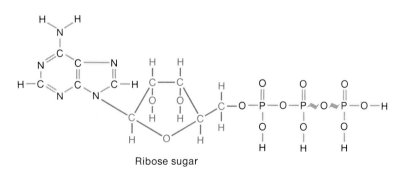

Ribose sugar

Fig. 4.9 Adenosine Triphosphate (ATP). Adenosine triphosphate (ATP) is an important biological molecule that has a simple sugar as part of its structure.

Lipids

Lipids are large organic molecules that do not usually dissolve in water. There are a number of different kinds of lipids, but we will consider only three: fats, phospholipids, and steroids.

Fats are molecules that do not dissolve in water very easily. Fats are similar to carbohydrates in that they contain only carbon, hydrogen, and oxygen atoms; but fats differ from carbohydrates in that they contain much less oxygen per molecule. Fats are made up of two smaller molecules called **glycerol** and **fatty acids.** Glycerol is an alcohol having the following structure

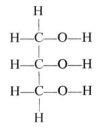

and fatty acids consist of carbon chains of various lengths having a

group at one end; this is called an acid group. Remember it because you will see it again later. An example of a fatty acid is shown in the following structure.

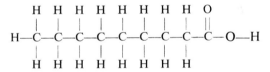

Figure 4.10 illustrates how glycerol and fatty acids are combined together to form a fat.

Fats such as those present in animals do not usually have double bonds between any of the carbons in the fatty acid portion of the molecule. These kinds of fats are called **saturated fats** and are usually solid at room temperature. Lard, whale blubber, and suet are saturated animal fats. Most fats of plants, however, do have double bonds between carbons in the fatty acid portion of the molecule. These kinds of fats are **unsaturated fats** and are usually liquid at room temperature. Some examples of plant fats are olive oil, linseed oil, corn oil, and cottonseed oil.

Fats are important molecules for storing energy. There is twice as much energy in a gram of fat as in a gram of sugar. This is important to an organism, since fats can be stored in a relatively small space and still yield a high amount of energy. However if the cells of an organism need energy,

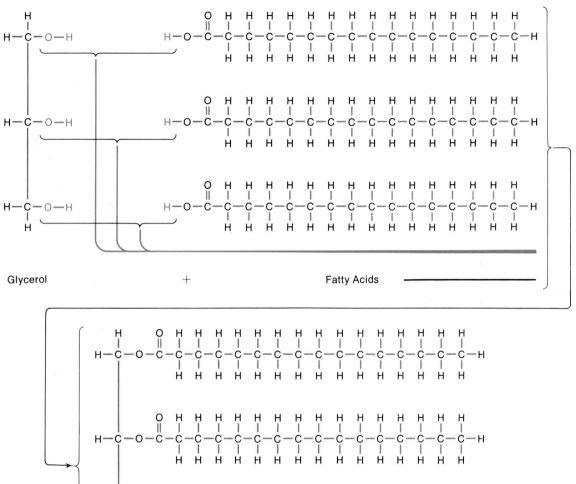

Glycerol   +   Fatty Acids

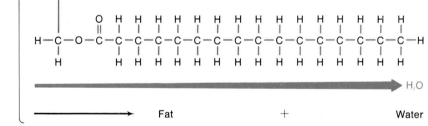

H₂O

Fat   +   Water

Fig. 4.10 *Fat Molecule.* A fat molecule is composed of glycerol and fatty acid molecules combined into a single unit.

they tap the carbohydrate source before the stored fat. This is very evident when a person tries to lose some weight. A successful diet is one in which the carbohydrate and fat intake is greatly reduced. This places a strong demand for energy on the stored fat molecules. Since fat has twice as much energy per gram as carbohydrate, the process of losing weight is often slow.

Another function of fats in animals is to provide protection. Some animals have a layer of fat under the skin that acts like a layer of insulation between the animal and its surroundings. The thick layer of blubber in whales, walruses, and seals prevents the loss of internal body heat to the cold, watery environment in which they live. This same layer of fat, together with the fat deposits around some internal organs, such as the kidneys and heart, serves as a cushion, which protects these fragile organs from physical damage.

Phospholipids are a particular class of water insoluble molecules that resemble fats but contain phosphate groups (PO_4) at some place in their structure (fig. 4.11). Phospholipids are involved in the structure of all cells. Nerve and brain cells contain a great deal of this type of molecule, including many different kinds of phospholipids. These are all essential to the operation of the nervous system of an animal. Phospholipids will be discussed again in chapter six, "Cell History, Structure, and Function."

Fig. 4.11 *A Phospholipid Molecule.* This molecule is similar to a fat, but it has a phosphate in the structure of the molecule. The phosphate is highlighted in color.

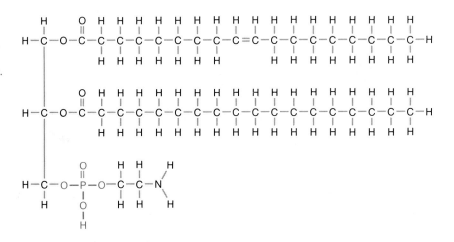

Steroids are a group of complex molecules that usually consist of ring-like arrangements of atoms. They are often **hormones** that aid in regulating body processes. One steroid molecule that you are probably familiar with is cholesterol. This steroid has been implicated in many cases of atherosclerosis, or clogging of the arteries. On the other hand, cholesterol is necessary for the manufacture of vitamin D. The cholesterol molecules are found in the skin and react with the ultraviolet light to produce vitamin D, which is used to assist in the proper development of bones and teeth. Figure 4.12 shows a cholesterol molecule.

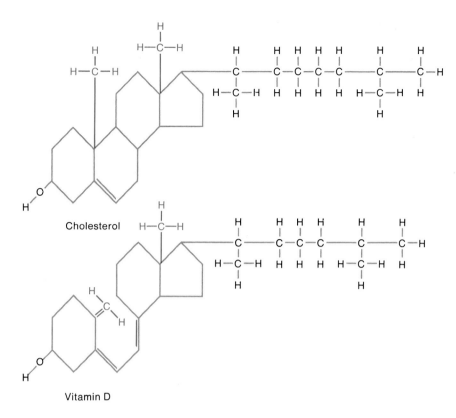

Cholesterol

Vitamin D

Fig. 4.12 *The Structure of Common Steroids.* Cholesterol and vitamin D are both steroids. Cholesterol is converted to vitamin D by the action of sunlight on the skin. The differences between these two molecules are shown in color.

A large number of steroid molecules are hormones. Many of them regulate various reproductive processes, such as egg production; others regulate the salt concentrations of the blood. Figure 4.13 shows progesterone and testosterone molecules as examples of common steroid hormones.

Proteins

Proteins are molecules that are made up of subunits known as **amino acids.** Amino acids contain nitrogen in an **amino group** at one end of the molecule and an **acid group** at the other end of the molecule (fig. 4.14).

There are about 20 different kinds of amino acids that are identical except for the side chain that differs from one amino acid to another. These amino acids can be combined to form chains. Just as the twenty-six letters of the alphabet can be combined to make millions of words, these amino acids can be arranged in millions of different ways. When the chain is short (about 100 amino acids or less) it is called a **polypeptide** chain. When the chain is longer than 100 amino acids, it is usually called a protein (fig. 4.15).

The structure of a protein is intimately related to the function of the protein. In most cases, a change in the structure of a protein will alter its

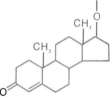

Testosterone
(the primary male
sex hormone)

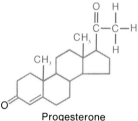

Progesterone
(one of the female
sex hormones)

Fig. 4.13 *Sex Hormones.* Many hormones are steroids. Two are shown here. Their differences are shown in color.

Some Not So Simple Stuff of Life

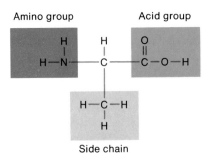

Fig. 4.14 *The Structure of an Amino Acid.* All amino acids have an amino group and an acid group. They differ from one another in the structure of their side chains.

Amino group   Acid group

Side chain

function. We will consider two aspects of the structure of proteins; the sequence of amino acids within the protein and the overall three-dimensional shape of the molecule. Any changes in the arrangement of amino acids within a protein can have far-reaching effects on the function of a protein. For example, normal hemoglobin found in red blood cells consists of two kinds of polypeptide chains called the alpha and beta chains. The beta chain has about 140 amino acids along its length. If a particular amino acid is changed from one form to another, the hemoglobin molecule does not function properly and thus results in a disease condition known as sickle-cell anemia.

In addition to the sequence of amino acids in the protein, the long chains of amino acids can coil and be folded into rather complex three-dimensional shapes. This three-dimensional structure is partly determined by the sequence of amino acids, since some of the amino acids at different places in the chain may chemically bond with one another. This results in a folding of the protein into a three-dimensional shape. For example, some amino acids have sulfur in them, and two sulfur atoms will form covalent bonds to hold the chain of amino acids in a particular shape. Other forces, such as hydrogen bonds, are also important in maintaining a particular shape for a protein molecule (fig. 4.16).

Fig. 4.15 *The Formation of a Protein Molecule.* Proteins are constructed by attaching amino acids end to end, much the same as a train is constructed by attaching railroad cars end to end.

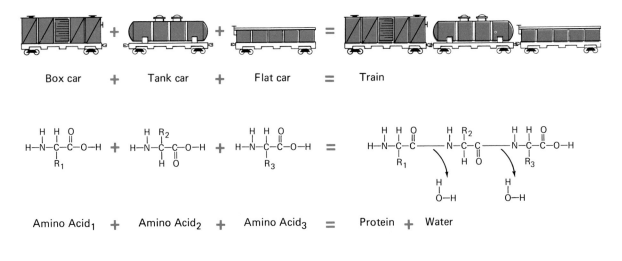

Box car   +   Tank car   +   Flat car   =   Train

Amino Acid$_1$ +   Amino Acid$_2$ +   Amino Acid$_3$ =   Protein   +   Water

Fig. 4.16 *A Protein Molecule.* The protein myoglobin is found in the muscles and helps to provide oxygen for muscle activity. A part of the molecule contains iron.

There are thousands of different kinds of proteins that can be placed into two categories. Some proteins are important for holding cells and organisms together, and are usually referred to as **structural proteins.** The other kinds of proteins are either hormones or **enzymes.** The enzymes are responsible for controlling the activities of cells and organisms. Enzymes are very important molecules and will be dealt with in greater detail in chapter seven. Two hormones that are protein in nature are insulin and oxytocin. Insulin is produced by the pancreas and regulates the amount of glucose found in the blood. If insulin production is too low or if the molecule is improperly constructed, glucose molecules are not removed from the bloodstream at a fast enough rate. As the glucose level increases in the blood, it is lost in the urine, which results in excessive thirst, and unconsciousness. This disease condition is known as diabetes. Oxytocin is a hormone that stimulates contraction of the uterus during childbirth. It is also an example of an organic molecule that has been produced artificially and is used by doctors to speed up the birth of a baby.

Nucleic Acids

Nucleic acids are complex molecules constructed of fundamental units known as **nucleotides.** There are eight common nucleotides and they are constructed from three kinds of subunits. These subunits are phosphates, sugars, and organic bases.

Phosphates consist of phosphorus with oxygen and hydrogen attached (fig. 4.17). There are two different sugars that can be components of nucleotides: ribose and deoxyribose. Each is a simple sugar having five carbons (fig. 4.18).

There are five common organic bases that are components of nucleic acids. They are adenine, guanine, cytosine, thymine, and uracil (fig. 4.19). Because these bases contain nitrogen, they are often called nitrogenous bases. A nucleotide is a large unit made up of one phosphate, one of the two sugars, and one of the five nitrogenous bases in the following arrangement (fig. 4.20).

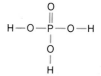

Phosphoric acid

A phosphate ion

Fig. 4.17 *Phosphate Group.* One of the components of the structure of nucleic acids is the phosphate group.

Fig. 4.18 *Two Sugars.* The two sugars found in nucleic acids are ribose and deoxyribose. Their differences are shown in color.

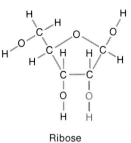

Ribose

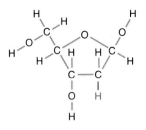

Deoxyribose

Fig. 4.19 *Nitrogenous Bases.* Five bases are found in nucleic acids.

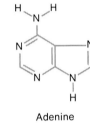

Adenine

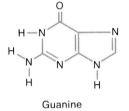

Guanine

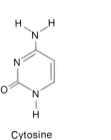

Cytosine

Uracil

Thymine

Fig. 4.20 *An RNA Nucleotide.* The unit from which large nucleic acids are built is the nucleotide. A nucleotide is made up of a phosphate, a sugar, and a nitrogenous base.

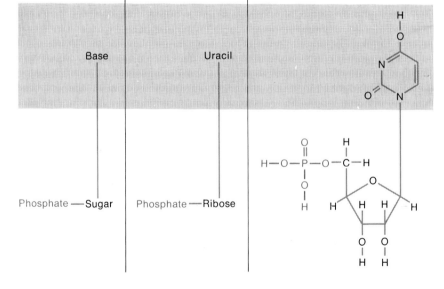

Base

Uracil

Phosphate — Sugar   Phosphate — Ribose

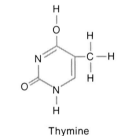

Nucleotides can be connected together to form long chains. These larger chains of nucleotides are of two different types: ribonucleic acid (RNA) and deoxyribonucleic acid (DNA). Ribonucleic acid (RNA) is a single chain of nucleotides. In RNA all the nucleotides contain the sugar ribose and a phosphate group. The bases adenine, guanine, cytosine, and uracil are also present in RNA, but thymine is not.

Deoxyribonucleic acid (DNA) is a more complicated molecule that consists of nucleotides containing deoxyribose, phosphate, and one of the following four bases: adenine, guanine, cytosine, or thymine. The base uracil is not present in DNA nucleotides. DNA differs from RNA in that the DNA molecule consists of two long strands of DNA nucleotides that are held together by matched pairs of bases. Adenine always pairs with thymine, and guanine always pairs with cytosine (fig. 4.21).

Another molecule that has a very important function in all cells is the molecule known as adenosine triphosphate (ATP). ATP is a nucleotide with two extra phosphates, and is used in energy transfer within the cell. The way in which this molecule functions will be covered more extensively in the discussion on cellular metabolism, chapter eight, "Biochemical Pathways."

Fig. 4.21 *The Structure of RNA and DNA.* DNA and RNA differ in structure in that DNA is a double strand and RNA is a single strand.

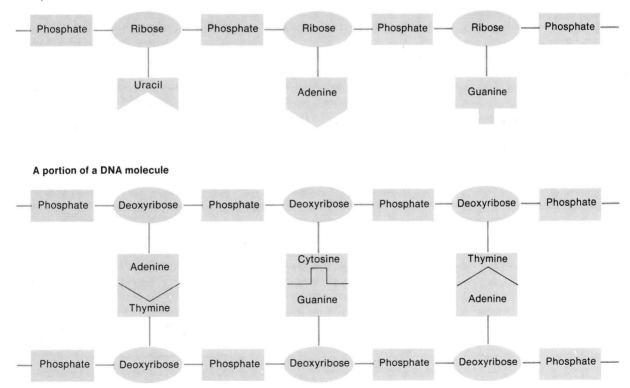

A portion of an RNA molecule

A portion of a DNA molecule

Summary The chemistry of living things involves a variety of large and complex molecules. It is based on the chemistry of the carbon atom and the fact that carbon atoms can be connected together to form long chains or rings. This results in a vast array of molecules. The structure of each molecule is important in determining which function the molecule is able to perform. Changes in the structure may result in abnormal functions, which we call disease. Some of the most common types of organic molecules found in living things are carbohydrates, lipids, proteins, and nucleic acids. Table 4.1 summarizes the major types of biologically important organic molecules and their role in living things.

Table 4.1   *A Summary of the Kind of Organic Molecules Found in Living Things*

Type of organic molecule	Basic subunit	Function	Examples
Carbohydrate	Simple sugar	Provide energy Provide support	Sugar Cellulose
Lipids 1. Fats	Glycerol and fatty acids	Provide energy Provide insulation Serve as shock absorber	Lard Olive oil Linseed oil Tallow
2. Steroids	A complex ring structure	Some hormones which control the body	Testosterone Vitamin D Cholesterol
3. Phospholipid	Glycerol, fatty acids and phosphorous compounds	Structure of the cell membrane	Cell membrane
Protein	Amino Acid	Structure of cells and parts of organisms	Cell membrane Hair Muscle
		Enzymes which regulate chemical reactions	Ptyalin in the mouth
		Some hormones	Insulin
Nucleic Acid	Nucleotide	Contains genetic information which controls the cell	DNA RNA

Amino acids and fatty acids are both organic acids. What property must they have in common with the inorganic acids, for instance sulfuric acid, and how do they differ? Consider such aspects as structure of molecules, size, bonding, and pH.

1. Diagram an example of each of the following molecular types: amino acid, simple sugar, glycerol, and fatty acid.
2. Give an example of each of the following classes of organic molecules: carbohydrate, protein, lipid, nucleic acid.
3. What is the structural difference between an unsaturated fat and a saturated fat?
4. Give an example of a hormone that is protein in nature, and state its function.
5. Give an example of a hormone that is steroid in nature, and state its function.
6. What two characteristics of the carbon atom make it unique?
7. What is the difference between inorganic and organic molecules?
8. What are the three main types of lipids? Give an example of each.

acid group   A portion of an organic molecule that is composed of one carbon atom, two oxygen atoms, and one hydrogen atom, arranged as

$$-\overset{\overset{\displaystyle O}{\|}}{C}-O-H$$

adenosine triphosphate (ATP)   An organic molecule that is able to store the energy needed for immediate use by the cell.

amino acid   A simple organic molecule that has an *acid group* $(-\overset{\overset{\displaystyle O}{\|}}{C}-O-H)$ on one end and an *amino group* $(-N\overset{\diagup H}{\diagdown H})$ on the other end—the building block of proteins.

amino group   A portion of an organic molecule containing a nitrogen atom and two hydrogen atoms.

$$(-N\overset{\diagup H}{\diagdown H})$$

biological chemistry   The study of the chemistry of living things.

carbohydrate   An organic molecule that contains carbon, hydrogen, and oxygen in the following ratio: CH_2O.

covalent bond   The attraction between two atoms formed by the sharing of electrons.

double bond   The attraction between two atoms in which two pairs (4) of electrons are shared covalently. It is usually denoted by two lines between atoms. Example: $O=C=O$.

enzyme   A special kind of protein that is produced by living cells and is able to speed up the rate at which chemical reactions take place, in otherwise normal conditions.

fat   Large organic molecule that is composed of three fatty acids and a single glycerol molecule.

fatty acid   A long carbon chain with an acid group ($-\overset{\overset{\displaystyle O}{\|}}{C}-O-H$) at one end.

glycerol   The three-carbon molecules that combine with fatty acids to form fats.

hormones   Molecules that act as regulators of a variety of activities.

inorganic molecules   Molecules that do not usually contain carbon atoms in chains.

lipid   A type of organic molecule that contains carbon, hydrogen, and oxygen, and usually does not dissolve in water.

macromolecule   Large organic molecule typical of living things. Examples: protein, DNA, and RNA.

nucleic acid   Complex organic molecules made up of subunits called *nucleotides,* involved in storing and transferring information within the cell.

nucleotide   The basic subunit of nucleic acids.

organic molecules   Molecules that contain carbon chains and are particularly common in living things.

phospholipid   Special kind of lipid important as a part of cell membranes.

polypeptide   Chain of amino acids that is usually less than 100 amino acids long.

protein   Chain of amino acids that is usually more than 100 amino acids long.

saturated fat   Fat that is composed of fatty acids that do not contain double bonds between any of the carbons.

simple sugar   The simplest unit of a carbohydrate.

steroid   Complex lipid molecule characterized by ringlike arrangements of atoms.

structural formula   Shows the arrangement and bonding of the various atoms within a molecule.

structural protein   A protein that forms part of the framework of cells and holds the various parts of a cell together.

unsaturated fat   Fat that is composed of fatty acid that contains double bonds between some of the carbons.

Purpose　This chapter will deal with theories of the origin of cellular life, which involves the changing of inorganic materials to organic materials. These organic materials may have been combined into living units called cells. The development of these ideas illustrates how people in science go about gathering and determining the worth of information.

The Origin and Evolution of Cells

5

Mice from Mud, or Molecules!

Man's curiosity has, for centuries, spurred him to investigate the basic nature of his environment. The vast amount of chemical and biological information presented in the previous chapters indicates his ability to gather and analyze information. His efforts have resulted in solutions to many problems, and have also revealed new and more challenging areas of concern. One question, despite his efforts, has continued to be a subject of speculation: what is the nature and origin of life?

In simpler times, the origin of life from nonliving things was never doubted. The Greeks, Romans, Chinese, and many other ancients believed that maggots, lice, frogs, and even mice could spontaneously arise from mud. They thought they saw these events happening every day. It was thought that mice could be produced from a sweaty shirt if it was kept in a dark, cool room with several grains of wheat. Many prominent scientists believed in this concept. Only through the efforts of scientific investigators like Redi, Spallanzani, and Pasteur was this classical concept of **spontaneous generation** discarded (fig. 5.1).

The argument between the supporters of spontaneous generation and the supporters of **biogenesis** has lasted over 300 years. Persons believing in biogenesis thought that all living things came from preexisting life. During this period, the cleverness and imagination of those involved were used to the fullest in the attempt to disprove the others' position. It was Francesco Redi (1668) who set up the first **controlled experiment** to disprove those who supported spontaneous generation. This is the best type of experimental setup from which to draw conclusions, since there is only one unknown in question. Redi used two sets of dishes and varied only one part of the experiment (fig. 5.2). These experiments put to rest the concept of spontaneous generation for only a short period of time. It was 1676 when the idea of spontaneous generation was accidentally revived, due to the tinkerings of a Dutch clothier

Fig. 5.1 *Life from Non-life.* The theory of spontaneous generation is as old as man himself. Many classical works of art, such as shown here, point out the idea that living things could originate from non-living matter or even from very different types of organisms. M. C. Escher's work entitled "The Reptiles 1943" shows the life cycle of a little alligator. Amid all kinds of objects, a drawing book lies open, and the drawing on view is a mosaic of reptilian figures in three contrasting shades. Evidently, one of them has tired from lying flat and rigid amongst his fellows, so he puts one plastic-looking leg over the edge of the book, wrenches himself free, and launches out into real life. He climbs up the back of a book on zoology and works his laborious way up the slippery slope of a set-square to the highest point of his existence. Then after a quick snort, tired but fulfilled, he goes downhill again, via an ashtray, to the level surface, to that flat drawing paper, and meekly rejoins his erstwhile friends, taking up once more his function as an element of surface-division. (Courtesy of the Escher Foundation— Haags Gemeentemuseum— The Hague.)

Anton van Leeuwenhoek. His discovery of "animalcules," little animals, while using lenses reopened the debate. Where did these new life forms come from? Spallanzani benefited from Redi's use of controlled experiments and was successfully able to put to rest the spontaneous generation theory once more. In 1745, in response to a challenge by Joseph Needham, an English priest and naturalist, Spallanzani devised an experiment that not only settled the argument, but demonstrated that heating followed by an airtight seal would prevent spoilage of foods. No "animalcules" were generated in his experiment. It was this experiment, on the origin of life, that ultimately led to the basic preservative methods used in the commercial canning industry (fig. 5.3).

Spallanzani's evidence supported the theory of biogenesis until 1775 when Lavosier and Priestly discovered oxygen. This discovery brought on another wave of interest in spontaneous generation. It was suggested that since oxygen was excluded from Spallanzani's experiment, the spontaneous generation of life was prevented. With this new challenge to the theory of biogenesis, Louis Pasteur (1869) began to experiment with the origin of bacteria and their need for oxygen. He successfully defended the biogenic theory. Even though Pasteur's original work was designed to investigate bio-

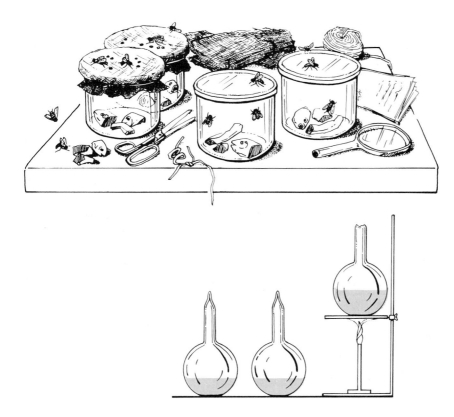

Fig. 5.2 Redi's Experiment. The two sets of jars here are identical in every way with one exception—the gauze covering. The set on the left is called the control group, and the set on the right is called the experimental group. Any differences seen between the control and the experimental groups are the result of a single variable. In this manner, Redi concluded that the presence of maggots in meat was due to flies laying their eggs on the meat, and not to spontaneous generation.

Fig. 5.3 *Spallanzani's Experiment.* Spallanzani carried the experimental method of Redi one step further. By sealing the flasks after they had been boiled, he demonstrated that spontaneous generation could not occur unless the broths were exposed to the "germs" in the air.

genesis, he gathered much other information that helped to control disease in the wine and silkworm industries, and led to the production of a vaccine to protect cattle against deadly anthrax. He also demonstrated the presence of bacteria in the air, a fact that later led to the development of sterilizing techniques (fig. 5.4).

Most important in the research of the origin of life was the understanding of the chemical similarity between living and nonliving things. Chemical reactions that could occur in a test tube or a living thing were identified. Chemical compounds once thought to be made only by organisms, **organic compounds,** were soon produced in the chemistry laboratory. Urea, an animal waste product, was the first organic compound to be synthesized in the lab (1828). Today vitamins, hormones, and a half-million other organic compounds have been synthesized. These advances in chemistry once again led to probing the question of the origin of life. However this time, the study was from a chemical point of view. Was it possible that spontaneous generation did, in fact, occur at some previous time on earth by a process that did not produce mice from mud, but produced the macromolecules characteristic and necessary for the origin of a "first organism"? These **protobionts,** first living things, may have evolved into the various life forms recognized today.

Fig. 5.4 *Pasteur's Experiment.* The gooseneck flasks of Pasteur were designed to allow for the flow of air into the flasks, but not airborne organisms. Pasteur demonstrated that germfree air with its oxygen does not support spontaneous generation of life. The autoclave shown on the right is designed to destroy all life forms and was developed on the basis of Pasteur's experimentation. (Photo courtesy of American Sterilizer Company.)

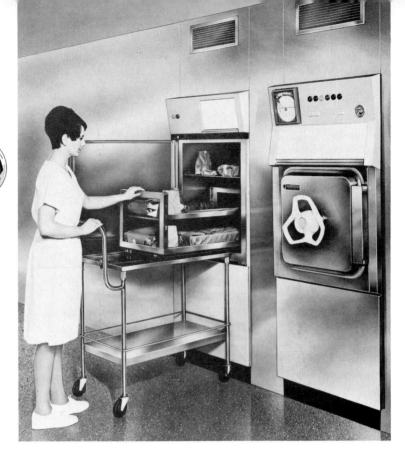

The Present State of Affairs: Spontaneous Generation Revisited

The spontaneous formation of macromolecules (examples: proteins and carbohydrates) and their organization into new cells does not happen today. Present environmental conditions are not favorable for their survival due to the presence of competing living organisms and destructively high concentrations of oxygen in our atmosphere.

Any atmosphere that contains molecular oxygen is called an **oxidizing atmosphere.** Recall the discussion in chapter three on how easily oxygen reacts with iron to change it from a strong, stable material to a powdery rust. Astrophysicists' investigations have indicated that the primitive earth's atmosphere may have differed greatly from that found at present. There was no oxygen (O_2); but hydrogen (H_2), methane (CH_4), water vapor (H_2O), and ammonia (NH_3) were present. Such an atmosphere is called a **reducing atmosphere.**

It was in 1924 that a Russian scientist, A. I. Oparin, developed a testable idea while speculating that nonbiologic synthesis of organic compounds could have occurred under reducing conditions. During the cooling process of the newly formed earth, water vapor condensed into rain and began to form the oceans. As rivers ran to the oceans they carried dissolved gases (methane, ammonia, etc.) from the atmosphere, and a variety of minerals (iron, calcium, etc.), and salts (sodium chloride, potassium sulfate, etc.) from the land. The energy sources available at the time included lightning, ultraviolet light, and geothermal heat, which encouraged chemical reactions to take place in the ocean. These dissolved molecules could have served as basic building blocks for use in the construction of larger molecules such as amino acids, sugars, or nucleic acids (fig. 5.5).

Twenty-nine years later (1953), Stanley Miller assembled an experimental apparatus, which simulated these primitive earth conditions as a test of Oparin's theory. He successfully demonstrated the spontaneous, nonbio-

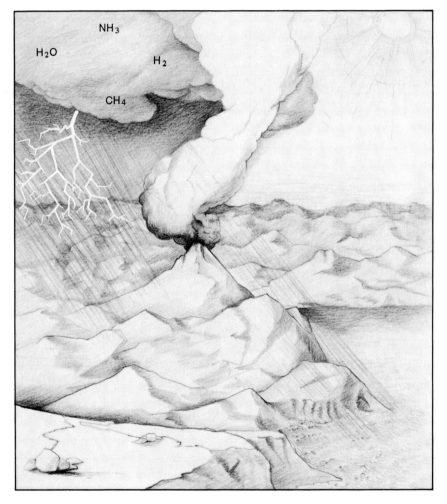

Fig. 5.5 *Primitive Earth.* The environment of the primitive earth was harsh and lifeless. But many scientists believe it contained the basic molecules necessary to fashion the first living things, spontaneously.

logic formation of organic molecules. He found large numbers of amino acids (the building blocks of proteins) and some energy-containing sugar molecules (fig. 5.6). Since all water eventually drains into the ocean, some scientists have speculated that these organic molecules would have been concentrated in the ocean in the same manner as salts.

Many are in agreement that a 1 percent concentration of organic compounds existed in that primitive sea and was adequate enough to allow for the nonbiologic synthesis of such macromolecules as DNA, proteins, and ATP (a chemical source of energy for the protobiont). These speculations have also been reinforced by experiments.

The existence of these complex molecules on the primitive earth *has not been proven*. The possibility of their nonbiologic formation *has been demonstrated* by experiment. This same experimental approach has been used to investigate the likelihood of cell-like structures (protobionts) forming under simulated, primitive earth conditions. Two such structures have been demonstrated. Protobionts are thought to have formed by the clustering of macromolecules within an orderly covering of water molecules. Oparin speculated that such a structure could have been the protobiont. Even today, similar droplets formed in the lab have been confused with true living cells because of their appearance, ability to selectively absorb surrounding molecules, and tendency to form discrete internal structures. A different type of cell-like

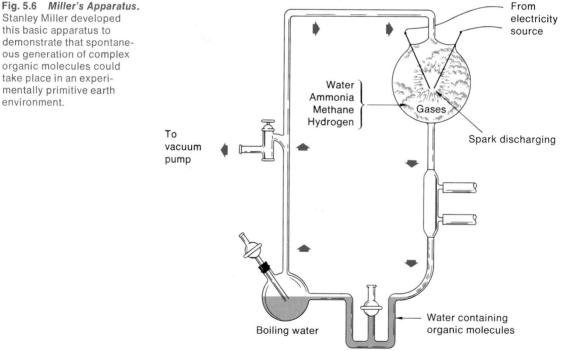

Fig. 5.6 *Miller's Apparatus.* Stanley Miller developed this basic apparatus to demonstrate that spontaneous generation of complex organic molecules could take place in an experimentally primitive earth environment.

From electricity source

Water
Ammonia
Methane } Gases
Hydrogen

To vacuum pump

Spark discharging

Boiling water

Water containing organic molecules

structure composed of protein was proposed by Sidney Fox. Its properties demonstrated movement, growth, and a type of "reproduction." Any type of primitive cell would need to control the nature of its chemical reactions in order to grow and reproduce. This could very well have been done by primitive proteins called enzymes.

Oxygen: Good or Evil?

During this primitive period the earth was undergoing a change from a re-ducing atmosphere to an oxidizing atmosphere. The oxygen was being released from two sources: the splitting of water molecules by ultraviolet light (fig. 5.7) and the release of oxygen from some of the chemical reactions of living cells.

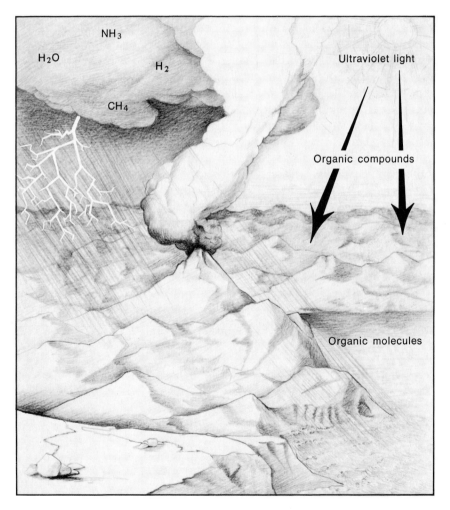

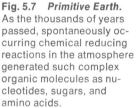

Fig. 5.7 *Primitive Earth.* As the thousands of years passed, spontaneously occurring chemical reducing reactions in the atmosphere generated such complex organic molecules as nucleotides, sugars, and amino acids.

All of the orderly chemical reactions that take place in a cell are referred to as **metabolism.** Metabolism that requires complex organic molecules as a food source is called **heterotrophy** (fig. 5.8). The alternative is **autotrophy** and is the means by which the cell is capable of utilizing carbon dioxide and other simple inorganic molecules to manufacture its food (fig. 5.9). The foods are used by the cells as building materials for new cell parts, repair of worn-out parts, and as a source of energy (fig. 5.10). Today these two major types of metabolism still exist, but are much more complicated than they were on the primitive earth. Any food-eating organisms, such as humans, snakes, mosquitoes, and fungi, are present-day examples of heterotrophs. The most significant autotrophs are such green plants as algae, mosses, ferns, and trees.

The gradual accumulation of oxygen had many effects. The production of macromolecules was greatly decreased because a form of oxygen known as ozone (O_3) effectively blocked out the ultraviolet light energy used in synthesizing food molecules. This meant that the protobionts had to find a new source of macromolecules for energy and food. Ozone that is present today as the atmospheric layer called the ozonosphere still serves today as it did two-billion years ago, to screen out harmful ultraviolet radiation.

The increase in oxygen (O_2) served to stop nonbiologic synthesis of macromolecules and to stop chemical evolution. It also favored those protobionts that had methods for surviving under these oxidizing conditions. Since no new food molecules were produced, the survival and reproduction of "cells" that were capable of autotrophic metabolism were favored. This atmospheric change also favored those heterotrophs with metabolic systems that did not rely on the "old" food molecules. These different forms of metabolism made them more likely to survive in the presence of the highly reactive oxygen molecules, and in fact, some may have used this oxygen in their metabolism. These new chemical reactions made the conversion of sugar to a chemical form of energy (ATP) more efficient. This conversion of sugar

$$\text{Organic molecules} + O_2 \longrightarrow CO_2 + H_2O + \text{Energy}$$

Fig. 5.8 ***Oxidation of Organic Molecules.*** Complex organic molecules, such as sugar, react with atmospheric oxygen to release the stored energy found in the chemical bonds.

$$CO_2 + H_2O + \text{Energy} \longrightarrow \text{Organic molecules} + O_2$$

Fig. 5.9 ***Photosynthesis.*** Photosynthesis is the series of chemical reactions as shown in this equation. The basic reactions result in the conversion of simple molecules of carbon dioxide and water to the complex organic molecules necessary to support life.

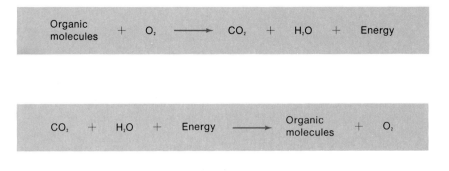

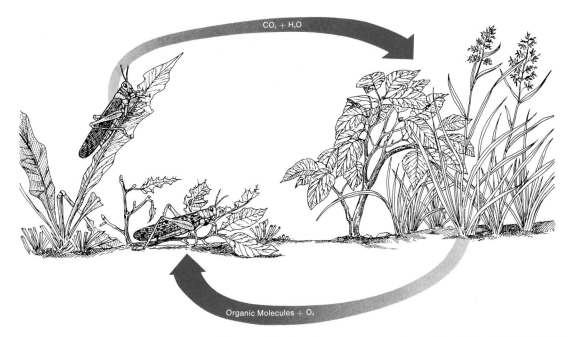

$CO_2 + H_2O$

Organic Molecules + O_2

Fig. 5.10 *Autotroph-Heterotroph Interdependency.* An interdependence of autotrophs and heterotrophs has developed. Each type of living thing supports the life processes of the other.

to ATP is a sequence of chemical reactions and is found in many complex plants and animals today. The process is called aerobic respiration and will be dealt with in detail in chapter eight, "Biochemical Pathways."

Heterotrophs and autotrophs have since become interdependent. Each type relies on the other for the necessary molecules to survive and reproduce. A cycle of dependency has been formed in which the autotroph serves as an energy-capturing and macromolecule-making system. The energy and molecules are then passed on for use by the heterotrophs in their lives, and they return the used, simple molecules to the autotrophs for recycling. As the population of organisms grew, the food supply decreased, and varied forms of organisms began to occur. These were better able to survive, reproduce, and compete for the available foods. The organisms that were successful we see today, while the not so successful organisms have become extinct (fig. 5.11).

Time

"Given so much time, the impossible becomes possible, the possible probable, and the probable virtually certain" (George Wald, Harvard University). The probability of being dealt a perfect hand in bridge may be one in a million. That does not mean that it will not happen. As a matter of fact, it happens every year. The really important fact is how many hands of bridge are dealt in a year. If only one hand is dealt, then the chance of it being a perfect hand is one in a million. However, if fifty million hands are dealt, there would probably be about fifty perfect hands. Likewise, the probability of certain of these steps happening in chemical evolution is very small, but

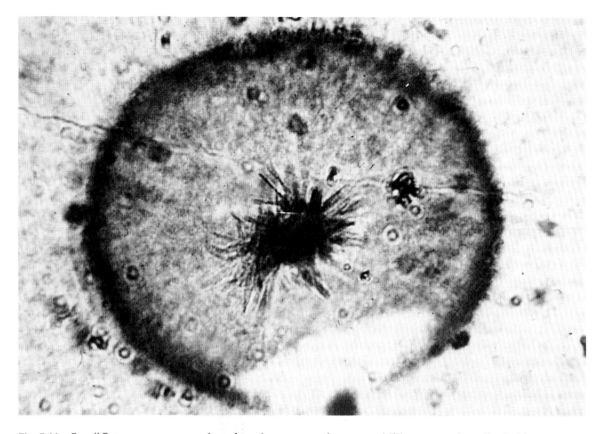

Fig. 5.11 *Fossil Procaryotes.* The fossil bluegreen algae shown here is estimated to be 2.7 billion years old. This is one of many such cells found by Elso S. Barghoorn of Harvard University while he was investigating the Gunflint geological formation in southern Ontario. (Courtesy of Dr. Elso S. Barghoorn.)

remember that there were about two billion years for all of this to occur. How many hands of bridge could you deal in two billion years, or how many could be dealt by two billion people in a year? If what has been hypothesized by Oparin and others is true, then life as we presently understand it was probably formed through the process of chemical, spontaneous generation and evolution (change). Have researchers, like Miller and Fox, gathered enough data to again support this theory? Has there been enough time? Maybe it is time for another Redi, Spallanzani, or Pasteur to appear on the scene to again challenge the idea of spontaneous generation. No doubt this will occur and result in new scientific advancements. But whether or not this "new" spontaneous generation theory will be shown to be false cannot be said at present. The argument supporting chemical, spontaneous generation is being supported by a wide variety of evidence from many different fields. To disprove this evidence will require much more effort than was ever exerted before.

One step in the process of the evolution of cells is still receiving much attention today. The question is, how did simple protobiont structures assemble to form the complex cell machinery we recognize in today's cells? In addition, the spin-off from this research has benefited man greatly. These current investigations into the origin of life have increased our knowledge in many fields. For example, viruses are very simple particles and may resemble some of the first "living things." How they are constructed and how they behave may give some additional clues into the origin of life. In the mean time, increased knowledge of viruses has resulted in new methods of controlling virus-caused diseases. They have also provided insights into how the genetic material of a cell functions. Just as in Pasteur's time, investigations of the origin of life have led to discoveries that were not directly related to answering that question, but have been useful in other ways.

The Scientific Method

All of the separate investigations into the origin of life have followed a particular pattern. In each case, the investigator has made an **observation** and questioned what was really going on. Did those mice scurrying from the dirty shirt and grains of wheat really grow there, or is there another explanation? Spallanzani observed maggots on meat, but did they really grow out of the meat? These questions did not go unanswered. A guess was made, and we call this possible explanation a **hypothesis.** To simply guess at an answer doesn't make it true. A good hypothesis accounts for all of the facts observed, and is able to be tested. In many cases, this testing is done by experiment. A single experiment does not always determine whether a hypothesis is correct. Usually a large number of experiments by many different people testing the same hypothesis is needed to make a good judgement of the accuracy of a hypothesis. Some hypotheses cannot stand the test of time. As new methods of testing the hypothesis are introduced, you may find that the hypothesis was wrong and must be discarded in favor of another. This has happened a number of times with spontaneous generation and biogenesis. Each time new information and methods have been introduced, the hypotheses were challenged. New experiments were performed and more information was gained, and yet we still are unable to answer the question, can living things arise from nonliving matter? This pattern of observation, hypothesis formation, and experimentation is known as the **scientific method.** If the scientific method is to be a valuable way of confirming observations and discovering new information, the users of the method must be unbiased, open-minded, and constantly questioning the results.

Summary

The centuries of research outlined in this chapter point out the development of an approach to understanding life. The scientific method is used to follow man's attempt to answer one question. The use of the method produces more questions than it answers in any single try, some of which may remain unanswered. The current theory of the origin of life speculates that the primitive earth's environment led to the spontaneous organization of chemicals into macromolecules which, in many cases, became organized into primitive cells. These basic units of all life then changed through time in response to a changing environment. The likelihood of these occurrences is supported by experimental evidence in simulated primitive earth environments, and are not to be found to occur in nature. The creation of life, as we know it, has not taken place in a test tube as yet. Despite the generation of volumes of worthwhile information, the question still remains unanswered (fig. 5.12).

Fig. 5.12 *Summary of the Reactions on Primitive Earth.*

CHANGES IN:				
I Radiation	ultra-violet light	ultra-violet light	less ultra-violet light	low level of ultra-violet light
II Atmosphere	H_2 CH_4 H_2O NH_3	H_2 CH_4 H_2O NH_3	Ozone, NH_3 O_2 H_2O, H_2	Ozone, O_2 CO_2 H_2O N_2
III Cell life forms	none present	none present	protobionts formed	present-day cell forms
IV Molecules in sea	simple molecules	complex molecules formed spontaneously	fewer complex molecules	organic molecules produced by living cells
TIME	5 billion years ago		2.5 billion years ago	Present

Consider This   It has been speculated that there is "life" on another planet in our galaxy. The following data has been obtained from "reliable" sources concerning the nature of this life. Using these data, what additional information is necessary, and how would you go about verifying these data in developing a theory on the origins of life on planet X?

1. The age of the planet is ten billion years.
2. Water is present in the atmosphere.
3. The planet is farther from its sun than our earth is from our sun.
4. The molecules of various gases in the atmosphere are constantly being removed.
5. Chemical reactions on this planet occur at approximately one-half the rate that they occur on the planet earth.

1. In what sequence did the following things happen: first living cell, oxidizing atmosphere, autotrophy, heterotrophy, reducing atmosphere, first organic molecules, ozone formation?
2. What is meant by spontaneous generation? What is meant by biogenesis?
3. Which of the following scientists provided evidence that was in support of the theory of spontaneous generation? In support of biogenesis?

   Pasteur / Fox / Spallanzani / Oparin / Redi
4. Can spontaneous generation occur today? Why or why not?
5. The scientific method cannot be used to deny or prove the existence of God. Why?
6. What are controlled experiments, and why are they necessary to support a hypothesis?
7. Why do most scientists believe that life originated in the seas?
8. What were the circumstances on the primitive earth that favored the survival of an autotrophic type of organism?
9. The current theory of the spontaneous chemical generation of life on earth depends on our knowing something of the history of the earth. Why is this so?
10. List two important effects caused by the increase of oxygen in the atmosphere.

autotroph   An organism that can manufacture its own food from simple inorganic molecules.

biogenesis   A theory that states that a living thing can arise only from a living parent.

controlled experiment   A comparison of two systems identical in all but one respect.

heterotroph   An organism that cannot manufacture its own food, but requires complex organic molecules from living organisms or other sources.

hypothesis   A possible explanation of, or answer to, a problem or question. This guess should account for all facts observed, and be a testable answer.

metabolism   All of the series of complex chemical reactions within living things.

observation   The process of realizing that a problem or question exists and that there are several facts related to the problem, which one can perceive using sight, sound, etc.

organic compound   Molecules containing carbon and (in the past) thought to be formed only by living organisms.

oxidizing atmosphere   Containing oxygen (O_2) molecules.

protobiont   First life.

reducing atmosphere   Containing molecular hydrogen (H_2) or other molecules bound to hydrogen. Example: nitrogen with hydrogen—ammonia (NH_3).

scientific method   A logical approach to problem solving using observation, questioning, and experimentation.

spontaneous generation   The theory of the origin of life stating that living things arise from nonliving material.

Purpose   The *cell* is the simplest structure capable of existing as an individual living unit. Within this unit, called the cell, there are certain chemical reactions required for maintaining life. These reactions do not occur at random, but are associated with the specific parts of all the many different kinds of cells. This chapter deals with certain cellular structures found within most types of cells, and discusses their functions. By developing an understanding of cell structure and function, you will be better able to understand and decide on the value of current information being publicized by TV, radio, and other media.

Cell History, Structure, and Function

6

Cell Concept

The concept of a cell did not arise spontaneously, but has been added to and modified over many years. It is still in this process of modification today.

Several events associated with particular individuals represent milestones in the construction of the cell concept. Anton van Leeuwenhoek is generally given credit for developing the first **microscope.** When he discovered that he could see things moving in pond water, his curiosity stimulated him to look at a variety of things through his crude microscopes. He studied blood, semen, feces, pepper, tartar, and many other things. Van Leeuwenhoek was the one who first saw individual cells, and recognized them as living units. He did not, however, call them cells; instead he called them "animalcules," little animals.

The honor of first using the term *cell* goes to Robert Hooke of England, who was also interested in how things looked when magnified. He chose to study thin slices of cork from a tree. What he saw was a mass of cubicles that fit neatly together, reminding him of the barren rooms in a monastery. Hence, he called them by the same name, *cells.* Ironically, we have come to use the word *cell* with respect to a living unit, when in fact what Hooke saw was only the walls that had surrounded the living portions of cells. The cell wall, as this nonliving part is called, is composed of layers of a complex carbohydrate called cellulose. This arrangement of living material inside the confining, cellulose cell wall lends strength and protection to the cell but hampers its flexibility and movement (fig. 6.1). The plants, one major group of organisms, are composed of cells that have cell walls. Animal cells do not have cell walls, but acquire strength and protection in other ways. The cell wall appears to be a rigid solid layer of material, but is really a loosely woven layer resembling a leaky basket through which many types of molecules can easily pass.

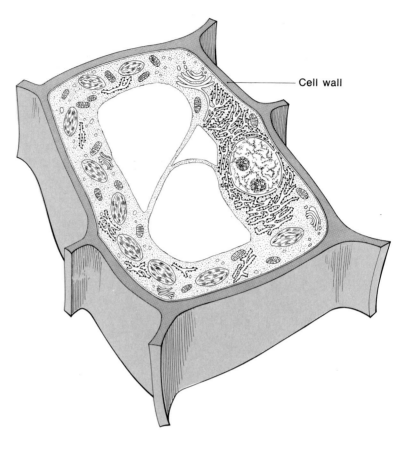

Fig. 6.1 *Cell Wall.* Plant cells have a layer of cellulose outside of the cell membrane that gives support and protection to the protoplasm.

Cell wall

Hooke's use of the term *cell* was really only the beginning. Soon after Hooke's term caught on, it was determined that the vitally important portion of the cell was inside. This was called **protoplasm,** which literally means 'first-juice' or 'juice of the first importance.' The term *protoplasm,* then, allows us to distinguish between the nonliving cell wall and the living portion inside. As with any new field of study, this early attempt at terminology was not a complete success. Very soon microscopists were able to distinguish two different regions of protoplasm. One type of protoplasm was more **viscous** and darker than the other and appeared as a central body within a more fluid juice. This early concept of cell structure can be better understood if you look at a hen's egg. The yolk resembles the nucleus of a cell suspended in the white. Both the yolk and the egg white are part of the egg, but the difference between the two is quite obvious. The term egg is not definite enough, neither is the term protoplasm. Therefore, two new terms were introduced: **cytoplasm** (literally cell juice), and **nucleus** (the kernel). Both the cytoplasm and the nucleus are parts of the protoplasm, just as the white and the yolk are both parts of the egg (fig. 6.2).

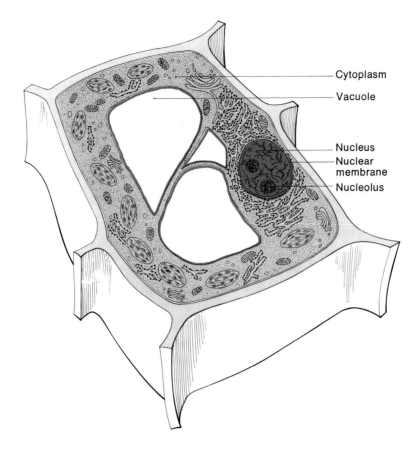

Cytoplasm

Vacuole

Nucleus

Nuclear membrane

Nucleolus

Fig. 6.2 *Protoplasm.* The living material in a cell is called protoplasm. It is composed of a more viscous central nucleus and a less viscous liquid—the cytoplasm.

The development of better light microscopes and ultimately the **electron microscope** revealed that protoplasm contained many structures not previously seen. These structures are called **organelles** (little organs), and each has a particular structure that is related to its function. These organelles are divided into two different categories—those that are composed of **membranes** and those that are not.

Membranes and Their Activities

A membrane is a thin sheet of material similar in many ways to sandwich wrap or waxed paper. Many of the structures in cells are made of a particular kind of membrane that is composed of two phospholipid layers sandwiched between two outside layers of protein. This is similar to two buttered pieces of meat with the two buttered surfaces touching. The butter would represent the phospholipid layers, and the meat would be the protein. This membrane is an active, functional part of the cell. Some of the proteins of the membrane are enzymes, and are involved in important chemical reactions. Other mole-

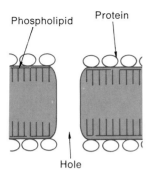

Phospholipid   Protein

Hole

Fig. 6.3 *Membrane Structure.* Membranes in cells are composed of layers of lipids sandwiched between two layers of protein.

cules are involved in moving materials from one side of the membrane to the other (fig. 6.3). In addition to all of this activity, there are holes in the membrane that allow the movement of some molecules from one side of the membrane to the other. Certain of these molecules can dissolve in the lipid layers of the membrane, and thereby pass across it. An example of this might be an oily substance entering or leaving the cell.

The cell membrane (sometimes called the plasma membrane) is the container of the protoplasm and is the outside edge of the cell. It acts as a barrier that separates the inside from the outside of the cell, and therefore materials must cross this barrier if they are to enter or leave the cell. **Diffusion,** which results from the random movement of molecules, is an important process that allows materials to cross the membrane. Molecules are not always evenly distributed. Many times there may be a high concentration of a particular type of molecule in one place and a lower concentration of that molecule in another (fig. 6.4). When this occurs, the random motion of the molecules will eventually result in the net movement of the molecules from the area of highest concentration to the area of lowest concentration. In other words, the net movement of molecules is downhill. This difference in concentration is referred to as the **diffusion gradient.** When the molecules are equally distributed, no such gradient exists. Diffusion can only take place as long as there are no barriers to their free movement. In the case of a cell, the membrane permits some molecules to pass through while others are held back. But the cell membrane does not distinguish between outside and inside. The restriction on molecules passing into the cell is just as effective for those leaving the cell. The cell membrane allows some molecules to pass while others are prevented from traveling through. Membranes that function in this way are called **differentially permeable.**

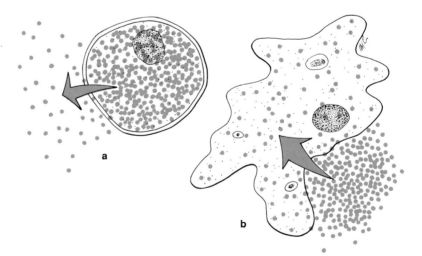

Fig. 6.4 *Diffusion.* Notice that the gases are moving into and out of the cells from the areas where they are in greater concentration to areas where they are in lower concentration.

The process of diffusion is an important method for exchanging materials between cells and their surroundings. Since the cell has no control over this process the molecules move at random. For example, animals that require oxygen constantly use up this gas from their cells. The cells, then, will contain a low concentration of oxygen in comparison to the oxygen level outside the cell. This diffusion gradient goes from the outside of the cell to the inside. It means that the animal cells will constantly gain oxygen as long as they use it. In large animals, many of the cells are buried deep inside the body and if it were not for their circulatory systems, there would be little opportunity for cells to exchange gases directly with their surroundings. The circulatory system is a transportation system within a body that carries molecules from one place to another.

Oxygen may diffuse into the blood through the membranes of the lungs, gills, or other moist surfaces of the animal's body. The circulatory system then transports the oxygen-rich blood throughout the body, where the oxygen will automatically diffuse into cells because they are low in oxygen. The opposite is true in the case of the gas carbon dioxide. Animal cells constantly produce carbon dioxide, and there is always a high concentration of these molecules within the cell. These molecules of carbon dioxide diffuse from the cell into the blood, where the concentration is lower. The blood is pumped to the moist surface, and the carbon dioxide again diffuses into the surrounding environment, which has a lower concentration of this gas. In a similar manner, many other types of molecules constantly enter and leave cells (fig. 6.5).

Water is one of the kinds of molecules that easily diffuses through cell membranes. The net movement of water molecules through a differentially permeable membrane is a special case of diffusion known as **osmosis.** A proper amount of water is required if a cell is to function efficiently. Too much

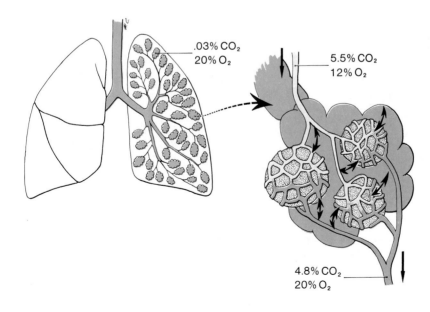

.03% CO_2
20% O_2

5.5% CO_2
12% O_2

4.8% CO_2
20% O_2

Fig. 6.5 *Diffusion in the Lungs.* Notice that two gases can be diffusing in opposite directions simultaneously.

water in a cell may dilute the cell contents and interfere with the chemical reactions necessary to keep the cell alive. Too little water in the cell may result in the buildup of a high concentration of poisonous waste products. As with the diffusion of other molecules, the cell has no control over the diffusion of water molecules. This means that the cell can only remain in balance in an environment that does not cause the cell to lose or gain too much water. If a cell does not contain the same concentration of water as its surroundings, it will either gain or lose water. Many organisms have a concentration of water that is equal to their surroundings. This is particularly true of simple organisms that live in the ocean. If an organism is going to survive in an environment that has a different concentration of water from its cells, it must expend energy to maintain this difference. Organisms that live in fresh water have a lower concentration of water than their surroundings. Since animal cells tend to gain water by osmosis, they must expend energy to eliminate this excess if they are to keep from swelling and bursting. Plant cells will not burst because they are surrounded by a rigid cell wall. Osmosis will also occur if the water concentration outside the plant cell is higher than the concentration inside the cell. Since more water molecules are entering than are leaving the cell, an internal pressure is created. If the water concentration is higher on the inside of the cell than on the outside, the cell will collapse because more water molecules are leaving than are entering. This will occur in both animal and plant cells. This can be seen in many vegetables that have become soft and wilted. The solution to this problem is a simple one. Placing the vegetable in a bowl of water will result in more water molecules entering its cells than are leaving. The pressure will increase inside each of the cells so that they press against one another. This will make the vegetable crisp again (fig. 6.6).

So far we have only considered those situations in which the cell had no control over the movement of molecules. Cells cannot rely solely on diffusion, since many of the molecules they require are relatively rare in their surroundings. Therefore they must actively take in these molecules if they are to survive, creating a storehouse of supplies to be used in their normal life processes. *This means that the molecules must be moved from an area of low concentration to an area of higher concentration.* Since this is going against the normal diffusion gradient of molecules, the cell must expend energy and use other cellular machinery, such as enzymes, to pull these molecules into the cell. This **active transport** process is extremely significant. For example, amino acids, which are essential for the construction of structural proteins and enzymes, are actively transported into cells of the intestine, kidney, and some glands of man. In this situation, the amino acid is attached to a carrier enzyme that ferries it across the cell membrane and drops it off on the other side (fig. 6.7). In some cases molecules are actively transported out of the cells. The kidney is involved in the transport of a number of different types of molecules from the blood into the urine (fig. 6.8).

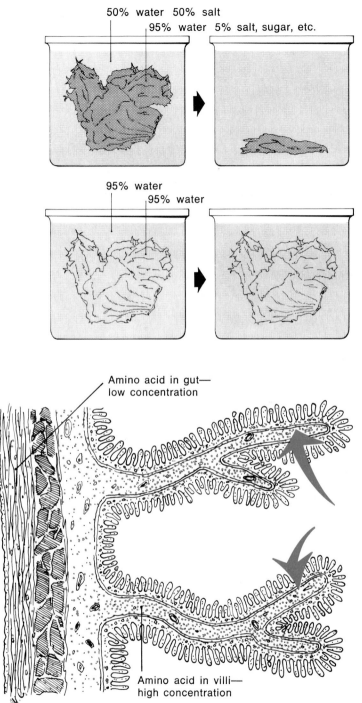

50% water 50% salt

95% water 5% salt, sugar, etc.

Fig. 6.6 *Osmosis.* Osmosis is the diffusion of a solvent (usually water) through a membrane. Notice that the water moves from the area of its higher concentration to the area of its lower concentration.

95% water

95% water

Amino acid in gut—low concentration

Amino acid in villi—high concentration

Fig. 6.7 *Active Transport of Materials into a Cell.* When a material moves against the concentration gradient, the cell must be expending energy to cause this movement. In this case, the cells are actively accumulating amino acids from the intestine.

Fig. 6.8 *Active Transport of Materials Out of a Cell.* The amino acids are being actively removed from the cells into the bloodstream of the kidney.

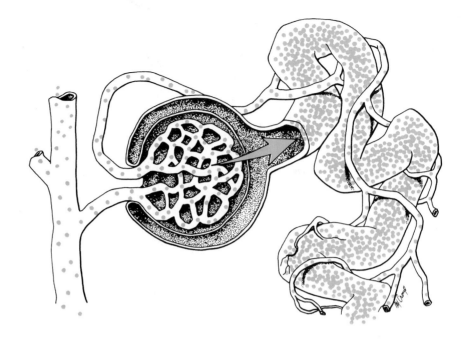

Fig. 6.8 *Active Transport of Materials Out of a Cell.* The amino acids are being actively removed from the cells into the bloodstream of the kidney.

Membranous Organelles

Internal Surfaces

The **endoplasmic reticulum,** ER, is a set of folded membranes found throughout the cell. This system of membranes provides a large surface upon which sequences of chemical reactions can occur. Enzymes and certain other structural units are attached to the membranes in a specific order resembling an assembly line, which results in an overall increase in the efficiency of the cell. The space between the folded membranes may serve as canals for the movement of molecules within the cell. Some researchers suggest that this system of membranes allows for rapid distribution of molecules within a cell (fig. 6.9).

Assembly Line

Most cells produce specialized chemical products that must be released from the cell in a manner that does not interfere with the other metabolic processes. These products are often assembled in a specialized portion of the ER known as the **Golgi apparatus.** The final reactions in the synthesis of these products occur in the Golgi apparatus, where these products are then assembled in packages that are surrounded by membrane. Once the packages are produced, they may move to the outer edge of the cell and release their contents (fig. 6.10).

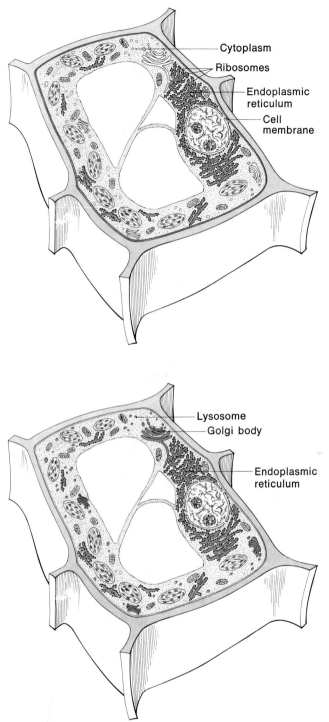

Cytoplasm

Ribosomes

Endoplasmic
reticulum

Cell
membrane

Fig. 6.9 *Endoplasmic Reticulum.* The infoldings of the cell membrane that permeate the cell are called endoplasmic reticulum, or ER. ER increases the surface area of a cell.

Lysosome

Golgi body

Endoplasmic
reticulum

Fig. 6.10 *Golgi Apparatus.* Special areas of the endoplasmic reticulum that are associated with secretion of materials are known as the Golgi apparatus.

Fig. 6.11 *Contractile Vacuole.* Some cells have specialized vacuoles that accumulate excess water. When the vacuoles become full, they eliminate the water by contracting.

Containers

Cells contain a number of storage areas. These are generally called **vacuoles.** In most plants, there is usually one huge centrally located vacuole in which water, food, wastes, and minerals are stored. In animals there are usually many smaller individual vacuoles that contain food or other materials. These storage areas are composed of a surrounding membrane and their contents.

Animal cells that receive too much water because of osmosis contain a specialized vacuole that increases in size as it collects this excess water. Once full, this vacuole has the ability to contract and force the extra water out through the cell membrane. It is called a **contractile vacuole,** and is the means by which these cells keep from swelling and bursting (fig. 6.11).

Another, different type of vacuole has been identified. This special vacuole is called a **lysosome** and contains enzymes that would digest the cell if they were not kept confined. These lysosomes are used in two major ways by cells. When a cell is damaged, the membranes of the lysosome break and the enzymes are released. These enzymes then destroy the cell and break down the large molecules into smaller components that can then be reused by other surrounding cells to repair the damaged area. Another use is demonstrated in the normal development of organisms. For example, frog tadpoles have a tail, but adult frogs do not. As the tadpole slowly changes into a frog, the cells of the tail are destroyed by the action of the lysosomes. Similarly, human embryos have paddle-shaped hands, while adults have individual fingers. As the embryo slowly changes, the cells between the bones of the fingers are destroyed by the action of the lysosomes, thus forming individual fingers (fig. 6.12). In some cases this process does not take place. People with this condition are born with webbed fingers, and the condition is called syndactylism.

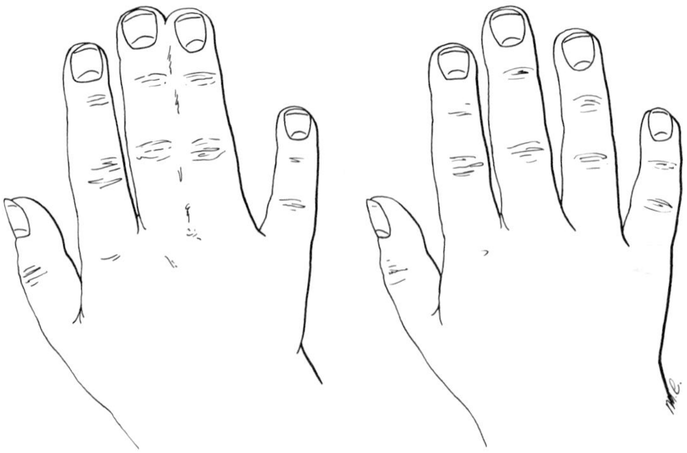

Fig. 6.12 *Action of Lysosomes.* Normally, while a child is developing, lysosomes cause the destruction of the web of tissue between the fingers. Sometimes the lysosomes do not function properly and the child is born with webbed fingers.

Energy Converters

Another membranous structure in the cytoplasm of cells is the **mitochondrion.** Its shape resembles a small bag with a larger bag inside. In order to fit, the larger bag must be folded back on itself. Contained within the mitochondria are specific enzymes responsible for the chemical reactions that release usable energy (ATP). These enzymes are not arranged in a haphazard manner, but are in a sequence that speeds the breakdown of food molecules (fig. 6.13). Another energy converting organelle is the **chloroplast**—a membranous sac that is found in the cells of green plants and contains **chlorophyll.** It is in these organelles that light energy is converted to chemical-bond energy by a process called **photosynthesis.** This form of energy is found in food molecules. Study of the **ultrastructure** of chloroplasts shows that the entire organelle is enclosed by a membrane, and other membranes are folded and interwoven throughout. In some areas, there are concentrations of these membranes stacked up or folded back on themselves. Chlorophyll molecules are attached to these membranes. It is almost as if daubs of chlorophyll were placed on sheets of membrane. The membrane is then folded in such a way that daubs of chlorophyll are stacked on top of one another. These areas of concentrated chlorophyll are called the **grana** of the chloroplast. The membrane without the chlorophyll that interconnects the grana is known as **stroma** membrane (fig. 6.14).

Nuclear Membrane

The nucleus has a boundary membrane called the nuclear membrane, which separates the nucleus from the cytoplasm.

All of the structures just examined are composed of modified membranes. Each membrane is built on the basic plan of two layers of lipid sandwiched between two layers of protein. These membranous organelles suspended in a watery environment give the cytoplasm of the cell a jellylike consistency (fig. 6.15).

Nonmembranous Organelles

The rest of the organelles discussed here are not basically composed of membranes, and are therefore a much more diverse group. You will want to pay particular attention to their structure and function.

Ribosomes

In the cytoplasm, there are many very small structures composed of protein and **ribonucleic acid** (RNA). These are called **ribosomes** and are involved in assembling proteins from amino acids. They are often found on the surface

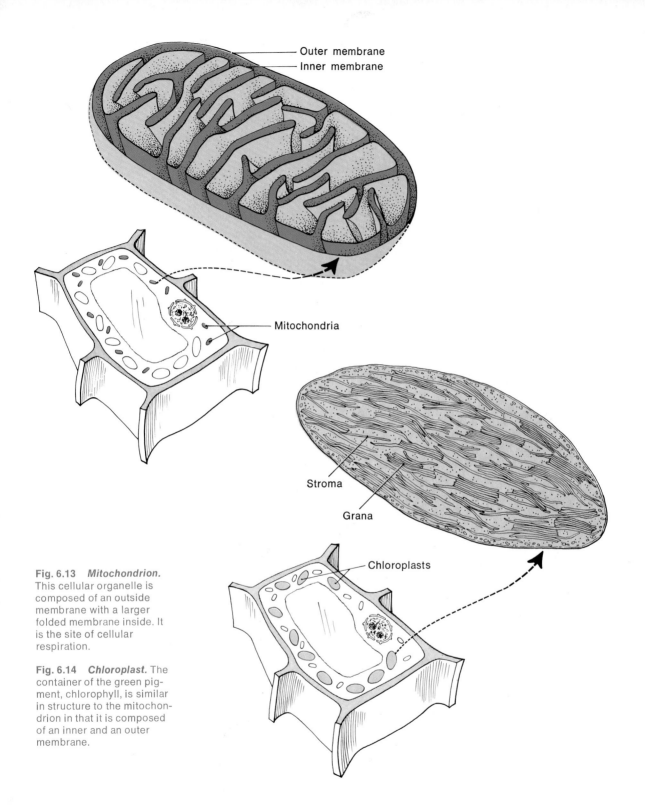

Outer membrane
Inner membrane

Mitochondria

Stroma

Grana

Chloroplasts

Fig. 6.13 *Mitochondrion.* This cellular organelle is composed of an outside membrane with a larger folded membrane inside. It is the site of cellular respiration.

Fig. 6.14 *Chloroplast.* The container of the green pigment, chlorophyll, is similar in structure to the mitochondrion in that it is composed of an inner and an outer membrane.

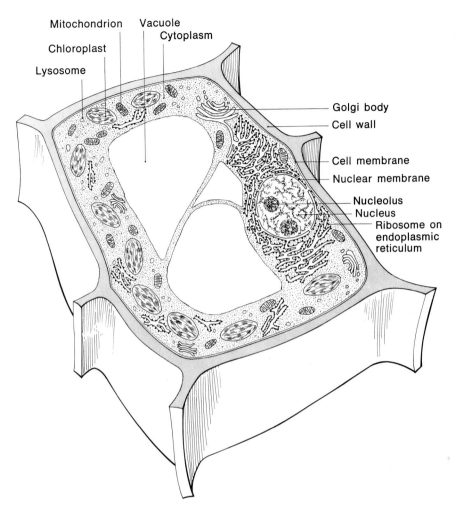

Mitochondrion
Vacuole
Chloroplast
Cytoplasm
Lysosome

Golgi body

Cell wall

Cell membrane

Nuclear membrane

Nucleolus
Nucleus
Ribosome on endoplasmic reticulum

Fig. 6.15 *Cellular Organelles.* Although you might not see all of the structures shown in this composite diagram of a cell when using a light microscope, this illustration shows their relative size and placement.

of the endoplasmic reticulum. In some highly magnified pictures of the cell, the ER seems to have so many of these attached ribosomes that it is called rough ER as opposed to smooth ER. Many ribosomes are also found floating freely in the cytoplasm.

Centrioles

Another nonmembranous structure found in many cells is the **centriole.** It is usually located just outside the nuclear membrane. The centriole is generally composed of two sets of short tubules that are set at right angles to each other (fig. 6.16). It is during cell division that the centriole may perform a function. This structure will be referred to again later.

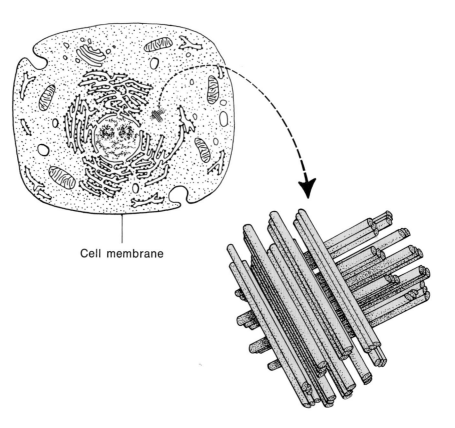

Fig. 6.16 *Centriole.* These two sets of short fibers are located just outside the nuclear membrane in most animal cells.

Cell membrane

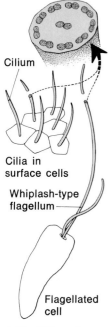

Cilium

Cilia in surface cells

Whiplash-type flagellum

Flagellated cell

Fig. 6.17 *Cilia and Flagella.* These structures function like oars by moving the cell through its environment, or by moving the environment past the cell.

Cilia and Flagella

Many cells have microscopic hairlike structures sticking out from the cell surface. These are the **cilia** or **flagella** (fig. 6.17). We generally call them flagella if they are few in number and long. They are called cilia if they are more numerous and short. Both are similar in structure and perform the function of moving the cell through its environment or moving the environment past the cell surface as a result of their motion.

Inclusions

Not all of the things in the cytoplasm have such a well-defined structure as those we have just examined; some are quite variable. We lump these structures together as miscellaneous material or **granules;** for example, starch granules and oil droplets. In the past many cell structures were called granules, since their structure and function were not clearly known. The ribosomes, mitochondria, and chloroplasts are examples of this. As scientists gain more knowledge of other unidentified particles in the cells, they will be named and more fully described.

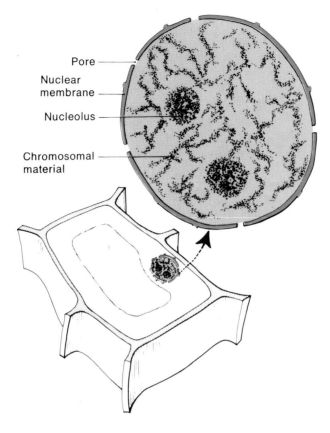

Pore

Nuclear
membrane

Nucleolus

Chromosomal
material

Fig. 6.18 *Nucleus.* The nucleus is a spherical structure containing the genetic data for the cell.

Nuclear Components

As stated at the beginning of this chapter, one of the first structures to be identified in cells was the nucleus. The nucleus was referred to as the cell center. It has been demonstrated that cells cannot live without the nucleus (fig. 6.18).

When nuclear structures were first identified, it was noted that the material in the nucleus became more stained by certain dyes than the rest of the cell. This material was called colored material or **chromatin.** Chromatin is composed of long molecules of **deoxyribonucleic acid** (DNA) in association with protein. These DNA molecules are the information center for the cell. Unwound and loosely organized DNA in the nucleus is called chromatin material. When the DNA and the protein coil into a shorter structure, it is called a **chromosome** (colored body). You should realize that chromatin and chromosomes are really the same thing, but in different forms. They contain the blueprints for the construction and maintenance of the rest of the cell. In addition to the chromatin material, the nucleus may also contain one or more **nucleoli.** We do not know much about these particular structures, but we do know that they are composed of ribonucleic acid.

Summary The concept of the cell has developed over a number of years. It passed through a stage where only two regions, the cytoplasm and the nucleus, could be identified. At present numerous organelles are recognized. Some of these organelles with their structure and function have been tabulated in table 6.1.

The cell is a unit of life common to all living things. The study of individual cells and their structure enables us to understand how they may function as individual living organisms and as parts of many-celled beings.

Table 6.1 *Comparison of the Structure and Function of the Cellular Organelles*

Organelle	Structure	Function
Plasma membrane	Typical membrane structure, phospholipid, protein sandwich.	Controls passage of some materials to and from the environment of the cell.
Endoplasmic reticulum	Folds of membrane forming sheets and canals.	Surface for chemical reactions and canal systems.
Golgi apparatus	Membranous stacks, specialized folded region of the E. R.	Associated with the production of secretions.
Vacuoles	Membranous sacs.	Containers of materials.
Lysosome	Membranous container.	Isolates very strong enzymes from the rest of the cell.
Contractile vacuole	Membranous container.	Expels excess water.
Mitochondria	Large membrane folded inside of a smaller membrane.	Associated with the release of energy from food; site of cellular respiration.
Chloroplast	Double membranous container of chlorophyll.	Site of photosynthesis or food production in green plants.
Nuclear membrane	Typical membrane structure.	Separates the nucleus from the cytoplasm.
Ribosome	Protein and RNA structure.	Site of protein synthesis.
Centriole	Fibrous structure.	Associated with cell division.
Granules	Too small to ascribe a specific structure.	May have a variety of functions.
Nucleolus	Group of RNA molecules located in the nucleus.	Function unknown.
Chromatin material	Composed of DNA and protein.	Contains the hereditary information which the cell uses in its day to day life and passed on to the next generation of cells.

A primitive type of cell consists of a membrane and a few other cell organelles. This protobiont lives in a sea that contains three major kinds of molecules having the following characteristics:

X	Y	Z
Inorganic	Organic	Organic
High concentration outside of cell	High concentration inside of cell	High concentration inside of cell
Essential to life of cell	Essential to life of cell	Poisonous to the cell
Small and can pass through the membrane	Large and cannot easily pass through the membrane	Small and can pass through the membrane

With this information and your background in cell structure and function, osmosis, diffusion, and active transport, decide whether or not this proto-biont will continue to live in this sea, and explain why or why not.

1. Make a list of the membranous organelles of the cell, and describe their functions.
2. Describe how the concept of the cell has changed over the past two hundred years.
3. What three methods allow for exchange of molecules between cells and their surroundings?
4. How do diffusion, osmosis, and active transport differ from one another?
5. What are the differences between the cell wall and the cell membrane?
6. Diagram a cell and show where proteins, nucleic acids, carbohydrates, and lipids would be located.
7. Make a list of nonmembranous organelles of the cell, and describe their functions.
8. Define the following terms: cytoplasm, stroma, grana, chromatin material, and chromosome.
9. Why does putting salt on meat preserve it from spoilage by bacteria?
10. In what way do mitochondria, lysosomes, and chloroplasts resemble one another in function?

active transport   A method whereby a cell exchanges material with its surroundings, and in the process, expends energy.

cells   The general structure of all life. Microscopic in size, and composed of organized living material called protoplasm. Named by R. Hooke.

centriole   A tubular organelle located just outside the nucleus; it functions in cell division.

chlorophyll   The green pigment associated with energy conversion.

chloroplast   Organelles in green plants where the chlorophyll is located. It is the site of food production, photosynthesis.

chromatin material   The genetic material composed of DNA and protein; it is called a chromosome when it is coiled.

chromosomes   Coiled-up chromatin material. Contains a package of genetic information. The number of chromosomes in the cells of a species is consistent.

cilia   Many small hairlike structures that project through the cell membrane. They function like oars for locomotion.

contractile vacuole   A special water container in a cell. It accumulates and then expells excess water.

cytoplasm   One of the two types of protoplasm; that portion of the cell excluding the nucleus.

deoxyribonucleic acid (DNA)   The chemical that contains the hereditary information.

differentially permeable membrane   A membrane that selectively allows some particles to pass through it and prevents ohers.

diffusion   The net movement of a diffusing substance from an area of higher concentration to an area of lower concentration. This net movement is due to randomly moving particles.

diffusion gradient   The difference in concentration of a substance in two areas.

electron microscope   A tool that uses electrons rather than light to expose the structure of small objects. It has a greater magnification capability than the light microscope.

endoplasmic reticulum (ER)   Continuation of the cell membrane, forming canals throughout the cell.

flagella   A few hairlike structures, that are longer than cilia and project through the cell membrane. They function like oars for locomotion.

Golgi apparatus   A specialized region of the ER that functions in secretion and/or packaging of these secretions.

grana   Areas of concentrated chlorophyll within the chloroplast.

granules   The miscellaneous stuff in a cell. Too small to have a well-defined structure.

lysosome   Special vacuole that contains strong enzymes.

membrane   A very thin sheet of material; may be molecular in size or several cells thick.

microscope   A tool that is used to magnify objects. May use light and lenses or other forms of energy and photographic equipment.

mitochondria   Membranous organelles that function in energy release from food. Their structure is a double membrane arranged into rod-shaped organelle.

nucleolus   A lump of RNA that is located in the nucleus and disappears during cell division. It's function is unknown.

nucleoplasm   That portion of protoplasm in the nucleus.

nucleus   Control center of cell that contains DNA.

organelle   Organized region in the protoplasm that has a specific structure and a specific function. Literally means 'little organs.'

osmosis   Diffusion of water through a differentially permeable membrane.

photosynthesis.   The process of converting light energy to chemical-bond energy in the form of food.

protoplasm   A general term meaning living juice. It is the term for the living contents of cells.

ribonucleic acid (RNA)   A molecule that is similar to DNA and functions in the decoding of the hereditary information as it is used in the cell.

ribosome   Small glob made of protein and RNA, located throughout the cytoplasm wherever protein is being constructed.

stroma   Membranous region of the chloroplast not associated with chlorophyll.

ultrastructure   The cellular structures not visible using a light microscope.

vacuole   A membranous container inside a cell. Specialized vacuoles may be termed food vacuole, water vacuole, etc.

viscous   A measure of degree of runniness. Example: molasses is more viscous in winter than in summer.

Purpose Living cells require various chemical reactions to conduct their vital functions. It is essential that these reactions be conducted rapidly and be controlled to prevent the malfunctioning and death of the cell. The problem is not one of starting reactions, but of controlling the rate of reactions. Regulating the rate of reactions is the task of the enzymes.

Enzymes

7

Catalysts and Enzymes

Most chemical reactions require an input of **energy** to get them started. This is called **activation energy.** Some reactions occur naturally at room temperature, since there is sufficient activation energy present. Hydrogen peroxide normally breaks down into water and oxygen ($H_2O_2 \longrightarrow H_2O + O$). You have probably experienced this reaction when some hydrogen peroxide was placed in a cut to prevent infection. The bubbles that came off were oxygen bubbles. The rate of this reaction can be increased when the chemical manganese dioxide (MnO_2) is mixed with the hydrogen peroxide (but not in a cut!). The manganese dioxide is a **catalyst,** an inorganic substance that speeds up this chemical reaction and is recovered unchanged.

If you were to put some saliva into a test tube of hydrogen peroxide, there would also be a rapid increase in the breakdown of hydrogen peroxide. This occurs because the saliva contains a complex organic molecule that interacts with hydrogen peroxide much like manganese dioxide. This molecule is called an **enzyme.** Enzymes are types of catalysts made of protein that speed up the rate of chemical reactions. The genes of the cell control the production of enzymes. How the genes function to do this will be discussed in chapter ten.

Working Hand-in-Glove, or Enzymes: Key Molecules

In the reaction of hydrogen peroxide with saliva, the hydrogen peroxide is referred to as the **substrate.** Substrates are molecules with which certain enzymes react, this results in a change in the substrate molecule. All molecules have their own specific three-dimensional shape. A given enzyme will only react with a substrate if the three-dimensional shape of the enzyme molecule and the substrate molecule are such that both can physically fit together. A new temporary molecule, an **enzyme-substrate complex,** is formed by this physical joining of the original enzyme with the substrate molecule.

Figure 7.1a illustrates a general reaction for all enzymatic reactions. The enzyme and substrate first unite to form the enzyme-substrate complex. While in this complex, the substrate molecule will be changed into a new molecule known as the **end product.** At the end of the reaction, the enzyme will leave unchanged.

Figure 7.1b illustrates an analogy of an enzymatic reaction. The key represents the enzyme and the bicycle lock represents the substrate. In order for a key to work on a lock, the key must have the correct shape. The key and the closed bicycle lock first join together to form a complex. When the key is turned the closed bicycle lock is separated, thus the lock is changed. The key is not modified in any manner. In all enzymatic reactions the substrate, represented by the bicycle lock, is changed into different end products. The enzyme, represented by the key, is unchanged.

Figure 7.1c illustrates a specific reaction. The enzyme is sucrase and the substrate is sucrose,* common table sugar. The sucrose is changed into the end products glucose and fructose, but the sucrase is the same at the end of the reaction as it was at the start.

No key can fit every lock in the world. It only works on a specific type of lock, or if it is a master key, a small group of very similar locks. Likewise, no enzyme will work on all materials. A given enzyme only works on one type of substrate or on substrates having a somewhat common shape. This is known as enzymatic **specificity.** The enzyme sucrase is specific for the substrate sucrose because the molecules of sucrase and sucrose will physically fit together.

The whole key does not work on a lock; the important part is the shape of the notches of the key. Likewise, enzymes have specific portions of their structure that interact with the substrate. These areas are known as **active sites.** The active site may only be a small portion of a large enzyme molecule, but this is where the chemical reaction really occurs.

In order for a substrate to be changed into the end product, a certain amount of energy must be supplied to start the reaction. For instance, the rate of a chemical reaction may be increased by applying more heat. But, in a living cell, the addition of large amounts of heat would raise the temperature to a point that would result in the death of the cell. Enzymes allow the rate of a reaction to increase without the addition of heat energy. Thus an enzyme can bring about the desired increase in reactions without having a destructive increase in the temperature of the cell.

---

* Traditionally, the names of enzymes are determined by the name of the substrates upon which they operate. The last syllable of the substrate name is dropped and the new syllable -ase is added. For example:

Substrate	Enzyme
lactose	lactase
deoxyribonucleic acid	deoxyribonuclease

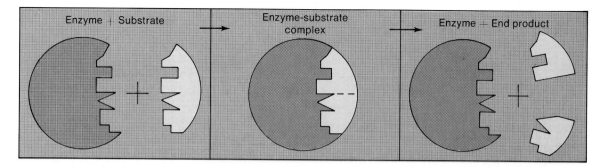

Enzyme + Substrate → Enzyme-substrate complex → Enzyme + End product

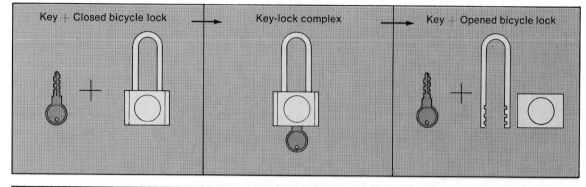

Key + Closed bicycle lock → Key-lock complex → Key + Opened bicycle lock

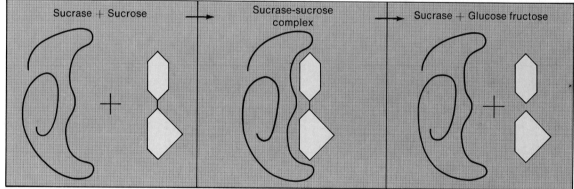

Sucrase + Sucrose → Sucrase-sucrose complex → Sucrase + Glucose fructose

Fig. 7.1 Enzyme Action.
(a) An enzyme and its substrate physically join together to form the enzyme-substrate complex. The enzyme emerges from this complex unaltered; the substrate changes into the end product. (b) If the key doesn't fit the lock, no change results in the lock. (c) When together, sucrase and sucrose represent a specific enzyme-substrate complex.

In figure 7.2, the original substrate molecule contains four units of energy. The end products contain one unit of energy. In order for this reaction to start, energy must be added that will make the substrate more reactive. Without an enzyme, you would need to add three units of energy to the substrate to get this particular reaction started. But with an enzyme, you only need to add one unit of energy. The peak of the top line represents the energy needed to start the reaction without an enzyme. The peak of the lower line represents the energy needed to start the reaction in the presence of an enzyme. Thus an enzyme speeds up a reaction by lowering the amount of energy required to start the reaction. Enzymatic reactions may aid in breaking down a substrate into smaller pieces, or the reaction may be one in which small molecules are bonded to one another forming a more complex molecule.

If a key is used to unlock a lock, the same key is usually used to lock that lock. Figure 7.3a illustrates how the process of unlocking a lock is the reverse of locking a lock. Thus the reaction may go in either direction as indicated by the double-headed arrows (↔). Enzymes influence only the rate and not the direction of a reaction. If an enzyme such as sucrase can speed up the formation of the end products, glucose and fructose, then sucrase may also speed up the reverse of this reaction (fig. 7.3b). If fructose and glucose are com-

Fig. 7.2. *How an Enzyme Works.* An enzyme reduces the amount of energy needed to bring about a chemical reaction.

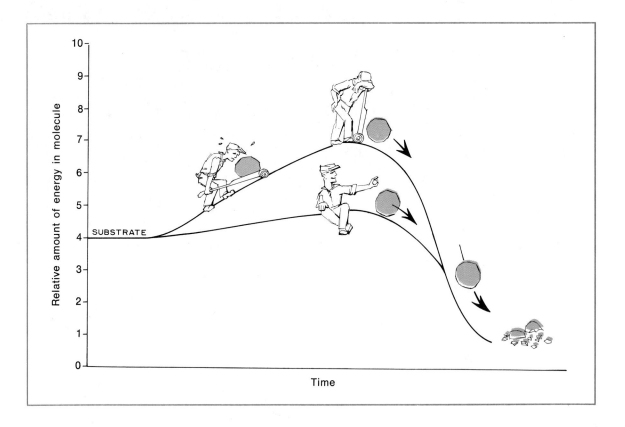

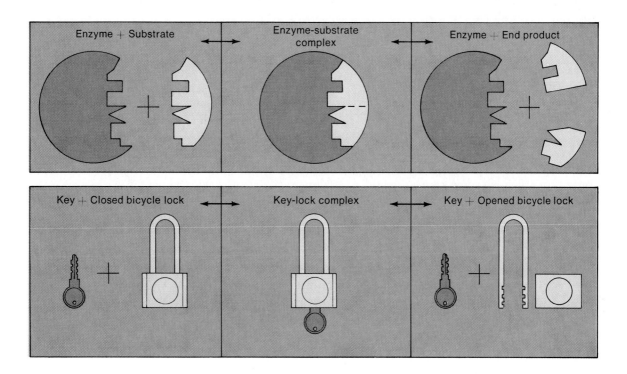

bining to form sucrose, then the addition of sucrase would speed the formation of sucrose. The enzyme is now working on fructose and glucose; they are the substrates, and sucrose is the end product.

Many enzymes do not work by themselves. They require the cooperation of some sort of a helper. This helper is a molecule that aids in the reaction by removing one of the end products, or it may aid by bringing in part of the substrate. Such helpers are called **coenzymes.** Without the coenzyme, the enzyme will not function as well as it could. An example of this enzyme-coenzyme cooperation is shown in figure 7.4. Alcoholic fermentation is a series of reactions resulting in the conversion of glucose to ethyl alcohol. Figure 7.4 illustrates the final reaction in this series.

In this reaction, the acetaldehyde is converted to alcohol. The rate of reaction is increased by an enzyme. But notice that there are two more hydrogen atoms in a molecule of ethyl alcohol than there are in a molecule of acetaldehyde. Two hydrogen atoms are needed to convert the acetaldehyde

Fig. 7.3. *Reversibility of a Reaction.* The same key opens and closes a lock. In the same manner, an enzyme usually causes a chemical reaction to go in either direction. The sucrase uses sucrose as a substrate and forms the end products, fructose and glucose. The sucrase also may use fructose and glucose as the substrate, and forms sucrose as an end product.

Fig. 7.4 *Role of Coenzyme.* The NADH₂ is a coenzyme; it works with alcohol dehydrogenase. The coenzyme NADH₂ furnishes the hydrogens necessary for the formation of alcohol.

into alcohol. The NAD with two hydrogens attached to form NADH$_2$ furnished these hydrogens. This is more efficient than just randomly obtaining the hydrogens from the environment of the reaction. The NAD molecule, which carries the hydrogen atoms, is the helper or coenzyme.

Environmental Effects on Enzymes

The number of molecules of substrate that one molecule of enzyme can react with in a given period of time is the **turnover number.** Under ideal conditions the turnover number is usually large, up to 50,000 per minute. This means that one molecule of enzyme could react with 50,000 different molecules of a substrate in a minute. Without the enzyme, perhaps only 50 to 100 substrate molecules might be altered. Many environmental factors can change this turnover rate either in the test tube or a living cell. Figure 7.5 illustrates a generalized graph of the influence of temperature on the turnover number. An increase in the amount of heat energy results in an increase in the turnover number until the maximum turnover number is reached. After this temperature has been reached, the turnover number will decrease. In the cell, the **optimum** turnover number (best for the cell) is not usually the maximum turnover number. Since all enzymes are proteins, a high temperature will change the structure of the enzyme by breaking some of the chemical bonds that hold the enzyme in its particular shape. The new shape will not allow the enzyme to form an enzyme-substrate complex; they will not fit together anymore. As a result of the higher temperature, the turnover rate will decrease. When excess heat is applied to a protein in this way, the protein is **denatured;** the protein changes in structure. An example of the denaturing of proteins is the change in consistency of eggs when they are cooked. The egg white, which is protein, changes its molecular structure. The opposite environmental change—lowering the temperature—also has a direct effect on the activity of an enzyme and its turnover number. For example, we store foods in refrigerators because the low temperature reduces the turnover number of bacterial enzymes and thus inhibits the spoiling of foods by bacteria.

Fig. 7.5 *Influence of Temperature on Turnover Rate.* As the temperature increases, the rate of enzymatic reaction increases until the heat changes the shape of the enzyme. When the enzyme does not fit the substrate, the enzymatic reactions decrease and eventually stop.

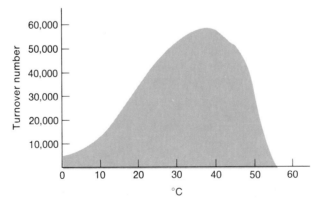

Chapter 7

Another environmental factor that will cause a variation in the turnover number is the hydrogen ion concentration, or pH. Each enzyme has its own optimum pH at which it attains the highest turnover number. Many enzymes function best at a pH close to neutral, which is seven on the pH scale. However, don't be misled, since a number of enzymes perform best at pHs quite different from seven. Pepsin, an enzyme found in the stomach, works well at an acid pH of 1.5 to 2.2; while arginase, an enzyme found in the liver, works well at a basic pH of 9.5 to 9.9.

Temperature and pH are not the only factors that influence the rate of enzyme activity. The concentration of enzymes, the concentration of substrate, the presence or absence of coenzymes, and many other factors also influence the rate of enzymatic reactions.

Enzymes in Real Life Situations

In any cell there are thousands of different kinds of enzymes. Each is sensitive to changing environmental conditions and controls specific chemical reactions. These enzymes operate in cooperation with each other to satisfy the cell's needs, such as immediate energy needs, growth, reproduction, and storage of materials for future use. All of these needs may be met by using the same nutrients. What results is enzymatic competition for specific substrate materials. The success of any one of these enzyme systems during competition will depend on the number of enzymes available and a suitable environment for their optimum operation. For example, if a cell requires immediate energy to move away from danger, it can shift the flow of nutrients to generate this energy. This can be done by increasing the number of enzymes involved in the reaction or by changing the environment so that the enzymes operate at a faster rate. Figure 7.6 illustrates such a situation. Acetyl is a molecule that can be a substrate for three different reactions. When the need for energy is greater than the need for protein and fat production in the cell, the enzyme citrate synthetase does its job more efficiently than either fatty acid synthetase or malate synthetase. This means that more acetyl molecules are converted into citric acid, and the energy needs of the cell are met. On the other hand, if the cell is not expending a great deal of energy, the acetyl is converted to either protein or fatty acids. The number of enzymes produced is regulated by genes. We will deal with this in chapter ten. Some molecules can speed up the rate of activity of enzymes present in the cell. You are familiar with some of these already, for example, coenzymes, vitamins (niacin, riboflavin, etc.), and minerals (Mg, Ca, etc.).

Enzyme reactions may also be slowed. If worn-out enzymes are not replaced, the chemical reactions that they speed up will be slowed down. Slowing of reactions may also be brought about by specific inhibitor molecules.

Some **inhibitors** are so specific that they only work on certain types of enzymes. These will occupy the active site of enzymes, so that there can be no normal enzyme-substrate complex formed (fig. 7.7). Certain pesticides that contain arsenic kill the pest by slowing down the enzymes, and the organism soon dies. The same thing can happen to human enzymes. Organophosphates are pesticides that inhibit several enzymes necessary for the operation of the nervous system in man. When the pesticide finds its way into the nerve cells, it disrupts the regular movement of nerve impulses and causes the person to die because of uncontrollable muscle twitching.

Other inhibitors have a shape that closely resembles the normal substrate of the enzyme. The enzyme can't distinguish the inhibitor from the normal substrate, and combines with the inhibitor and not the substrate. Some of these enzyme-inhibitor complexes are permanent. Such an inhibitor completely removes the enzyme as a functioning part of the cell, and the end product is no longer formed. Even if the inhibitor does not form a permanent enzyme-inhibitor complex, the formation of such a temporary complex results in a lower turnover number for that enzyme.

In disease control we use this principle of enzyme inhibition. The sulfa drugs are used to control a variety of different kinds of bacteria, such as the bacteria *Streptococcus pyogenes*—the cause of strep throat and scarlet fever. The drug resembles one of the bacteria's necessary substrates and prevents some of the enzymes from producing essential cell components. As a result, the normal metabolism of the bacterial cell cannot be maintained, and the cell dies.

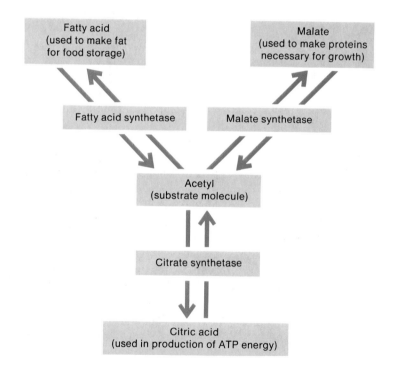

Fig. 7.6 *Enzymatic Competition.* Acetyl serves as a substrate for a number of different enzymes. The requirements of the cell help determine which of the enzymes react with the substrate.

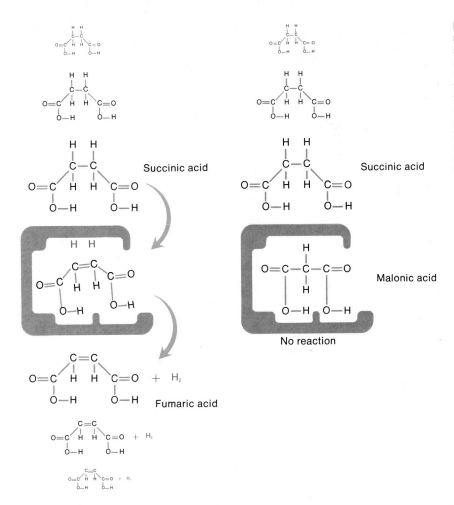

Succinic acid

Succinic acid

Malonic acid

No reaction

Fumaric acid + H₂

Fig. 7.7 *Enzymatic Inhibition.* Malonic acid's shape is similar to that of succinic acid. The malonic acid is capable of combining with the enzyme; this prevents the enzyme from reacting with its usual substrate, succinic acid. This reduces the number of enzymes available for the reaction, and fewer fumaric acid molecules are produced.

Summary

Enzymes are protein catalysts that speed up the rate of chemical reactions without any significant increase in the temperature by lowering activation energy. Enzymes have a very specific structure that matches the structure of a substrate molecule. Actually a specific part of the enzyme molecule—the active site—is the place where the substrate molecule comes in contact with the enzyme. The enzyme-substrate complex reacts to form end products. Because of this, enzymes are very specific as to the kind of substrate molecules with which they will interact. The protein nature of the enzyme suggests that they are sensitive to environmental conditions such as temperature and pH that will change the structure of proteins. The numbers and kind of enzymes are ultimately controlled by the genetic information of the cell. Other kinds of molecules such as coenzymes, inhibitors, or competing enzymes, can influence the fate of specific substrate molecules. Changing conditions within the cell can result in a shift in the enzymatic priorities of the cell by influencing the turnover number.

Consider This   The following data were obtained by a number of Nobel Prize winning scientists from Lower Slobovia. As a member of this group, interpret the data with respect to:

1. Enzyme activities.
2. Movement of substrates into and out of the cell.
3. Competition of different enzymes for the same substrate.
4. Cell structure.

Data

a. A lowering of the atmospheric temperature from 22°C to 18°C causes the organisms to form a thick protective coat.
b. Below 18°C no additional coat material is produced.
c. If the cell is heated to 35°C and then cooled to 18°C, no coat is produced.
d. The coat consists of a complex carbohydrate.
e. The coat will be formed even if there is a low concentration of simple sugars in the surroundings.
f. If the cell needs energy for growth, no cell coats are produced at any temperature.

Questions   1. What is the difference between a catalyst and an enzyme?
2. Describe the sequence of events that occurs in an enzyme controlled reaction.
3. How does changing temperature affect the rate of enzyme controlled reactions?
4. Would you expect a fat and sugar molecule to be acted upon by the same enzyme? Why?
5. Enzyme reactions may be speeded up or slowed down by what factors in the cell?
6. What is the turnover number, and why is it important?
7. How does a coenzyme differ from an enzyme?
8. What is enzymatic competition, and why is it important to all cells?
9. What effect might a change in pH have on enzymatic activity?
10. Where would you look for enzymes in a cell?

Chapter Glossary   **activation energy**   The energy required to start a chemical reaction.

active site   The part of the enzyme that reacts with the substrate.

-ase   A suffix that identifies a word as an enzyme.

catalyst   A material that increases the rate of a chemical reaction.

coenzyme   A material that works with an enzyme in carrying out a reaction.

denature   To change a protein in such a way that it can no longer function as an enzyme.

end product The new molecules formed from the substrate.

energy An ability to do something. Various forms are heat, light, electricity, etc.

enzymatic competition Several different enzymes competing for the same substrate molecule.

enzyme An organic protein molecule that regulates the rate of a chemical reaction.

enzyme-substrate complex The physical union of an enzyme molecule with a substrate molecule.

inhibitor A material or condition that decreases the effectiveness of an enzyme.

optimum The best condition.

specificity A property that only one enzyme can physically fit with a particular substrate.

substrate The material that the enzyme combines with in the reaction. The materials are changed into the end products.

turnover number The number of molecules of substrate that one molecule of enzyme can react with in a given unit of time.

Purpose This chapter deals with some of the major chemical reactions that occur in living things. Because these reactions are dependent on one another and occur in specific series, they are commonly referred to as *biochemical pathways*. An understanding of these biochemical pathways will help you understand how energy is utilized within an organism.

There are hundreds of such pathways, which all interlink, but we will deal only with those that form the central core of all chemical reactions of a living cell. The two major pathways are *photosynthesis* and *cellular respiration*.

Biochemical Pathways

8

Living Things Are Energy Transformers

All living organisms require **energy** to conduct the many functions necessary to sustain life. The immediate source of energy for cells is found in the chemical bonds of food molecules. Some organisms (green plants) are capable of trapping sunlight energy and converting it to these chemical bonds in food molecules. Photosynthesis is a biochemical pathway that traps sunlight energy and converts low energy-containing inorganic molecules into higher energy-containing organic molecules. In other words, plants can combine carbon dioxide and water to form food. A by-product of these reactions is oxygen gas: O_2.

Cellular respiration is the second major biochemical pathway. It results in the release of energy from food molecules. In this process, the chemical energy in the food is released, and the organism can carry on the functions necessary to maintain life. During respiration, the cell releases carbon dioxide, water, and energy as waste products. However, a portion of this released energy is stored in the chemical bonds of the molecule **adenosine triphosphate (ATP).** All organisms require a constant supply of energy. They get their energy directly from ATP molecules. However, the ATP molecules may be produced in a variety of ways. Both photosynthesis and cellular respiration are biochemical pathways that produce ATP molecules, but in different ways. No matter how an organism may generate ATP, the energy in these molecules can always be traced back to the sun. The sunlight energy is converted to chemical energy in the chloroplasts of green plants. This energy can be used by that plant in its life processes, or it may be used by organisms that use plants as food. Even animals that only eat meat are getting this sunlight energy indirectly, since they feed upon animals that have eaten plants (fig. 8.1). Think of the food you have eaten in the last twenty-four hours; what proportion is direct sunlight energy and what proportion is indirect sunlight energy?

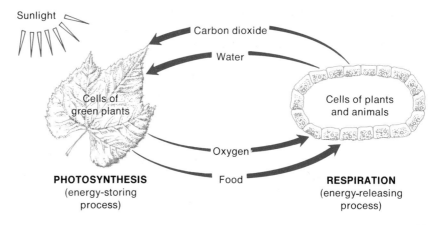

Fig. 8.1 *The Relationship Between Photosynthesis and Respiration.* The raw materials for photosynthesis—carbon dioxide and water—are the end products of respiration. The raw materials for respiration—food and oxygen—are the end products of photosynthesis.

The Currency of the Cell

The chemical bonds that hold the atoms of a molecule together contain energy. If a bond is broken, the energy is released and may be converted into other forms. The conversion of energy from one form to another is a common occurrence. For example, electrical energy may be changed to heat energy, light energy, or mechanical energy. In order for energy to be used it must be in a suitable form. Crude oil possesses large amounts of chemical energy; however, the engine of a car is unable to use all of the energy that is potentially available in that oil. Crude oil must be processed in order to select out only the useful gasoline. In other words, the oil must be converted into gasoline before being used in the car. Living cells also require chemical energy as a means of accomplishing the many complex reactions that occur in living cells. Food has large amounts of chemical energy, just as crude oil has large amounts of chemical energy. This energy is released when the bonds in a molecule are broken. Living cells cannot directly use this food energy; it must be converted to a form that the cell can use. This form is ATP.

A basic law of energy states that some usable energy is lost whenever energy is converted from one form to another. In a car, the goal is to convert chemical energy into mechanical energy in order to move the car. Much of the energy is lost in the form of heat. The car's radiator has the task of removing this useless heat from the engine system. In a similar way the surface of your body serves to radiate heat.

The chemical bonds in a molecule of food are broken, releasing small amounts of energy. Many small amounts of energy are combined in special bonds of ATP molecules. When these special bonds are broken, a form of energy usable to the cell is released (fig. 8.2). Note in figure 8.3 that there is a single bond (represented by a single straight line) between the ribose and the first phosphate. A curved line is used to represent the bond between the first and second phosphate, as well as between the second and third phosphate. This curved line represents a single bond, a bond yielding a great deal of energy. This is a **high-energy phosphate bond.** When the bond is broken, usable energy is released, and the components remaining are **adenosine diphosphate** (ADP) and the third phosphate.

In order to better understand the idea of high-energy bonds, let's compare a chemical bond to money since ATP is often called the energy currency of the cell. Both money and the energy in ATP can be converted into many things that are necessary for everyday living. A single one-dollar bill can be broken and spent to acquire the needed things of life. A single two-dollar bill is still only one bill. It is the same size and weight as a one-dollar bill, but spending a two-dollar bill allows you to buy more than you could with a one-dollar bill. So we may call the two-dollar bill a high-energy bill. The curved line in the ATP represents a single high-energy bond. Breaking a high-energy chemical bond yields about twice as much energy as that obtained from breaking an ordinary single chemical bond.

The high-energy bond in ATP can be manufactured from the breakdown of other organic molecules, and it can also be formed from captured light energy during the process of photosynthesis. The molecule **chlorophyll,** which is the green stuff of plants, is directly involved in the light-trapping process. This chemical-bond energy is used in later steps to combine water

Fig. 8.2 *Energy Conversion.* When ADP and phosphate combine, a high-energy bond is formed. Either light energy or food energy is converted into this high-energy bond. The breakdown of ATP releases life energy and forms ADP and phosphate. As long as there is a source of energy to form ATPs, there is a source of energy for the processes of life.

Fig. 8.3 *Adenosine Triphosphate.* A molecule of ATP consists of five smaller molecules: adenine, ribose, and three phosphates. The two end phosphates are bonded by high-energy phosphate bonds.

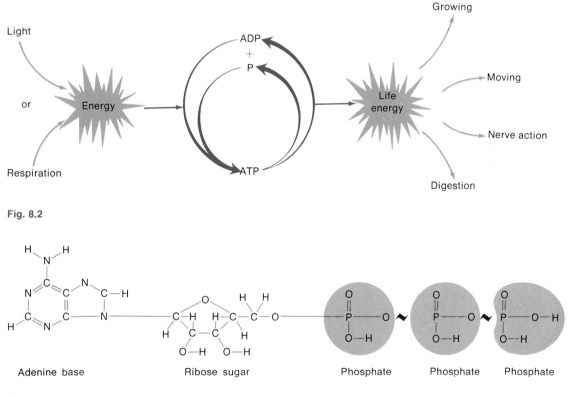

Fig. 8.2

Fig. 8.3

and carbon dioxide to form a simple sugar molecule. As a result of the manufacture of simple sugar, oxygen is released into the atmosphere. Once the plant has manufactured the simple sugar, it can use it to construct other kinds of molecules, provided there are a few additional raw materials such as minerals and nitrogen-containing molecules. The shorthand chemical equation for this entire process can be written:

$$\text{sunlight energy} + \text{carbon dioxide} + \text{water} \xrightarrow[\text{chlorophyll}]{\text{helped by}} \text{simple sugar} + \text{atmospheric oxygen}$$

The total process of photosynthesis can be divided into two main stages on the basis of how things occur in the cell. The first of these we will call the **light energy conversion stage,** since light energy is converted into chemical-bond energy. Refer to figure 8.4 as the light energy conversion stage of photosynthesis is explained.

Light Energy Conversion Stage

Chlorophyll, which is present in the chloroplasts of plants, is a complex molecule with many loosely attached electrons. Some of the electrons can be kicked off of the chlorophyll molecule when they are struck by sunlight energy. These electrons contain more energy than they did previously and will release this energy as they return to their normal position on the chlorophyll molecule. Some of these high-energy electrons transfer this energy to form a molecule of ATP as they return. Other high-energy electrons may be trapped by an electron carrier known as **NADP.** Each NADP molecule has the ability to capture two electrons. As a result, a molecule of NADP is converted to a molecule with a double negative charge ($NADP^{--}$). Hydrogen ions (H^+) become attached to these electron carrying molecules forming $NADPH_2$, since unlike charges attract one another. The hydrogen ions are available for this process because water normally breaks down into hydrogen ions and hydroxyl ions ($HOH \longrightarrow H^+ + OH^-$).

Since the hydrogen ions that ordinarily combined with the hydroxyl ions are now part of the $NADPH_2$, they are no longer available to form part of a water molecule. As a result, the excess hydroxyl ions are combined with each other to form water, atmospheric oxygen, and free electrons (fig. 8.5). These free electrons are attached to the chlorophyll molecule that had previously lost electrons to NADP. At the completion of the light energy conversion stage, the plant has a source of energy (ATP), a source of hydrogen ($NADPH_2$), and has released oxygen (O_2) into the atmosphere. The shorthand chemical equation for this portion of photosynthesis can be written:

$$\text{sunlight energy} + \text{water} \xrightarrow[\text{chlorophyll}]{\text{helped by}} NADPH_2 + ATP + \text{atmospheric oxygen.}$$

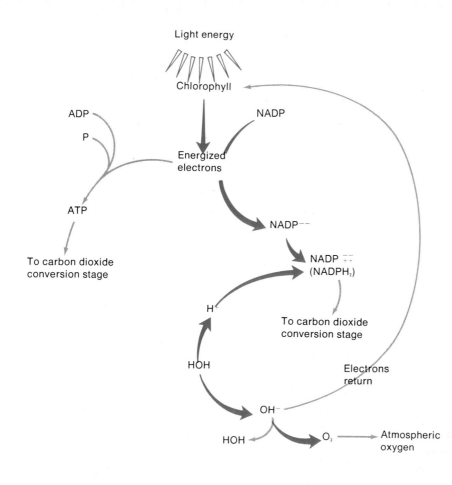

Light energy

Chlorophyll

ADP

P

ATP

To carbon dioxide
conversion stage

NADP

Energized
electrons

NADP⁻⁻

NADP ⁻⁻
(NADPH₂)

To carbon dioxide
conversion stage

H⁺

HOH

Electrons
return

OH⁻

HOH ←   O₂ ——→ Atmospheric
oxygen

Fig. 8.4 *Light Energy Conversion Stage of Photosynthesis.* In the light energy conversion stage, light is the source of energy. This stage results in the formation of ATP, NADPH₂, and O₂.

Both the NADPH₂ and ATP molecules are used in the next stage called the **carbon dioxide conversion stage.** Refer to figure 8.6 as the carbon dioxide conversion stage of photosynthesis is explained.

Carbon Dioxide Conversion Stage

This second set of reactions occurs in the chloroplasts of green plants and uses ATP, NADPH₂, CO₂, and a five-carbon starter molecule (fig. 8.6). The ATP and NADPH₂ come from the light energy conversion reactions, the CO₂ comes from the air, and the starter molecule is already present in the cell. In this stage a molecule of carbon dioxide is used as raw material to produce a simple carbohydrate called **PGAL.** The carbon dioxide molecule does not directly become PGAL. It is first removed from the atmosphere and attached to a previously existing five-carbon compound to form a new six-carbon molecule. This six-carbon molecule quickly breaks down into two three-carbon molecules. The three-carbon molecules undergo a series of

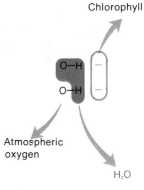

Chlorophyll

O—H

O—H

Atmospheric
oxygen

H₂O

Fig. 8.5 *The Fate of Hydroxyl Ions.* In the light energy conversion stage, the OH− ions combine to form water, oxygen for release into the atmosphere, and electrons to replace the energized electrons that leave the chlorophyll.

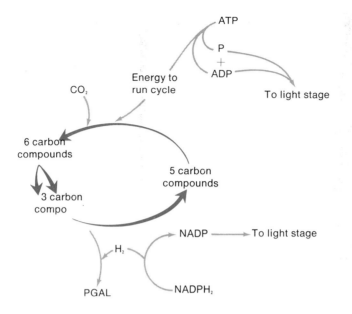

Fig. 8.6 *The Carbon Dioxide Conversion Stage of Photosynthesis.* This stage results in the incorporation of carbon dioxide into the process of photosynthesis. This stage produces PGAL, a source of food.

reactions that transfer energy from the ATP molecules and H_2 from $NADPH_2$ to these molecules. The result of these reactions is the three-carbon molecule PGAL. Most of these PGAL molecules go through a series of complicated reactions that regenerate the five-carbon starter molecule. The light energy conversion stage furnished the necessary ATPs and $NADPH_2$s for the carbon dioxide conversion stage.

PGAL: An All-Purpose Molecule

What happens to all the PGAL produced by photosynthesis? PGAL may combine with other PGALs to form the simple sugar glucose. A number of these simple sugars may then combine to form a complex starch molecule. Amino acids may be constructed by adding ammonia to this basic three-carbon skeleton of PGAL. These various amino acids may then combine to form plant proteins. The energy supply for all these chemical reactions is furnished by the breakdown of other PGAL molecules releasing their chemical-bond energy. The method for releasing energy from such reactions will be covered later in this chapter (fig. 8.7).

At the end of the carbon dioxide conversion stage, the plant has a source of food (PGAL) and has regenerated the raw materials NADP, ADP, and P. The shorthand chemical equation for this portion of photosynthesis can be written:

$$CO_2 + ATP + NADPH_2 + \text{5-carbon starter} \longrightarrow PGAL + NADP + ADP + P$$

Figure 8.8 shows how both the light and CO_2 stages are linked.

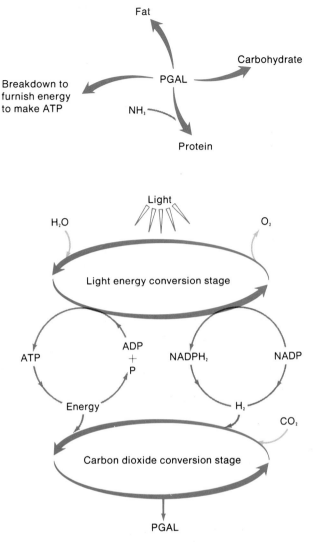

Fig. 8.7 *The Fate of PGAL.* The PGAL produced in the carbon dioxide conversion stage serves as the substrate for a number of reactions. It may be a source of energy or it may be converted into fat, carbohydrate, or protein.

Fig. 8.8 *Photosynthesis.* The process of photosynthesis is composed of the interrelated stages of the light energy conversion stage and the carbon dioxide conversion stage. The carbon dioxide conversion stage requires the ATP from the light energy conversion stage. It also requires the NADPH$_2$ as a source of hydrogen. The light energy conversion stage requires the ADP and phosphate from the carbon dioxide conversion stage as the substrate to form ATP. It also requires the NADP as a hydrogen carrier. Each stage is dependent upon the other stage.

We All Do It!

Even though the process of photosynthesis provides plants with PGAL, plants as well as animals must break down the food in an orderly fashion to release usable energy. Nearly all organisms rely on the same basic chemical pathways to release this energy. **Cellular respiration** is the name of the process. In cellular respiration, food and oxygen combine to yield energy and release carbon dioxide and water. In chemical shorthand this may be written:

$$\text{sugar} + \text{oxygen} \longrightarrow CO_2 + \text{water} + \text{energy (ATP)}$$

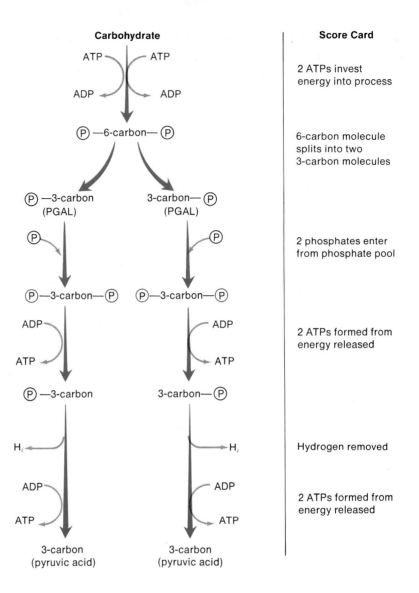

Fig. 8.9 Glycolysis. The glycolysis pathway results in the breakdown of six-carbon sugars under anaerobic conditions. As a result of this breakdown, each molecule of sugar releases enough energy to produce a net of 2 ATPs and two molecules of pyruvic acid.

Carbohydrate

ATP   ATP

ADP   ADP

P —6-carbon— P

P —3-carbon   3-carbon— P
(PGAL)   (PGAL)

P   P

P—3-carbon— P   P—3-carbon— P

ADP   ADP

ATP   ATP

P —3-carbon   3-carbon— P

H₂   H₂

ADP   ADP

ATP   ATP

3-carbon   3-carbon
(pyruvic acid)   (pyruvic acid)

Score Card

2 ATPs invest energy into process

6-carbon molecule splits into two 3-carbon molecules

2 phosphates enter from phosphate pool

2 ATPs formed from energy released

Hydrogen removed

2 ATPs formed from energy released

The first stage in carbohydrate respiration, known as **glycolysis,** involves the breakdown of a sugar without the use of free oxygen (fig. 8.9). In any chemical reaction that occurs in the cytoplasm, some energy must be put in to start the process. In the case of glycolysis, this energy is supplied by two ATPs. The two phosphates released from these two ATPs attach to the six-carbon simple sugar to form a **phosphorylated** sugar molecule ($P—C_6—P$). Any molecule that gains phosphates is said to be phosphorylated. This compound is broken into two three-carbon compounds, each with an attached phosphate ($C_3—P$). This is the PGAL molecule that is so important in photosynthesis. These three-carbon compounds with phosphates attached acquire a second phosphate from a phosphate pool normally found in the cell. Now we have two three-carbon compounds, each with two phosphates attached ($P-C_3-P + P-C_3-P$). A series of reactions follows in which energy is released by the breaking of chemical bonds, causing each of these compounds to loose its phosphates. These high-energy phosphates are combined with ADP to form two ATP molecules for each three-carbon molecule. In addition, four hydrogen atoms are removed from the carbon skeletons and attached to two hydrogen-carrying molecules, NAD. These two molecules, now $NADH_2$, contain a large amount of potential energy, which may be released in a usable form in later chemical reactions.

In summary, the process of glycolysis starts with a six-carbon sugar and undergoes reactions that lead to the formation of four ATPs, two $NADH_2$s and two three-carbon molecules known as **pyruvic acid.** Since two ATPs were used to start the process and a total of four ATPs were formed, each simple sugar molecule that undergoes glycolysis results in a net production of two ATPs. Glycolysis is called an **anaerobic** process because no atmospheric oxygen (O_2) is used. If atmospheric oxygen is available, most cells continue to break down the pyruvic acid molecules and release even more energy. This is called an **aerobic** process. Refer to figure 8.10 for a diagram of the series of chemical reactions known as the Krebs' cycle.

Each molecule of pyruvic acid will lose a molecule of carbon dioxide and hydrogen. With the loss of these carbon dioxide molecules, the three-carbon pyruvic acid becomes a two-carbon acetyl compound. Carbon dioxide is a waste product that the cell will release into the atmosphere. The acetyl compound temporarily combines with a large molecule called coenzyme A (CoA) to form an acetyl-CoA compound. This molecule reacts with a previously existing four-carbon molecule. In this reaction the two-carbon acetyl is transferred to the four-carbon compound to form a new six-carbon molecule. The CoA may return to pick up a different compound. The function of CoA is to assist in combining the two-carbon compound with the four-carbon compound.

The new six-carbon compound is broken down in a series of reactions to a four-carbon compound by the release of two carbon dioxide molecules and a number of hydrogen atoms. The resulting four-carbon molecule is used to combine with a newly entering two-carbon acetyl compound, and the chemical reactions are repeated. Each time an acetyl group moves through the **Krebs' cycle,** an ATP is formed. Thus, each pyruvic acid has lost a carbon dioxide to form an acetyl group and additional carbon dioxides in the cycle. All of the six carbon atoms that were originally in the simple sugar are released into the atmosphere as the gas carbon dioxide. This process takes place in the mitochondria of plant and animal cells.

At this point, the breakdown of sugar has resulted in the net production of four ATPs—two from glycolysis and two from the Krebs' cycle. The

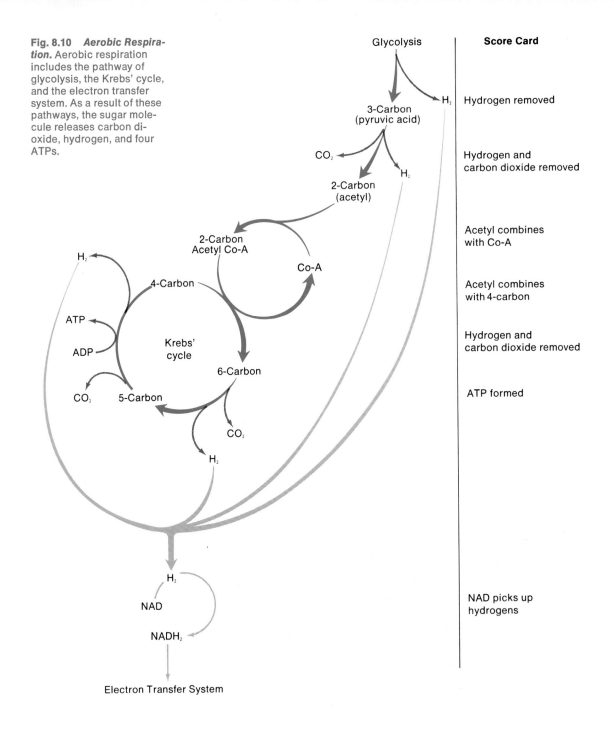

Fig. 8.10 *Aerobic Respiration.* Aerobic respiration includes the pathway of glycolysis, the Krebs' cycle, and the electron transfer system. As a result of these pathways, the sugar molecule releases carbon dioxide, hydrogen, and four ATPs.

Glycolysis

Score Card

3-Carbon
(pyruvic acid)

H_2 Hydrogen removed

CO_2

H_2

Hydrogen and
carbon dioxide removed

2-Carbon
(acetyl)

2-Carbon
Acetyl Co-A

Co-A

Acetyl combines
with Co-A

H_2

4-Carbon

ATP

ADP

Krebs'
cycle

Acetyl combines
with 4-carbon

CO_2 5-Carbon

6-Carbon

CO_2

Hydrogen and
carbon dioxide removed

ATP formed

H_2

H_2

NAD

NADH$_2$

NAD picks up
hydrogens

Electron Transfer System

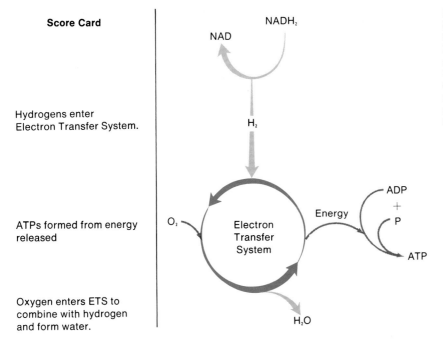

Score Card

Hydrogens enter Electron Transfer System.

ATPs formed from energy released

Oxygen enters ETS to combine with hydrogen and form water.

NAD

NADH₂

H₂

O₂

Electron Transfer System

Energy

ADP + P

ATP

H₂O

Fig. 8.11 *Electron Transfer System.* The electron transfer system utilizes the hydrogen released by the aerobic respiration in the Krebs' cycle, and releases energy during this series of chemical reactions. ATPs are formed by using this released energy.

hydrogen atoms released during glycolysis and the Krebs' cycle are all picked up by hydrogen acceptors and enter a third series of reactions known as the **electron transfer system (ETS).** This system converts the potential energy in the hydrogen carrying molecules to ATP (fig. 8.11). The reactions yield enough energy to form thirty-four additional ATPs. Add to this the two ATPs from glycolysis plus the two ATPs from the Krebs' cycle reactions, and the complete breakdown of a simple sugar will yield a total of thirty-eight ATPs if oxygen is available (fig. 8.12).

Oxygen is used in the ETS and is ultimately combined with hydrogen to form molecules of water as an end product. The twelve hydrogen atoms found in the original molecule of simple sugar are now part of six molecules of water. The simple sugar has now undergone many reactions, having been changed from sugar to carbon dioxide and water and released enough energy to form thirty-eight ATPs.

If no oxygen is present, the ETS system stops working, the Krebs' cycle stops, and acetyl is not formed from pyruvic acid. As a result, only glycolysis will occur to form only two ATPs.

$$\text{sugar} + \text{series of reactions} + O_2 \longrightarrow CO_2 + H_2O + 38 \text{ ATPs}$$

Glycolysis	Glycolysis = 2
Krebs'	Krebs' = 2
ETS	ETS = 34

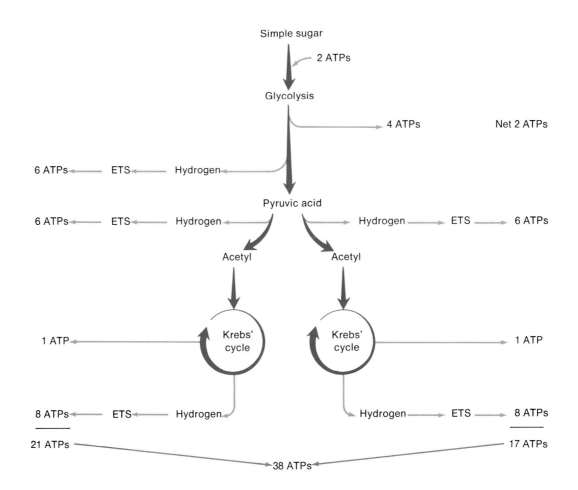

Simple sugar

2 ATPs

Glycolysis

4 ATPs   Net 2 ATPs

6 ATPs ← ETS ← Hydrogen ←

Pyruvic acid

6 ATPs ← ETS ← Hydrogen ←   → Hydrogen → ETS → 6 ATPs

Acetyl   Acetyl

1 ATP ← Krebs' cycle   Krebs' cycle → 1 ATP

8 ATPs ← ETS ← Hydrogen ←   → Hydrogen → ETS → 8 ATPs

21 ATPs   17 ATPs

38 ATPs

Fig. 8.12 *ATP Production from Glucose.* In the respiration of a six-carbon sugar, two ATPs are put into the reaction. Under anaerobic conditions, four ATPs are produced. The net profit to the cell is two ATPs. Under aerobic conditions, two ATPs are put into the reaction and forty ATPs are produced (four from glycolysis, two from the Krebs' cycle, and thirty-four from the electron transfer system). The net profit to the cell is thirty-eight ATPs.

Atmospheric oxygen is essential to higher forms of life because it means a release of thirty-six more ATPs from each simple sugar in comparison to that released during glycolysis (fig. 8.13). If cells can't get oxygen, ATP production falls below the point that furnishes enough energy for essential cell functions, and eventually the cells will die from this lack of energy.

Some cells can survive without atmospheric oxygen by making use of the glycolysis pathway and additional reactions that convert the pyruvic acid to other molecules. These processes are called **fermentation.** Organisms that use fermentations to produce ATP can only get two ATPs from each sugar molecule they break down. Therefore, fermentation is less efficient than aerobic respiration. All kinds of fermentation involve the glycolysis pathway, and only in the final steps do the processes differ. These differences occur because different organisms produce different enzymes.

Biochemical Pathways

In the presence of the proper enzymes glucose can be converted to PGAL

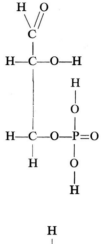

and then to pyruvic acid.

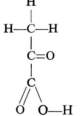

Some animal cells have enzymes that can convert the pyruvic acid to **lactic acid** (fig. 8.14). If the energy requirements for muscle movement are too great, your body will not have enough oxygen to process all the hydrogens through the ETS. As a result, some of the hydrogen atoms will combine with the pyruvic acid to form lactic acid. It is the buildup of lactic acid in the muscles that makes them tired when exercising. Later, when enough oxygen is taken into the muscle cells, the lactic acid will be changed back to pyruvic acid, and the tired feeling will disappear as the pyruvic acid is broken down in the Krebs' cycle.

In yeasts, there are different enzymes present that bring about the manufacture of **ethyl alcohol** and carbon dioxide from pyruvic acid (fig. 8.15). Fermentation is widely used in the food processing industry. The wine maker will squeeze some grapes, add yeast, and place the mixture in a container. The yeast will use the grape sugar as a source of energy and convert the sugar into alcohol and carbon dioxide. The wine maker allows the carbon dioxide to escape into the air. The champagne maker keeps the carbon dioxide in the wine. Other food products such as yogurt, sauerkraut, and cheeses are also the result of fermentation reactions by specific fermenting organisms. Now that you have a basic understanding of how organisms derive energy, we can use this background to show how other molecules may be used for energy.

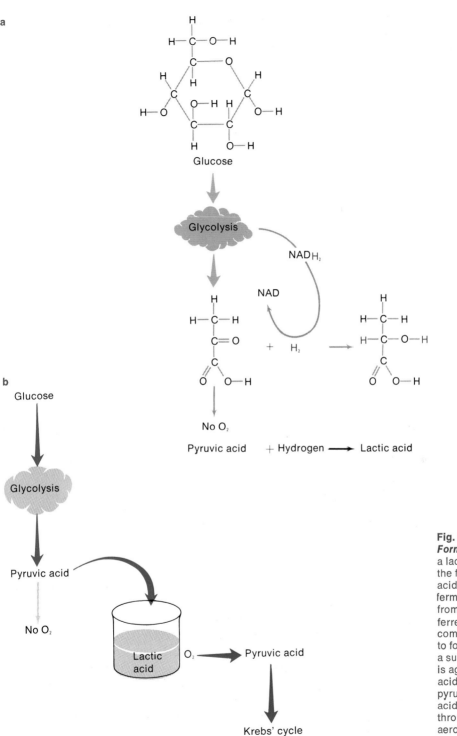

a

Glucose

Glycolysis

NAD H₂

NAD

No O₂

Pyruvic acid + Hydrogen ⟶ Lactic acid

b

Glucose

Glycolysis

Pyruvic acid

No O₂

Lactic acid

O₂ ⟶ Pyruvic acid

Krebs' cycle

Fig. 8.14 *Lactic Acid Formation. (a)* In animals, a lack of oxygen results in the formation of lactic acid—a process called fermentation. The hydrogens from glycolysis are transferred by NADH₂ and then combined with pyruvic acid to form lactic acid. *(b)* When a sufficient supply of oxygen is again present, the lactic acid will be converted to pyruvic acid; the pyruvic acid will then proceed through the pathways of aerobic respiration.

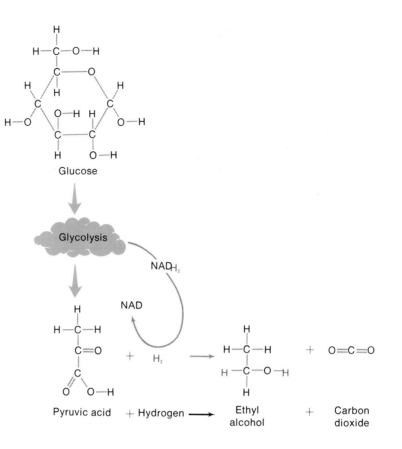

Fig. 8.15 *Alcoholic Fermentation.* In plants, a lack of oxygen results in the formation of alcohol and carbon dioxide during fermentation. The hydrogens from glycolysis are transferred by $NADH_2$ and combined with pyruvic acid to form alcohol and carbon dioxide.

Glucose

Glycolysis

$NADH_2$

NAD

H_2

Pyruvic acid + Hydrogen ⟶ Ethyl alcohol + Carbon dioxide

Fat Respiration

Before fats can undergo respiration and release energy, they must be broken down into glycerol and fatty acids. Refer to figure 8.16 as fat respiration is discussed.

Glycerol is a three-carbon compound.

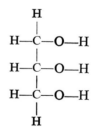

Once the glycerol is changed into pyruvic acid, it proceeds through the Krebs' cycle in the same way as did the pyruvic acid formed from simple sugars.

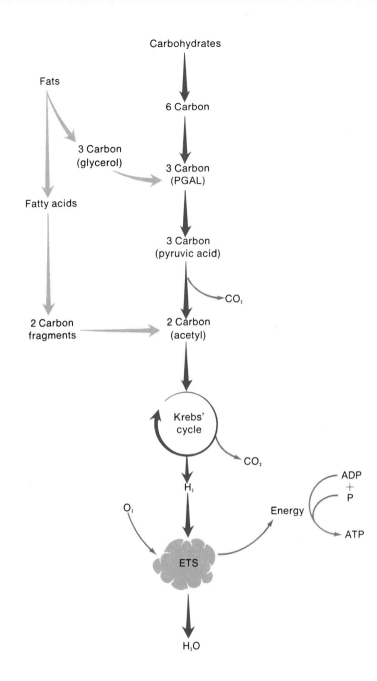

Carbohydrates

Fats

3 Carbon
(glycerol)

6 Carbon

Fatty acids

3 Carbon
(PGAL)

3 Carbon
(pyruvic acid)

CO_2

2 Carbon
fragments

2 Carbon
(acetyl)

Krebs'
cycle

CO_2

H_2

O_2

Energy

ADP
+
P

ATP

ETS

H_2O

Fig. 8.16 *Fat Metabolism.* Fats must be digested into glycerol and fatty acids before they can undergo respiration. The glycerol is converted into PGAL and then proceeds through the respiration pathways. The fatty acid molecules are broken down into two-carbon fragments; these are converted into acetyl, which then proceeds through the respiration pathways.

Fatty acids are long chains that can break apart into two-carbon compounds

Enzymes can change these two-carbon compounds into acetyl molecules.

Once the acetyl is formed, it proceeds through the Krebs' cycle. Each two-carbon fragment of a fatty acid chain will produce a number of ATPs. When all of these fragments from a molecule of fat are considered, a molecule of fat yields more energy than a molecule of simple sugar. When both the fat and carbohydrate molecules are completely broken down, they are changed to carbon dioxide and water. In addition to sugars and fats, proteins can be broken down to form ATP.

Protein Respiration

In order for proteins to release energy, they must first be broken into individual amino acids. The amino acid must have the amino group removed and be converted to a different molecule, ammonia. This new molecule, which lacks an amino group, will be changed and entered into the respiration cycle as pyruvic acid or one of the types of molecules found in the Krebs' cycle (fig. 8.17).

So far we have seen that the same basic metabolic pathways of glycolysis, the Krebs' cycle, and the ETS are involved in the breakdown of many different kinds of organic molecules to produce energy. Not all molecules entering these pathways are destroyed. Some of them are used in reactions that build new cells or their parts. In order to accomplish these synthesis reactions, one kind of molecule may be converted to another. This interconversion of molecular types will occur if a needed building block happens to be in short supply, or must be stored for later use.

Interconversion of Foods

Now let's consider how these foods can be converted from one form to another, such as carbohydrate to fat, or protein to carbohydrate. A person whose daily energy intake exceeds his daily energy requirements will only convert the necessary amount of food into energy. The excess food may be

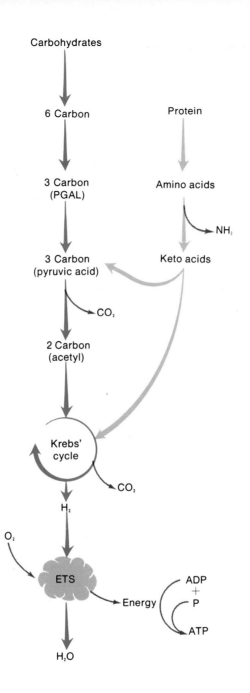

Carbohydrates

6 Carbon

3 Carbon
(PGAL)

3 Carbon
(pyruvic acid)

CO_2

2 Carbon
(acetyl)

Protein

Amino acids

NH_3

Keto acids

Krebs'
cycle

CO_2

H_2

O_2

ETS

Energy

ADP
+
P

ATP

H_2O

Fig. 8.17 *Protein Metabolism.* Proteins must be digested into amino acids before they can undergo respiration. The amino acids are converted into various keto acids. The keto acids enter the respiration pathway as pyruvic acid or one of the keto acids of the Krebs' cycle.

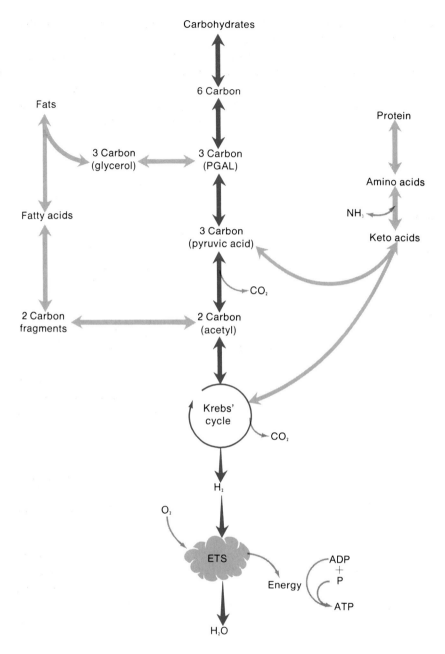

Fig. 8.18 *Interconversion of Fats, Carbohydrates, and Proteins.* The cells do not necessarily utilize all the food as energy. It is possible to change one type of food into another type, depending upon the requirements of the cell.

Carbohydrates

6 Carbon

Fats

3 Carbon (glycerol)   3 Carbon (PGAL)

Protein

Amino acids

Fatty acids

3 Carbon (pyruvic acid)

NH_3

Keto acids

CO_2

2 Carbon fragments   2 Carbon (acetyl)

Krebs' cycle

CO_2

H_2

O_2

ETS

ADP + P

Energy

ATP

H_2O

converted into fats or proteins depending on the needs of the organism at that particular time and the enzymes present (fig. 8.18). In fact, what glycolysis and the Krebs' cycle do is allow molecules of the three major food types (carbohydrates, fats, and proteins) to be interconverted.

In order to lose weight, it is necessary for the food intake to be less than is needed to supply the energy requirements. Then the stored fat will be converted to energy (fig. 8.16), and the person will lose weight.

Plants Can Do It All!

At the beginning of this chapter, we considered the conversion of carbon dioxide and water into PGAL through the process of photosynthesis. We also learned that PGAL is a very important molecule because it can be used for energy (fig. 8.8). Plants obtain energy from food molecules in the same manner as animals do. They process the food through the respiration pathways. This means that plants, like animals, require oxygen for the ETS portion of aerobic respiration. Many students believe that plants only give off oxygen and that somehow they have no need for it. This is incorrect. It is true that in the light energy conversion stage of photosynthesis plants do give off oxygen, but in respiration they use oxygen just like any other organism. However, during their life span, green plants give off more oxygen to the atmosphere than they take in for use in respiration. The surplus they give off is the source of oxygen for animals. Not only are animals dependent on plants for oxygen, but all animals are ultimately dependent on plants for the organic molecules necessary to construct their bodies and maintain their metabolism.

The plants, by a series of reactions, produce the basic foods for animal life. In order to produce PGAL, which can be converted into carbohydrates and fats, plants require carbon dioxide and water as raw materials. The carbon dioxide and water are put into the atmosphere as waste products of respiration by plants and animals. In order to make the amino acids needed for proteins, plants require a source of ammonia, which is a waste material from animals.

Thus, animals supply raw materials (CO_2, H_2O, and ammonia) needed by plants, just as plants supply raw materials (sugar, oxygen, amino acids, fats, and vitamins) needed by animals. This constant recycling is essential for life as we know it on earth (fig. 8.19). As long as plants and animals are in balance and the sun shines, the food cycles of all living organisms will continue to work properly.

Summary

This chapter discusses the manufacture of a form of energy, ATP, that can be utilized by all cells. In the light energy conversion stage of photosynthesis, plants use chlorophyll to trap sunlight to manufacture a source of energy,

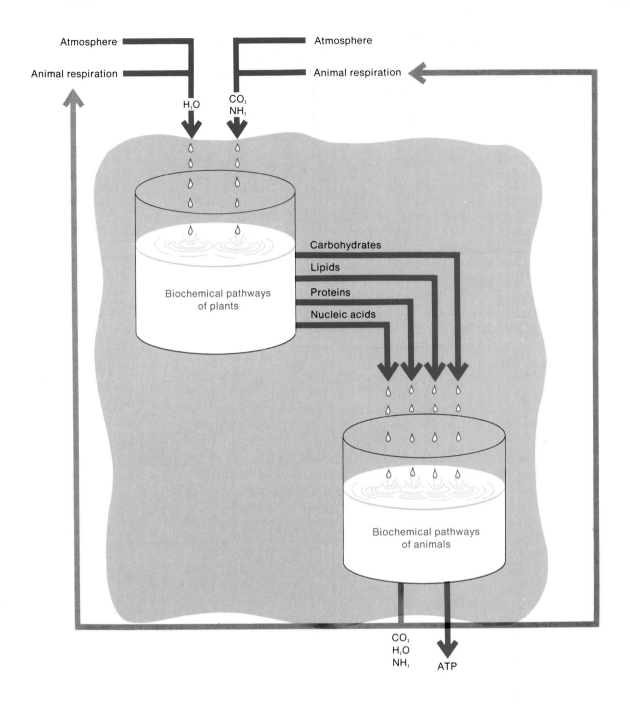

Fig. 8.19

ATP, and a source of hydrogen, NADPH$_2$. Atmospheric oxygen is released in this stage. This ATP energy is used in a series of reactions in the carbon dioxide conversion stage of photosynthesis to join the hydrogen from the NADPH$_2$ to a molecule of carbon dioxide to form a simple carbohydrate, PGAL.

In subsequent reactions, the plant uses the PGAL as a source of energy and raw material to make complex carbohydrates, fats, and other organic molecules. With the addition of ammonia as a raw material, the plant is able to form proteins (fig. 8.20).

In the process of respiration, organisms convert foods into energy (ATP) and waste materials (carbon dioxide, water, and ammonia). Those organisms that use oxygen (O$_2$) in this process receive much more energy from sugar than those which ferment sugar, since fermenters do not use the Krebs' cycle and the electron transfer system (ETS), but rely entirely on glycolysis. Glycolysis and the Krebs' cycle serve as a molecular interconversion system. Fats, proteins, and carbohydrates can all be interchanged depending on the needs of the cell.

The waste materials of respiration, in turn, are used by the plant. Therefore, there is a constant recycling of materials between plants and animals. Sunlight is essential in order to supply the initial energy to make the large organic molecules that are necessary to maintain the forms of life we know.

Fig. 8.19 *The Interdependency of Photosynthesis and Respiration.* Plants use the end products of animal respiration, carbon dioxide, water, and ammonia, to produce various foods. Animals use the end products of plants, food, and oxygen as a source of energy. Therefore, plants are dependent upon animals and animals are dependent upon plants.

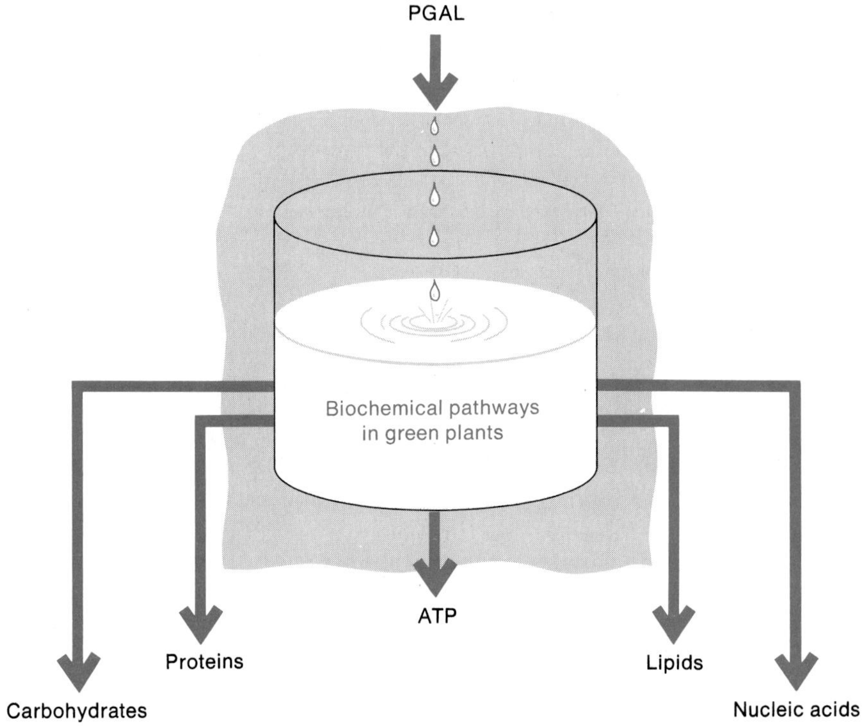

Fig. 8.20 *Uses of PGAL.* As a result of photosynthesis, plants produce PGAL. The PGAL can follow various pathways and be converted into a number of different products.

Both animals and green plants carry on metabolism. From a metabolic point of view, which is the most complex? This is not an easy question to answer. Include in your answer the following topics:

1. Cell structure
2. Biochemical pathways
3. Enzymes
4. Organic molecules
5. Autotrophy and heterotrophy

Questions

1. What is a metabolic pathway? Give two examples.
2. List four ways that photosynthesis and aerobic respiration are similar.
3. Photosynthesis is a biochemical pathway that occurs in two stages. What are they, and how are they related to one another?
4. Why does aerobic respiration yield more energy than anaerobic respiration?
5. Even though animals do not photosynthesize, they rely on the sun for their energy. Why is this so?
6. What is the importance of each of the following?
   NADP in photosynthesis
   PGAL in photosynthesis and respiration
   Oxygen in aerobic respiration
   Hydrogen acceptors in aerobic respiration
7. In what way does ATP differ from other organic molecules?
8. Pyruvic acid can be converted into a variety of different molecules. Name three.
9. What cellular organelles are involved in the processes of photosynthesis and respiration?
10. Aerobic respiration occurs in three stages. Name these and briefly describe what happens in each stage.

Chapter Glossary

adenosine diphosphate (ADP)   ADP plus phosphate and energy are used to make an ATP molecule.

adenosine triphosphate (ATP)   A source of usable cellular energy.

aerobic respiration   Metabolic process requiring the use of free oxygen.

anaerobic respiration   Metabolic process not requiring the use of free oxygen.

biochemical pathways   Specific series of major chemical reactions.

carbon dioxide conversion stage   Stage of photosynthesis that removes carbon dioxide from the atmosphere and uses it as a raw material to make a simple carbohydrate.

cellular respiration   Chemical breakdown of organic (food) molecules with subsequent release of energy.

chlorophyll   The green pigment associated with energy conversion.

electron transfer system (ETS)   A series of chemical reactions involving hydrogen, which yields energy to produce ATPs.

energy   The ability to do work. Different forms are interconvertible to other forms, such as light energy to chemical energy or chemical energy to heat.

ethyl alcohol   One of the end products of fermentation in plants and micro-organisms.

fermentation   An anaerobic process that converts pyruvic acid to alcohol and carbon dioxide in plants, or to lactic acid in animals.

glycolysis   The anaerobic stage of carbohydrate respiration.

high-energy phosphate bond   A type of bond found in ADP and ATP, which when broken yields more energy than regular covalent bonds.

Krebs' cycle   The breakdown of an acetyl group to carbon dioxide and hydrogen with the formation of one ATP. Hydrogens are then carried to the electron transfer system for further energy release.

lactic acid   The end product of fermentation in animals.

light energy conversion stage   Stage of photosynthesis that converts sunlight into electron energy with the subsequent production of $NADPH_2$, ATP, and atmospheric oxygen (O_2).

NADP   An electron acceptor and a hydrogen carrier.

PGAL   The simple sugar produced in the carbon dioxide conversion stage of photosynthesis.

phosphorylate   To add a phosphate group (PO_4) to another molecule.

photosynthesis   Major chemical pathway that converts light energy into chemical-bond energy in the form of food.

pyruvic acid   The three-carbon compound formed from glycolysis.

Purpose   The biochemical pathways described in the previous chapter all occur inside living cells. In man and many other organisms, available foods cannot directly enter these metabolic processes. The food eaten must be chemically prepared before it can be used in the cell's processes. This chapter will deal with the process called digestion and the factors that influence it.

Going Down the Right Tract

9

What's It All About?

The **digestive tract** is a long tube that passes through the body and has specialized sections for the breakdown of large food molecules into smaller molecules. The basic design and function of this system is to provide the cells of the body with the five essential ingredients that will keep them alive and well. These five classes of nutrients are the proteins, carbohydrates, lipids, vitamins, and chemical elements (minerals) (fig. 9.1). In order for you to remain in good health, foods that contain these five classes of nutrients must be a part of your diet. The carbohydrates, proteins, and lipids are the sources of energy. As noted in the previous chapter on cell metabolism, all these types of molecules may come together in the metabolic "mill" of the cell and be converted from one form to another. But the type and amount of foods you take into your body each day will have an effect on just how these conversions take place.

The digestive system does not absorb all of the proteins, carbohydrates, and lipid molecules that flow through it. In fact, there is a very specific uptake of these types of molecules. Usually, carbohydrates are taken into the body

Fig. 9.1 *Four Basic Foods.* The kinds of foods shown here contain the five classes of nutrients. Any one of these foods might not contain one of the necessary nutrients, but together they can supply the body with proteins, carbohydrates, lipids, vitamins, and chemical elements.

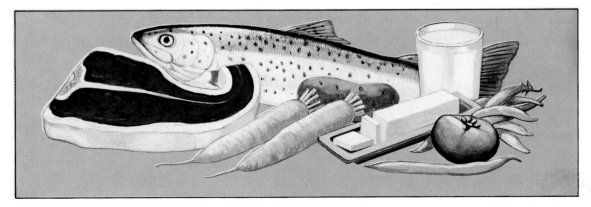

first, and proteins last. This is also true of the order in which each of the three types of molecules are respired in the cells. Your cells will begin the respiration of the carbohydrates first. About five hours later, your body shifts to burning the fats for energy, and the proteins are left for last. If you were to measure the amount of usable energy your body extracts from a gram of each of these types of molecules, it would come out to be 4.0 calories per gram of carbohydrate, 9.0 calories per gram of fat, and 4.0 calories per gram of protein.

2,600,000 Calories a Day—Ugh!

The unit used to measure the amount of energy available to the body is the **calorie.** It is the amount of heat it takes to raise the temperature of a gram of water one degree centigrade. People have, over the years, misused this term. When you talk about a person on a 1000 calorie diet, you really mean that he is on a one million calorie diet (table 9.1). That is because biologists measure energy value of foods in calories, while doctors measure food intake in terms

Table 9.1   *A Weight-Control Diet—1,500 Kilocalories or 1,500,000 Calories*

With any diet, there are general guidelines to follow. Baking, boiling, or broiling meats and fish adds the least amount of fat to the diet. Prepare all foods using measured amounts of fats or flour to be added, and measure the amount of foods. Remember, high carbohydrate foods (Ex.: candy, sugars, and beer) and high fat foods (Ex.: creamed foods) should be avoided.

	Measured	**Nonmeasured**
Breakfast	Orange juice, ½ cup Egg, 1 Milk, 1 cup Cereal, dry, ¾ cup Cream, sweet, 2 tbsp	Coffee or Tea
Lunch	Cheese, 1 slice Anchovies, 3 medium Bread, 1 slice Potato, ½ cup Butter, 1 tsp Apple, 1 medium Pear, 1 small Milk, ½ cup	Salad Coffee or Tea
Dinner	Roast beef, 3 slices (3 x 2 x ⅛ in) Green beans, 1 cup Carrots, ½ cup Bread, 1 slice Butter, 1 tsp Milk, ½ cup Peach, 1 medium	Broth Coffee or Tea

Table 9.2 Energy Requirements
This list of various activities shows the amount of energy expended (measured in calories) if the activity is carried out for an hour.

Kinds of activity	Calories (per hour)
Walking up stairs	1100
Running (a jog)	570
Swimming	500
Vigorous exercise	450
Slow walking	200
Dressing and undressing	118
Sitting at rest	100

of **kilocalories.** A kilocalorie is one thousand times the amount of a calorie. So don't be misled by the amount of calories generated by certain foods listed in this chapter. Remember you are really eating one thousand times the calories listed in dieting books! The energy you use for different types of activity are listed in table 9.2. These are all listed in "real" calories. Notice that all the activities include physical exercise. This is because the majority of energy expenditure is through muscular activities.

As a person engages in the activities of his everyday life, he constantly uses energy that he acquires from the food he eats. At no time are those molecules entering his body locked into some part of his cells. They are constantly being changed and exchanged; for example, fat molecules are completely exchanged about every four weeks. This exchange is easily seen when a person either gains or loses weight. In each case, the molecules of his body are rearranged. The nature of the rearrangement will depend on the amount of incoming food and the amount of activity. If a person's activity level increases and his eating habits remain the same, he will lose weight. On the other hand, if his activity level drops and his eating habits remain the same, he will gain weight. Of course, extremes in both of these cases can be seen. The one extreme in which a great deal of unnecessary weight is gained occurs in **obese** persons. Obesity occurs because some people take in more food energy than is necessary to meet the activity requirements of their life-style. Many physically inactive persons have become fat simply because society has made it acceptable to eat "three square meals" a day. In some cases it seems necessary to eat more food than is really required for good health. For example, most social gatherings have high-calorie snack foods available, and luncheon dates are an everyday occurrence for many businessmen. The solution to obesity is biologically simple, eat the amount of food calories that corresponds to your daily activity level. If you eat less and increase your activity, you will lose weight. Don't fall for fad diets; just cut down on portions and frequency of eating. It is rare that a person has a "glandular problem," but if you honestly

Fig. 9.2 Starvation and Stored Foods. Starving yourself will result in a very selective loss of the different kinds of nutrients stored in the body. Notice how the protein level in the body decreases the slowest of the three.

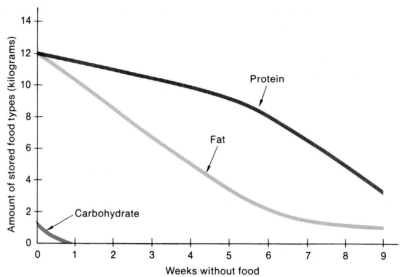

try and fail to rid yourself of that excess weight, you should check with a doctor.

Very little carbohydrate is stored in your body. This small amount will only last as a stored form of energy for about two days if you starve yourself. After the stored carbohydrate has been used, your body will begin to use its stored fat deposits as a source of energy; the proteins will be used last. During the early stages of starvation, the amount of fat in the body will steadily decrease, but the amount of protein will drop only slightly (fig. 9.2). This can continue only up to a certain point. During about six weeks of this starvation period, the fat acts as a protein protector. You can see the value of this kind of protection when you remember the vital roles that proteins play in cellular metabolism. After six weeks, however, so much fat has been lost from the body that proteins are no longer protected, and they will begin to be respired by the cells as a source of energy. This results in a loss of proteins from the cells of the body so that cells can no longer carry out their normal functions. When enough enzymes are not available to do the necessary cellular jobs, the cells die.

Remember—Quality, Not Quantity!

The amount of food you eat each day should be regulated to meet your activity needs. But even more important is the kind of food you eat. Most carbohydrates can be digested for use in the human body. This is also true of proteins and lipids. However, not all proteins contain the same amino acids. Proteins can be divided into two main groups, the **complete proteins** and the **partial proteins.** This division is based on the fact that some proteins contain all the amino acids necessary for good health (complete proteins) while other proteins (partial proteins) lack certain amino acids that must be available to the body if it is to function efficiently. Table 9.3 is a list of the ten so-called **essential amino acids.** Without minimal levels of these amino acids in the diet, a person may develop health problems that could ultimately lead to his death. In many parts of the world, large populations of people live on diets that are very high in carbohydrates and fats, but low in complete protein. This is easy to understand, since carbohydrates and fats are inexpensive to grow and process in comparison to proteins. For example, corn, rice, wheat, and barley are all high carbohydrate foods (fig. 9.3). Corn and its products (meal, flour) contain protein, but it is a partial protein, because it lacks the amino acid tryptophan. Without this amino acid, many necessary enzymes cannot be made in sufficient amounts to keep the person healthy. The symptoms of protein deficiency can be very easily seen in persons (fig. 9.4). A protein deficiency disease is called **kwashiorkor.** A person with this deficiency has a distended belly, slow growth, slow movement, and is emotionally depressed. If caught in time, brain damage may be prevented and death averted. To do this requires a change in diet that includes expensive complete protein. Such a diet might include poultry, fish, beef, shrimp, or milk. As the world food problem increases, these expensive foods will be in even shorter supply, and will become more and more costly.

Table 9.3 *Sources of Essential Amino Acids*
The essential amino acids are required in the diet for protein building, and along with the other nonessential amino acids, allow the body to metabolize all nutrients at an optimum rate. Combinations of different plant foods can provide essential amino acids even if the complete protein foods—such as meat, fish, and milk—are not in the diet.

Essential amino acid	Food sources
Threonine	Dairy products, nuts, soybeans, turkey
Lysine	Dairy products, nuts, soybeans, green peas, beef, turkey
Methionine Cystine	Dairy products, fish, oatmeal, wheat
Arginine (essential in infants only)	Dairy products, beef, peanuts, ham, shredded wheat, poultry
Valine	Dairy products, liverwurst, peanuts, oats
Phenylalanine	Dairy products, peanuts, calves liver
Tyrosine	Dairy products, calves liver, peanuts
Leucine	Dairy products, beef, poultry, fish
Tryptophan	Dairy products, sesame seeds, sunflower seeds, lamb, poultry, peanuts
Isoleucine	Dairy products, fish, peanuts, oats, macaroni, lima beans

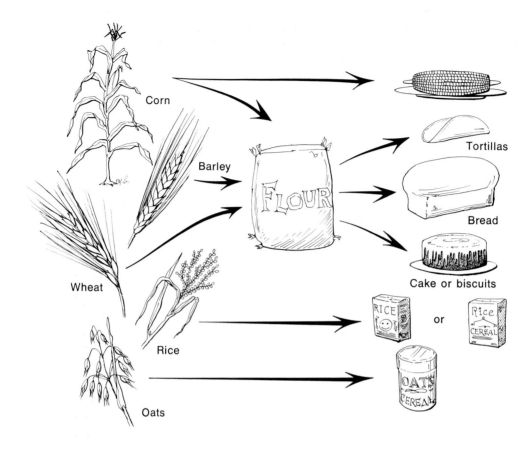

Corn

Barley

Wheat

Rice

Oats

FLOUR

Tortillas

Bread

Cake or biscuits

Fig. 9.3 *Carbohydrates in Your Diet.* Many of the world's food staples are plant carbohydrates that have been ground into flours or are eaten directly. Combinations of certain grains can supply the essential amino acids in a diet.

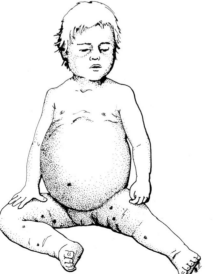

Fig. 9.4 *Kwashiorkor.* This starving child shows the symptoms of the protein-deficient disease kwashiorkor. If treated with a proper diet containing all amino acids, this disease could be cured.

Biologists have changed many inexpensive crops that were low in complete protein so that they now contain more amino acids. You may have driven past a sign next to a cornfield that had "L3369" written on it (fig. 9.5). What this means is that the corn being grown in this cornfield has been produced by biologists because of its exceptionally high content of the amino acid lysine, in comparison to other corn plants. Production of these special corn plants may help supplement the protein portion of the diets of many people throughout the world.

Another Important Factor

Even if all the proteins, carbohydrates, and lipids are supplied to the cells, good health may still not be attained. Almost all cells require small amounts of certain other materials that are important in aiding the functioning of the cell or are a necessary part of the cell's structure. These materials are called **growth factors,** but are more commonly referred to as **vitamins** and **minerals.** All minerals must be present in the diet, since the cells cannot manufacture chemical elements. Examples of minerals and their functions are listed in table 9.4. Small amounts of vitamins are also needed in the diet. Vitamins are not elements but organic molecules manufactured by some other organisms. Table 9.5 shows some of the sources of the various vitamins necessary to man and the roles they play in keeping a person healthy. The lack of a particular vitamin in the diet can result in a condition of ill health called a **vitamin deficiency disease.** These diseases are noted in table 9.6.

Fig. 9.5 *Hybrid Corn.* Selective breeding of grains can result in crops that are higher in certain essential amino acids than are the common varieties. These are especially high in the amino acid lysine. (Courtesy of Pioneer Seed Company.)

A great deal has been said about the need for vitamin and mineral supplements in diets. Some people claim that it is essential that supplements be made to the diet, while others claim adequate amounts are easily obtained from a well-balanced diet. Supporters of vitamin supplements have even claimed that extremely high doses of certain vitamins will prevent ill health, or even create supermen. It is very difficult to evaluate many of these claims, since the actual functioning of vitamins and minerals and their regulation in the body is not completely clear. In fact, the minimum daily requirement of a number of vitamins has not been determined. The information in tables 9.4 and 9.5 should be used in considering the kinds of foods you eat each day, and their value to you in maintaining good health.

Table 9.4 *Source and Uses of Minerals in the Human Body*

Mineral	Food source	Use in body
Calcium	Asparagus, beans, cauliflower, cheese, cream, egg yolk, milk.	Building of bones and teeth; aids in clotting of blood; regulation of heart, nerve, and muscle activity; enzyme formation; milk production.
Chlorine	Bread, buttermilk, cabbage, cheese, clams, eggs, ham (cured), sauerkraut, table salt.	Regulation of osmotic pressure; enzyme activities; formation of hydrochloric acid in stomach.
Cobalt	Liver, seafoods	Normal appetite and growth; prevention of a type of anemia.
Copper	Bran, cocoa, liver, mushrooms, oysters, peas, pecans, shrimp.	Formation of hemoglobin.
Iodine	Broccoli, fish, iodized table salt, oysters, shrimp	Formation of thyroxin.
Iron	Almonds, beans, egg yolk, heart, kidney, liver, soybeans, whole wheat.	Formation of hemoglobin; oxygen transport.
Magnesium	Beans, bran, brussels sprouts, chocolate, corn, peanuts, peas, spinach, prunes.	Muscular activity; enzyme activity; bone structure.
Phosphorus	Beans, cheese, cocoa, eggs, liver, milk, oatmeal, peas, whole wheat.	Tooth and bone formation; buffer effects in the blood; muscle contraction.
Potassium	Beans, bran, molasses, olives, parsnips, potatoes, spinach, oranges.	Normal growth, muscle function; maintenance of osmotic pressure; regulation of heart beat.
Sodium	Beef, bread, cheese, oysters, spinach, table salt, wheat germ.	Regulation of osmotic pressure; protection against excessive loss of water.
Sulfur	Beans, bran, cheese, cocoa, eggs, fish, nuts, peas.	Formation of proteins.
Zinc	Beans, cress, lentils, liver, peas, spinach.	Normal growth.

Adapted from Cornett Morrison et al. *Human Physiology.* New York: Holt, Rinehart, Winston, 1967, p. 186.

Chapter 9

Table 9.5 *Source and Uses of Vitamins in the Human Body*
These are only a few of the vitamins used in human metabolism. Notice that a number of them have been referred to earlier in the chapters on enzymes and respiration.

Vitamin	Food source	Use in body
Thiamine (B$_1$)	Peas, beans, eggs, pork, liver	Coenzyme use in Krebs' cycle
Riboflavin (B$_2$)	Milk, whole grain cereals, green vegetables, liver, eggs	Part of coenzyme used in electron transfer system (FAD)
Niacin (nicotinic acid)	Milk, poultry, yeast, cereal	Part of coenzyme used in electron transfer system (NAD)
Pyridoxine (B$_6$)	Most foods	Coenzyme used in synthesis of amino acids
Cyanocobalamin (B$_{12}$)	Meats, dairy products	Used in red blood cell formation
Ascorbic acid (C)	Citrus fruits, vegetables	Part of cell cement used to hold cells together
E	Green vegetables, vegetable oils in most foods	Maintains fertility
D	Dairy products, fish oil	Aids in calcium use in bones
A	Dairy products, vegetables	Used in formation of visual pigment; maintains skin (action not known)

Table 9.6 *Vitamin Deficiencies*

Vitamin	Symptoms of deficiency
B$_1$	Beriberi—breakdown of nerve cells and muscle, heart failure
B$_2$	Cracking of skin around the eyes and mouth; skin infections
Niacin	Skin infections, diarrhea, insanity
B$_6$	Vitamin is so readily available that no deficiency disease has been noted
B$_{12}$	Pernicious anemia—defective formation of red blood cells
C	Scurvy—small blood vessels break just under the skin and around mouth
E	Sterility and weakness in rats; human disease not fully known
D	Rickets—soft, misshaped bones
A	Night blindness; dry skin; leads to infections of skin

Through the Teeth and Over the Gums, Look Out Stomach Here It Comes!

All the processes involved in preparing foods (nutrients) for entry into a cell are called digestion. These events actually take place outside the cell. Many single-celled organisms such as bacteria release enzymes that break down large molecules of food so that they may enter the cell. This occurs when mold grows on bread. The fungus releases its enzymes into the bread and makes it soft as it breaks down the bread (fig. 9.6). In many-celled organisms, there is usually a large sac or cavity into which the nutrients are placed. Enzymes are then mixed with the nutrients in this cavity and the smaller food molecules are then taken into the body cells for use in metabolic pathways (fig. 9.7). In the case of man and many other very complex animals, the simple digestive sac has been replaced by a very complex and lengthy system of tubes and specialized cells, which make the digestive process much more efficient. This digestive tract includes many parts, each of which plays an important role in the breakdown of foods. These parts include the mouth, salivary glands, esophagus, stomach, small and large intestines, liver, gall bladder, pancreas, and anus (fig. 9.8).

The first portion of the digestive tract is the **mouth.** The mouth, teeth, and tongue function to physically break down the incoming foods into smaller pieces that can move easily through the esophagus into the stomach. This breakdown also increases the surface area of the foods so that the digestive

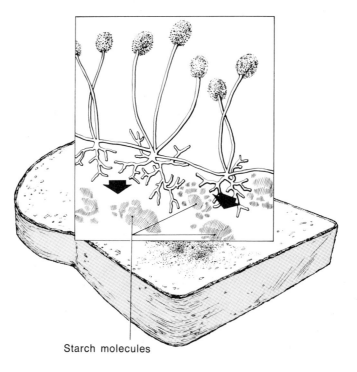

Fig. 9.6 *Extracellular Digestion.* The mold growing on this slice of bread releases its enzymes (arrow) onto the surface of the bread where it breaks down the substrate into smaller molecules for absorption into the filaments of the mold.

Starch molecules

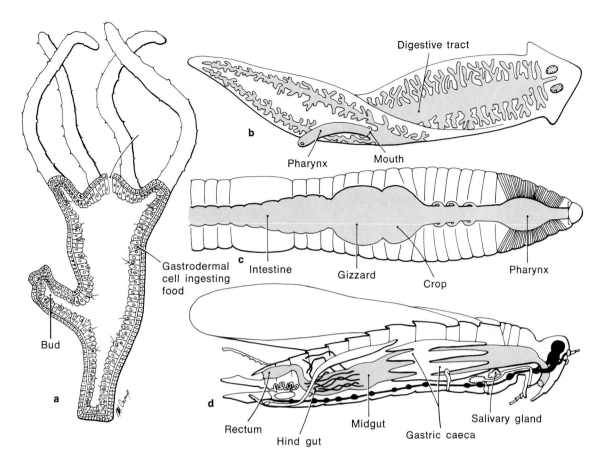

a Bud
Gastrodermal cell ingesting food

b Digestive tract
Pharynx
Mouth

c Intestine
Gizzard
Crop
Pharynx

d Rectum
Hind gut
Midgut
Gastric caeca
Salivary gland

enzymes may come in contact with more of their substrate molecules. During this process, the salivary glands produce the fluid **saliva,** which adds moisture and the enzyme amylase to the food. Amylase begins the breakdown of starch molecules to more simple sugars. Saliva also allows many of the flavor molecules of foods to be released, enabling the taste buds on the tongue to let you know what you are chewing. Once the food has been chewed, the tongue rolls it into a ball and presses it to the back of the mouth. This pressure acts as a trigger mechanism for swallowing, and the food begins its passage through the next portion of the digestive tract, the **esophagus.** Muscles squeeze the ball of food down the esophagus in a wavelike manner (fig. 9.9). This sequence of contractions, which moves the food to the stomach, is called **peristalsis.** These waves of contractions occur throughout the digestive tube and move the food all the way through to the anus (the opening from the digestive tract).

Once the food enters the **stomach,** it is usually kept there because a muscle between the stomach and esophagus remains closed. This muscle, called the **sphincter muscle,** wraps around the esophagus, and when con-

Fig. 9.7 *Digestive Tracts.*
All the organisms pictured have some form of digestive tube. The hydra *(a)* is the most simple while the digestive system of the grasshopper *(d)* is much more complex. Notice that when food is *in* the tube, it is really *outside* the animal cells.

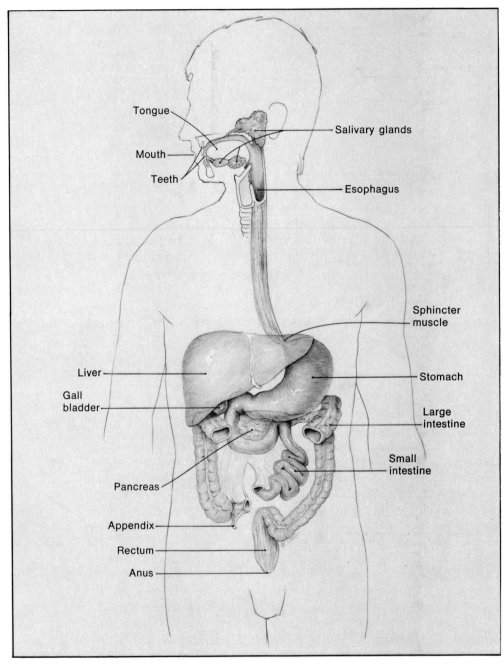

Fig. 9.8 *Human Digestive Tract.* The digestive system of man and the specialized organs that aid in the chemical breakdown of foods.

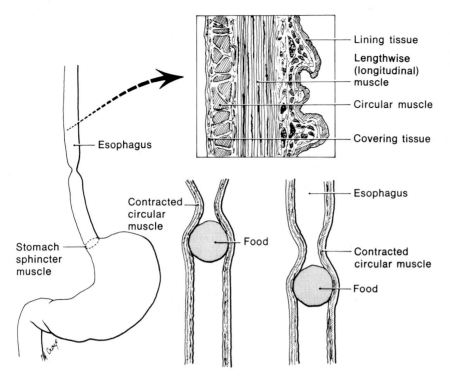

Lining tissue

Lengthwise (longitudinal) muscle

Circular muscle

Covering tissue

Esophagus

Esophagus

Stomach sphincter muscle

Contracted circular muscle

Food

Contracted circular muscle

Food

Fig. 9.9 *Peristalsis of Esophagus.* A series of rhythmic muscular contractions forces the food through the esophagus.

tracted, or tightened, it squeezes the tube closed. However, in some cases, the sphincter muscle may be relaxed or forcefully opened by pressures from the stomach. When this happens, a small amount of the contents of the stomach moves back into the esophagus. Since the stomach's contents are very low in pH (acid) and contain many strong enzymes, this backup may cause an irritation in the lower portion of the esophagus. When this occurs, a person feels what is called a "heartburn." In extreme cases of stomach irritation, **vomiting** might take place. The stomach is actually squeezed by the muscles of the sides of the body, violently forcing the contents of the stomach through the esophagus and mouth.

A Sour Stomach

The stomach receives about 2000 ml (2 qts) of fluid per day from the cells lining the stomach. This fluid contains the enzymes **pepsin** and **rennin** and has a low pH of 1.0–3.5 due to the presence of hydrochloric acid, HCl. This acid aids in the breakdown of foods, just as it would decompose most materials, and produces a very favorable environment for the operation of the enzyme pepsin. When the food reaches the stomach, the stomach muscles contract and relax in a regular manner to churn the contents. As the food is churned, it mixes with the HCl and the enzymes. Pepsin operates on protein

On the morning of 6 June 1822, a nineteen-year-old French-Canadian fur trapper named Alexis St. Martin was shot in the stomach by the accidental discharge from a shotgun. The Army surgeon at Fort Mackinac, Michigan, Dr. William Beaumont, was called to attend the wounded man. Since part of the stomach and body wall had been shot away, Beaumont quickly dressed the wound but expected the patient to die. When St. Martin was found to be alive the next day, Beaumont was surprised and encouraged to do what he could to extend his life. As a matter of fact Beaumont cared for St. Martin for two years, and the wound healed. However, the wound healed in such a way that the stomach formed an opening through the body wall. Beaumont found that he could look through the opening and observe the activities that occurred in the stomach. As a result, Beaumont was able to perform a number of experiments related to human digestion. He was able to obtain pure gastric juice from the stomach and note its effects on food outside of the body. He was also able to suspend food by a string and note the progress of digestion in St. Martin's stomach. St. Martin did not take kindly to these probings and twice ran away from Beaumont's care, but did not die until the age of 83, having lived over 60 years with a hole in his stomach.

foods and increases the rate of their breakdown into free amino acids. Because of the large amount of very dense food in the stomach, the pepsin doesn't reach all the protein and much remains untouched by this enzyme. The final breakdown of the proteins is accomplished at a later time in the digestive process.

The other enzyme, rennin, is only found in mammals that feed their young milk. Rennin reacts with milk protein, splitting it into two products. The products that form are a fluid portion called whey, and a more solid portion called casein (or curd). For this reason, rennin is used in the cheese-making process to speed up the formation of curds and whey. The stomach curd resembles cottage cheese. The protein casein also clumps into small curds in the stomach. The enzyme pepsin then begins to break the protein casein into amino acids. Rennin works best in a solution that is not highly acidic. Because children produce less acid in their stomachs than adults, the small amount of rennin in their stomachs has a better chance to work than the rennin found in adults. In fact, the pH of digestive juice in adults is usually so low that milk curd is never formed.

The digestive enzymes of the stomach operate on any protein. In fact, it is impossible for pepsin to distinguish the difference between the molecules of incoming foods and similar molecules that make up the actual structure of the stomach. Enzymes work on substrates, and as long as the two (enzyme and substrate) fit together properly, it makes no difference whether the substrate is food or your own cell material! How then does a person keep from digesting himself to pieces? The digestive tract is lined with many types of cells, some of which are specialized in the production of molecules of a thick, sticky substance called **mucous.** The mucous forms a lining on the inside of the stomach and many other structures, and helps to protect the tract from the digestive enzymes and acid by acting as a barrier.

As digestion occurs, the mucous lining wears away and must constantly be replaced. In some cases, this form of self-protection doesn't always operate. Some persons fail to produce enough mucous to prevent their own stomach juices from coming in contact with the cells lining the stomach. When this contact is made, the enzymes and acid react with the cells of the stomach and form a small cavity in the stomach wall. This is called an **ulcer** (fig. 9.10).

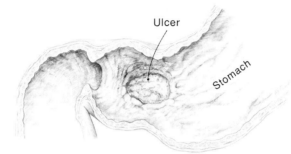

Ulcer

Stomach

Fig. 9.10 Stomach Ulcer. If the mucous lining in the stomach is lost, the pepsin and hydrochloric acid may produce a cavity in the wall of the stomach. Notice the ulcer at the end of the pointer.

If the ulcer is the result of too much pepsin being produced by the stomach, it is called a **peptic ulcer.** As you might know, the cavity can become quite extensive and may even destroy some of the blood vessels of the stomach wall. When this occurs, the ulcer causes a great deal of pain, begins to bleed, and sometimes there may be enough damage to cause death.

Some materials can actually speed up the ulcer forming process. Aspirin can pass through the mucous lining of the stomach and cause bleeding. It is important to take aspirin as recommended by a doctor. To take them more frequently, or in greater numbers may cause serious side effects. This is especially true of persons taking large numbers of aspirin to relieve the pain of arthritis. The ulcer causing property of aspirin may be speeded up if alcohol is also present in the stomach. Many people take a couple of aspirins after drinking alcohol to help prevent a hangover; but they may actually be encouraging the development of an ulcer. Doctors may recommend that a person with an ulcer eat more frequently each day. In this way the stomach will be kept partially full all the time, so as not to give the pepsin and acid a chance to digest the stomach wall. Instead, the acid and enzyme will be working on the incoming foods (table 9.7).

Solid food is kept in the stomach for about three to four hours before it is released to the next part of the digestive tract, the **small intestine.** The small intestine contains an even larger assortment of digestive enzymes and other related molecules than is found in the stomach. Some enzymes, such as amylase, continue the same processes as were started earlier, while other

Table 9.7 *Ulcer Diet*

Compare this ulcer diet to the 1500 calorie diet in table 9.1. Notice the different types of foods in both diets, and how these foods would better aid in the ulcer repair. What might be a problem if you were to remain on this diet for a long time?

General description:
1. Avoid overeating at any one meal. It is better to eat smaller amounts more often.
2. Eat slowly and chew thoroughly. Sip liquids slowly, especially hot or cold ones.
3. Avoid worry, tension, argument, hurry, and fatigue, particularly at mealtime.
4. Avoid monotony in diet by varying the foods used as much as the diet allows.
5. Use no spices or seasonings except salt. Avoid concentrated sweets. Small amounts of sugar may be used.
6. Do not drink over a glass of liquid with each meal, but drink as much as desired between meals.
7. Take medications regularly as directed.
8. Follow all directions carefully and include only that part of the following diet list which is prescribed. Make the additions to the diet only as the physician advises it.
9. Maintain regular hours for eating, and take meals regularly.

Food	Allowed	Not allowed
Milk	Regular or homogenized, buttermilk	
Cream	Plain or mixed with milk	
Fats	Fresh butter or fortified margarine	Any others
Eggs	Boiled, poached, coddled; plain omelet or scrambled in double boiler; eggnog with vanilla only	Fried eggs
Cereals	Cooked refined or strained; oatmeal, cream of wheat, Farina, Wheatena, precooked infant cereals; also plain buttered noodles, macaroni, spaghetti, or white rice Dry cereals such as cornflakes, puffed rice, Rice Krispies, without bran	Whole grain cereals; cereals containing bran or shredded wheat
Desserts	Plain custard, Jell-o, rennet, plain cornstarch, tapioca or rice puddings; plain vanilla ice cream (if allowed to melt in mouth)	Any other
Bread	Enriched white; fine rye or fine whole wheat bread at least one day old (may be plain or toasted soda crackers); zweibach, melba toast, hard rolls	Whole wheat and other whole grain bread; graham or coarse crackers; hot or fresh bread
Cheese	Cream, cottage cheese, mild processed American and Swiss	All other
Sweets	Jelly (clear, plain) honey, sugar (in moderation), strained cranberry sauce	Any other
Potato	White, baked, boiled, creamed; boiled or baked sweet potatoes or yams in moderate amounts	Any other
Cream soups	Homemade cream soups from the following pureed vegetables: asparagus spinach potato green bean pea tomato	Canned cream soups; soups from any other vegetables; dehydrated soups, chicken soups, broths, meat stock, bouillon

From Sue Rodwell Williams, 1973. *Nutrition and Diet Therapy*, 2d ed. St. Louis: The C. V. Mosby Co.

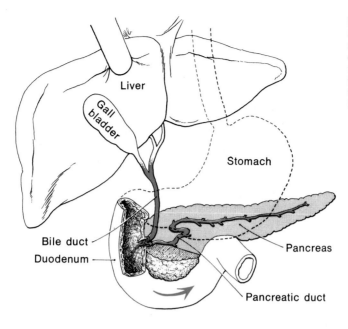

Fig. 9.11 *Enzymes and Digestion.* Digestive enzymes and other molecules enter the small intestine from the liver and pancreas through the tubes or from the lining of the small intestine.

enzymes begin the breakdown of other foods into their simpler, more useful parts. This assortment of enzymes and other molecules come from three different sources: the lining of the intestine, the liver, and the pancreas (fig. 9.11). As the food enters the first portion of the small intestine, the **duodenum,** the cells lining the intestine are stimulated to release their enzymes. As this occurs, both the **gall bladder** and the pancreas release their contents, which flow through tubes to the small intestine. The product of the liver, bile, is produced continuously while the products of the pancreas are only released as needed. When bile is not needed in the duodenum, it is stored in the gall bladder.

Growl, Growl, Growl

Table 9.8 lists the various digestive enzymes and related molecules, their source, and the chemical changes that they produce in the small intestine. It is here that all three main food materials are completely broken down into their simplest forms. Proteins are split into the amino acids. Fat molecules are broken down into fatty acids and glycerol. Carbohydrates are broken down into simple sugars.

The operation of all the intestinal enzymes will provide the person with the variety of simple nutrients he needs for proper cell metabolism. If any of the enzymes are lacking, the cells of the body will not receive the necessary nutrients and disruptions in the intestinal tract may occur. A good example of this can be seen in people who are *lactose intolerant*. In the normal individual, the wall of the intestine produces the enzyme *lactase*. Lactase breaks

Table 9.8 *Digestive Enzymes and Their Activity*

Digestible food types	Enzymes	Source	Product of reaction
Proteins	Pepsin	Gastric juice	Smaller proteins
	Trypsin	Pancreatic juice	Smaller proteins
	Carboxy-peptidase	Pancreatic juice	Amino acids
	Di-peptidase	Intestinal juice	Amino acids
Carbohydrates	Amylase	Saliva Pancreatic juice Intestinal juice	Disaccharides (double sugar)
	Disaccharidases	Intestinal juices	Simple sugars
Lipid	Lipase	Intestinal juice Pancreatic juice	Fatty acids and glycerol

the milk sugar, lactose, into its two simpler components, glucose and galactose. Since lactose is absorbed into the small intestine and enters the blood slower than the glucose or galactose molecules, this enzymatic reaction aids in getting sugar to cells at a faster rate. Some persons lack this enzyme. When they eat or drink dairy products, the lactose is not digested, but accumulates in the intestine. This accumulation wouldn't be a problem, except for the fact that the intestine contains a wide assortment of bacteria that are capable of fermenting lactose. As the lactose increases, these bacteria ferment the sugar, causing the person to have cramps, gas, growling, and diarrhea. People with lactose intolerance show this reaction to milk thirty to ninety minutes after eating dairy products. This intolerance really should not be considered serious. Usually, when the problem is discovered, it is easily controlled by simply not drinking milk or eating dairy products.

Through Thin and Thick

During the four to eight hours that the contents of the stomach are slowly emptied into the small intestine, a large amount of fluids are added to aid the digestive process. Along with the 2000 ml of stomach fluids added, there are about 6000 ml more fluids added to the contents of the digestive tract each day. This makes the contents of the small intestine very watery. Dissolving the food materials in this solution allows these molecules to be better digested and absorbed into the cells that form the wall of the intestine. In fact, most of the foods you eat are taken into the body from the small intestine. Direct contact with this lining is possible since the pH of the intestine is not as acid as the stomach. The pH of the small intestine is changed by the products of the pancreas. As they arrive, they change the pH to a more neutral condition. Because of this, it is less likely that a person will get an ulcer in the small intestine. The wall of the small intestine has on its surface a great many small fingerlike projections called **villi** (villus, sing.).

These greatly increase the surface area of the small intestine (fig. 9.12). Each villus contains many small blood vessels that take up the molecules and circulate the nutrients to the rest of the cells of the body.

Some nutrients are not easily absorbed through the villi, but are still necessary for the health of the animal. The fats are this kind of nutrient. They can be altered in a way that will allow them to pass through the villi by the action of the bile. The bile salts break down fat into smaller droplets so they can be acted upon by the enzyme lipase, which is produced by the pancreas and intestine. The bile actually contains many different types of molecules. One of these is the bile salts and another is **cholesterol.** No specific function has been identified for the cholesterol in the bile, but it is known that the bile salts are produced from the cholesterol. In most people, the cholesterol is pumped from the gall bladder into the small intestine, and does not build up. However, some people may produce more cholesterol or absorb a great deal of water from the bile in the gall bladder. The cholesterol molecules now form crystals in the gall bladder, which are called **gallstones.** Gallstones may reduce the flow of bile into the small intestine and thus reduce the amount of fat digestion that occurs there.

Very little digestion takes place in the next portion of the intestine. This next section is the large intestine, or **colon.** Any materials that were not absorbed in the small intestine are usually wastes and are changed in the colon in preparation for elimination from the body. In order to prevent an extensive loss of valuable water from the digestive tract, much of the water that was added to the food to aid in digestion is taken back into the body. This reabsorbing of water changes the contents from a thin watery material to a thicker mass. At this point, the material is called **feces.** The digestion in the intestines usually takes about twelve hours.

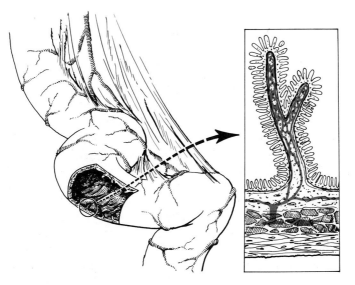

Fig. 9.12 *Villi of the Small Intestine.* The lining of the small intestine is not smooth, but covered with microscopic projections called villi (see inset). These greatly increase the surface of the small intestine and allow for better absorption of nutrients into the body.

Together, Wherever We Go

The processes of preparing the fecal material for elimination from the body are controlled by the cells of the colon and a great variety of bacteria that live in the colon. These bacteria decay the materials that were not digested in the small intestine. As these bacteria go about the business of surviving, they produce a variety of products, some of which benefit man. Vitamins are among these products. As changes in diet occur, the bacteria change in type and in the effects they have on the colon. A change in water, for example, may favor the bacterial production of gases. As the gas accumulates, it causes pain and bulging of the colon. In order to prevent such a catastrophe when you travel to another geographical area, you should enjoy the water and foods of that area very cautiously. Drink small amounts of the water to begin with and make sure that the foods are well cooked and cleaned. Once the bacteria in your intestine have become accustomed to these new foods, they should not give you a great deal of trouble.

Another disruption of the bacteria that live in your colon may result from the use of antibiotics. These drugs are used to help you defend yourself against bacterial infections. The drug, however, may not recognize the difference between infectious bacteria and the normal bacteria in your colon. You could destroy many of these helpful bacteria with the antibiotic. This could result in a case of diarrhea, and the loss of bacteria would also decrease the amount of vitamins you receive. In that case, your doctor may recommend that you take a vitamin supplement for a while and eat plenty of fresh fruit, since the bacteria on the fruit will help restock your colon with new bacteria.

The total number of bacteria in the colon is great. In fact, some people have estimated that one third of the fecal material is composed of bacteria. The final portion of the tract is called the **rectum.** After this section of the digestive tract has been filled, the feces are eliminated from the body through an opening from the rectum called the anus.

Summary   In order for an organism composed of many cells to live in good health, it must receive nutrient molecules that can enter the cells and function in the metabolic processes of the cells. The digestive tract of man is a tube that carries the food through a number of specialized portions: mouth, esophagus, stomach, small and large intestine, rectum, and anus (fig. 9.13). Each of these sections has become specialized in function. Through absorption of the digested food into the villi of the small intestine, small nutrient molecules are carried to all the cells of the body for use in cellular metabolism. The proper quantity and quality of nutrients (proteins, carbohydrates, lipids, and growth factors) are essential for the good health of the individual. Disruptions in the quantity or quality of the foods may result in metabolic problems such as obesity, starvation, kwashiorkor, vitamin deficiency diseases, or ulcers.

(Digestive tract)

Fig. 9.13 ***Human Digestive Tract.***

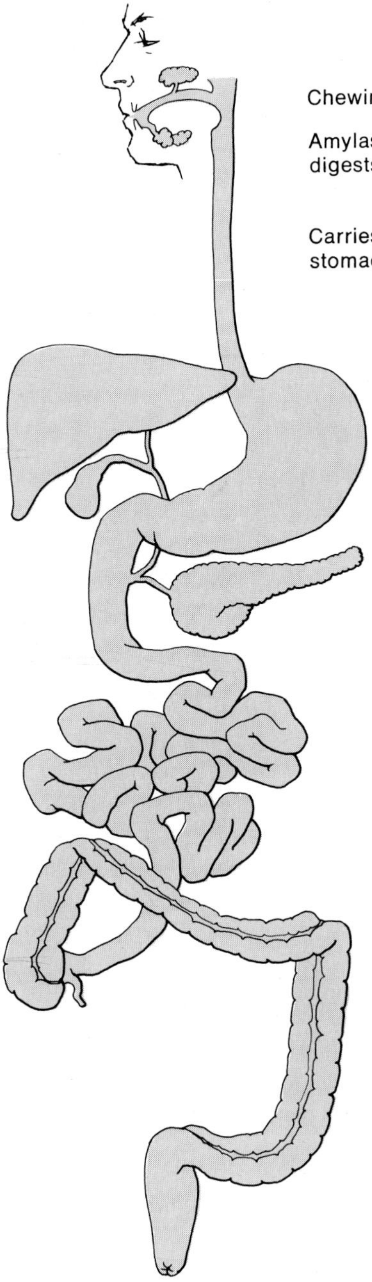

Name of structure	**Function of structure**
Mouth	Chewing
Salivary glands	Amylase in saliva digests starches
Esophagus	Carries food to stomach
Liver	Produces and holds bile and many other digestive materials
Gall bladder	
Stomach	Produces gastric juice, pepsin, rennin, HCl, etc.
Pancreas	Produces digestive enzymes
Small intestine	Produces digestive enzymes and also absorbs food which has been digested
Appendix	No known function
Large intestine	Reabsorbs water
Rectum	Holds undigested food until elimination
Anal opening	Opening through which undigested food is eliminated

Fantastic Journey

This is the title to a new movie just released from the studios of Hospital Productions, Inc. The plot involves a trip through the digestive tract of a lactose intolerant patient in an attempt to identify the exact nature of the patient's problem. In order to gain entry into the tract, the doctors are reduced in size and placed in a hamburger. They are mistakenly washed down with a glass of milk instead of water.

As the script writer, it is your job to describe in detail the events of their journey. (P.S. The hamburger has everything on it!)

Questions

1. Name two enzymes that are involved in the breakdown of proteins in the digestive tract of man.
2. What role does the liver play in fat digestion?
3. Why is chewing important in digestion?
4. What is a villus, and what is its function?
5. If a person wants to lose weight, what two things must he do?
6. How do the bacteria in the intestine aid in maintaining good health?
7. What is kwashiorkor, and why is it a serious health problem?
8. What factors aid in the movement of food through the digestive tract?
9. What particular malfunctions of the digestive tract result in each of the following conditions: gallstones, ulcers, heartburn, lactose intolerance?
10. How do the small and large intestines differ in structure and function?

Chapter Glossary

anus   The opening of the digestive system through which undigested food is eliminated.

calorie   The amount of heat necessary to raise the temperature of one gram of water one degree centigrade.

cholesterol   A steroid molecule found in the bile, which can be converted to vitamin D by sunlight. May crystallize to form gallstones.

colon   The large intestine. Water and salts are absorbed from the contents of the colon.

complete protein   Protein molecules that provide all the essential amino acids.

digestive tract   The series of tubes and structures that break down complex food molecules and absorb nutrients into the body.

duodenum   The upper portion of the small intestine into which flow various digestive enzymes and materials from the stomach, liver, and pancreas.

esophagus   A tube that conducts food from the mouth to the stomach.

essential amino acids   Those amino acids that are not made by the human body, but must be taken in as a part of the diet, examples: lysine, tryptophan, and valine.

feces   The name given to the undigested food material eliminated from the digestive tract through the anus.

gall bladder   A saclike structure that holds bile before it is released into the small intestine.

gallstones   Crystals of cholesterol formed in the gall bladder.

growth factor   A nutrient that is needed by the body for proper functioning, but only in very small amounts. Examples: vitamins and minerals.

kilocalorie   One thousand times larger than the calorie, a measure of heat energy.

kwashiorkor   A protein deficiency disease.

lactase   An enzyme produced by the cells lining the small intestine that breaks the complex sugar lactose into simple sugars.

lactose intolerance   A condition that results from the inability to digest lactose.

minerals   Growth factors, usually inorganic salts. Examples: calcium and magnesium.

mouth   The opening to the digestive tract.

mucous   A slimy material produced in various parts of the digestive tract; aids in the movement of food through the system, and protects the lining of the digestive tract from being digested by acids and enzymes.

obese   Extremely overweight.

partial protein   Protein molecules that do not provide all the essential amino acids.

pepsin   An enzyme that is produced by the cells lining the stomach and begins the breakdown of proteins.

peptic ulcer   A cavity formed in the wall of the digestive tract that is the result of the action of the enzyme pepsin.

peristalsis   Wavelike contractions of the muscles of the digestive tract, which move the food through the tube.

rectum   The final portion of the digestive tract in which undigested food is stored before being eliminated through the anus.

rennin   A digestive enzyme that is found in the stomach and curdles milk.

saliva   A digestive juice produced by the salivary glands, which aids in the digestion of starches and also moistens the food.

small intestine   The portion of the digestive tract in which most of the digestion occurs.

sphincter muscle   A circular muscle that when contracted closes the digestive tube.

stomach   The portion of the digestive tract that begins the digestion of proteins.

ulcer   An open sore.

villus   A microscopic fingerlike projection from the lining of the small intestine, which increases the surface area of the digestive tract.

vitamin deficiency disease   Poor health caused by the lack of a certain vitamin in the diet. Example: scurvy.

vitamins   Growth factors needed in the diet in small amounts.

vomiting   Forceful ejection of food from the stomach through the mouth.

Purpose In previous chapters we have considered a variety of biological structures and their functions. Organic molecules that are found in living cells are not haphazard arrangements of atoms, but are highly organized and may be classified into major groups. The nucleic acids, one of these groups, have a unique structure and function as the primary control molecules of the cell. This chapter will consider how the structure of complex molecules can be converted into the actions of living cells; and thus provide background information for later chapters on genetics and evolution.

Information Systems

Building Blocks

Like the other groups of organic macromolecules, the nucleic acids are made up of certain chemical elements. These are carbon, oxygen, hydrogen, nitrogen, and phosphorous. They are arranged into basic types of building blocks called **nucleotides.** Each of these is composed of a sugar molecule (S) containing five carbon atoms, a **phosphate** group (P),* and a kind of molecule called a **nitrogenous base** (B) (fig. 10.1).

There are eight common types of nucleotides available in a cell for building larger nucleic acids. Nucleotides differ in the kind of sugar and nitrogenous base they contain. Because of these differences it is possible to classify the nucleic acids into two main groups: **ribonucleic acid (RNA)** and **deoxyribonucleic acid (DNA).** The names of each give you information

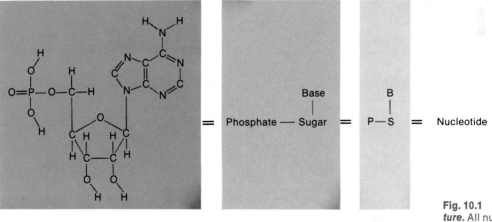

Fig. 10.1 Nucleotide Structure. All nucleotides are constructed in this basic way. The nucleotide is the basic structural unit of all nucleic acid molecules.

---

* In previous chapters, a phosphate has always been referred to with its complete chemical formula (PO_4). Now for simplicity, the phosphate group will be represented in the illustrations by a single capital (P).

about the structure of the molecules. For example, the prefix *ribo* in RNA tells you that the sugar part of this nucleic acid is **ribose.** Similarly, DNA contains a ribose sugar that has been deoxygenated (lost an oxygen atom) and is called **deoxyribose** (fig. 10.2). The nucleotide units contain nitrogenous bases that are of two different sizes, large and small. The larger ones are **adenine** (A) and **guanine** (G), which differ in the kinds of atoms attached to their double-ring structure (fig. 10.3). The smaller molecules are **cytosine** (C), **thymine** (T), and **uracil** (U). Each of these differs from the other by the atoms attached to its basic single-ring structure (fig. 10.4). These differences in size are important, as you will see later. Table 10.1 shows the basic differences between the makeup of RNA and DNA.

In chapter four you were shown ATP as an example of a nucleotide's structure (fig. 4.9). Chapter eight dealt with the function of this ATP molecule. Figure 10.5 illustrates a new example of a nucleotide commonly found in cells. These nucleotide building blocks can be bonded to one another

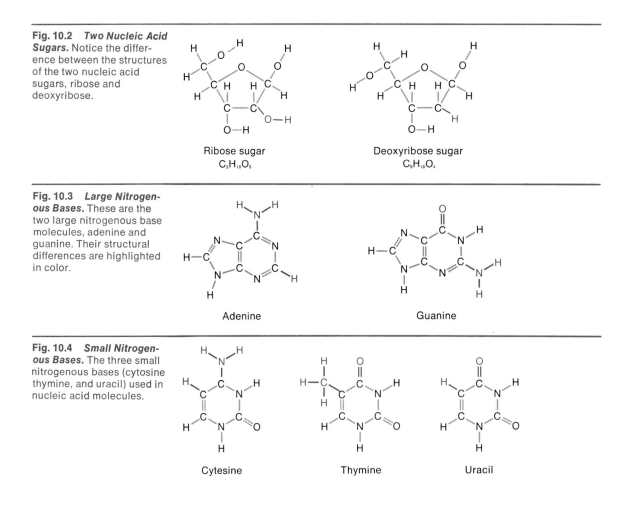

Fig. 10.2   *Two Nucleic Acid Sugars.* Notice the difference between the structures of the two nucleic acid sugars, ribose and deoxyribose.

Ribose sugar
$C_5H_{10}O_5$

Deoxyribose sugar
$C_5H_{10}O_4$

Fig. 10.3   *Large Nitrogenous Bases.* These are the two large nitrogenous base molecules, adenine and guanine. Their structural differences are highlighted in color.

Adenine

Guanine

Fig. 10.4   *Small Nitrogenous Bases.* The three small nitrogenous bases (cytosine thymine, and uracil) used in nucleic acid molecules.

Cytesine

Thymine

Uracil

Table 10.1 *Comparison of DNA and RNA*
The composition of the RNA molecule differs from that of DNA in both the categories of base type and sugar type.

Nucleic acid type	RNA	DNA
Base type	A,G,C,**U**	A,G,C,**T**
Acid type	Phosphoric acid	Phosphoric acid
Sugar type	**Ribose**	**Deoxyribose**

in a specific manner by a dehydration synthesis reaction involving a specific enzyme. The result of this nucleic acid synthesis is a long chain macromolecule, which resembles a comb. The protruding "teeth" (different nitrogenous bases) are connected to a common "backbone" (the sugar and phosphate molecules). This is the basic structure of both RNA and DNA. Notice in figure 10.6 that it is possible to "make sense" out of the sequence of nitrogenous bases. If you "read" them from left to right in groups of three, you can read three words: *CAT, ACT,* and *TAG.* It is possible to "write" a message in the form of a stable DNA molecule by combining different nucleotide units in particular sequences. You are using the four DNA nucleotides as an alphabet and restricting yourself to three-letter words. Realize, also, that in order to make sense out of such a code, it is necessary to read in a consistant direction. Reading the sequence in reverse doesn't always make sense just as reading this text in reverse would make no sense. DNA language is the language that the cell understands. The coded DNA serves as a central library; DNA contains all the information the cell needs to sustain, grow, and reproduce itself.

To accomplish all these processes, the library (DNA) must contain all the specifications necessary to manufacture the tools needed to perform every chemical job of the cell. If such information is missing or is not accurate, the cell will not work properly, and may even die. Enzymes, the tools that control the chemical reactions of the cell (discussed in chapters seven and eight), are constructed from DNA specifications. For this reason DNA is called the "blueprint of life." The necessary specification for mak-

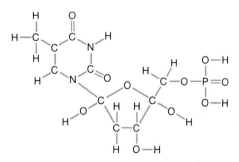

Fig. 10.5 *A DNA Nucleotide Containing Thymine.* A DNA nucleotide containing the nitrogenous base thymine. What change would have to be made if this was an RNA nucleotide?

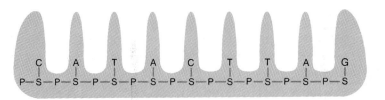

Fig. 10.6 *Single Strand of DNA.* A single strand of DNA resembles a comb. The molecule is much longer than pictured here and is composed of a sequence of linked nucleotides.

ing a particular enzyme is called a **structural gene.** In most cases structural genes are chemically linked together to form a large threadlike molecule. Each strand may have tens of hundreds of genes linked end-to-end. These threads can be dyed to make them more visible when looked at through a microscope. As a result they have come to be known as chromosomes (colored bodies).

Safeguards for Valuables

It is possible to continue the blueprint example even further. The blueprints for any essential tool must be protected from damage or the job for which it is to be used might never be completed. Such protection could be accomplished in a number of ways. For example, a protective cover could be placed over the valuable blueprint and then rolled into a tube and put in a safe place. Another method to protect the blueprint would be to use a copy instead of the original.

Living systems have adopted all of these protective measures to one degree or another, which, as a result, has better insured the continuation of their existence. The protective "cover" over the genetic material takes the form of a second long strand of DNA. Its structure is designed to provide maximum protection. It forms a smooth, parallel, molecular cover that can be removed easily when the blueprint needs to be read. The cover DNA is kept in place by the formation of weak hydrogen bonds between certain **complementary bases** of the gene and the cover. Three such bonds are formed between guanine and cytosine, and two such bonds are formed between adenine and thymine (fig. 10.7). This double-stranded DNA molecule is stabilized by the fact that its sides are parallel, just as a ladder with parallel sides is more stable than one having bulges or constrictions located at random from one end to the other. This parallel structure is maintained, since the large bases (G and A) always pair with the small bases (C and T). A is complementary to T, and C is complementary to G. Referring again to our blueprint idea, the DNA becomes coiled or twisted when not in use. This provides protection for the molecule, since the sugars and phosphates of the backbone cover the bases. This means that the most important part of the molecule, the chemical code sequence of bases, is tucked inside this **double helix** away from the potentially damaging effects of its environment. Further protection from the environment is gained in most cells by confining the DNA within a membrane. This enclosed area is the nucleus.

The Original Copy Machine

The third protective device involves the production of a copy of the blueprint. This is the first step in the process of using the blueprint information for the synthesis of protein **(protein synthesis).** The process of protein synthesis is similar to the series of events involved in the supervision and manufacture of a product in a factory. Keep in mind that the cell is a very complex chemical factory and must be capable of responding to changes in its environment.

For a factory to be efficient, it must produce a standardized product. This requires tools that operate on the parts in a very specific way. For example, 5mm wrenches only fit on 5mm bolts, and not on 8mm bolts. When wrenches wear out or become damaged, they must be replaced by another tool exactly like the original. The blueprint for that tool is opened so that it may be read. To take the original blueprint to the workbench for use during the toolmaking process would be a mistake because it could become damaged and worthless. Therefore, a copy of the original is made and taken to the workbench instead. If there is a great demand for these tools, many copies may be made. The original blueprint is then recovered, rolled up, and kept safe (fig. 10.8).

For the cell to be efficient, it must produce all the chemicals required to sustain, grow, and reproduce itself. To do this the cell requires enzymes to operate on substrates. After much use, enzymes become worn-out or dam-

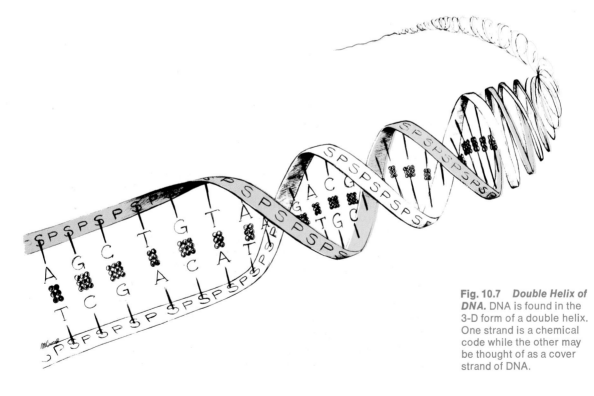

Fig. 10.7 Double Helix of DNA. DNA is found in the 3-D form of a double helix. One strand is a chemical code while the other may be thought of as a cover strand of DNA.

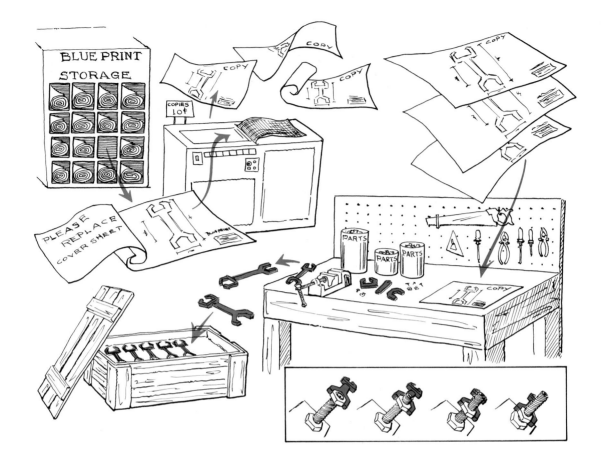

Fig. 10.8 *Tool Production.* The structure of DNA (and many other molecules) is closely linked with its function. Compare this factory assembly-line example with figure 10.9.

aged and must be replaced by another enzyme just like it. The DNA that codes for that enzyme is separated from the cover DNA. The DNA is not used directly by the cell to manufacture enzymes, but a copy of the gene is made to accomplish this. Many copies will be made if the cell has a great need for a specific enzyme. If the enzyme is rarely used, few copies will be made. This copying process is the first event in protein synthesis, and is called **transcription.** It involves the four types of RNA nucleotides: A, G, C, and U. (Remember, there is no thymine in RNA, but the base uracil is found in its place).

In order to guarantee accuracy, each nucleotide in the structural gene is copied or paired with an individual RNA nucleotide (fig. 10.9). These attach to one another by hydrogen bonding between the single RNA nucleotides and the nucleotides of the DNA strand. (Remember, the cover DNA has been removed and is now at a distance from the gene.) None of the RNA nucleotides base-pair with the cover DNA nucleotides. When the copying process is complete, the RNA nucleotides are attached to one another, and they form a single strand of RNA. This strand is removed with the aid of an

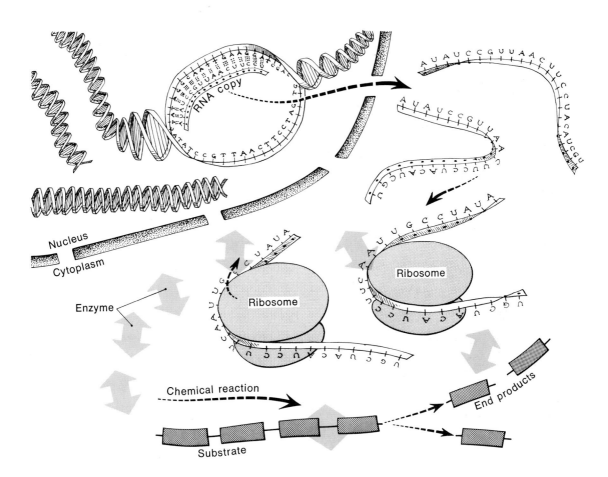

Labels in figure:
RNA copy
Nucleus
Cytoplasm
Enzyme
Ribosome
Ribosome
Chemical reaction
Substrate
End products

enzyme, and the blueprint is recovered and coiled into the double helix. This newly formed molecule is RNA, not DNA. It is an exact copy of the message of the structural gene and is called **messenger RNA,** or **mRNA** (fig. 10.10).

At the Workbench

The mRNA molecule is a coded message written in nucleic acid language. At the workbench it must be read and the information used to assemble amino acids into protein. This second event in the process of protein synthesis is called **translation.** In order to translate mRNA language into protein language, it is necessary to have a dictionary. The translation must account for the fact that there are only four letters in the nucleic acid alphabet, while the protein language has twenty in the form of twenty different amino acids. By using three-letter nucleotide words, it is possible to write sixty-four unique words, more than enough to translate for the twenty amino acid molecules (table 10.2). The name **codon** is given to each of the sixty-four mRNA triplet nucleotide words. Table 10.3 is a usable

Fig. 10.9 *Protein Production.* The assembly-line of the cell is very complex and requires DNA, RNA, ribosomes, amino acids, and a number of specific enzymes to function efficiently. The cell is not just a sac of water in which occurs a random assortment of chemical reactions.

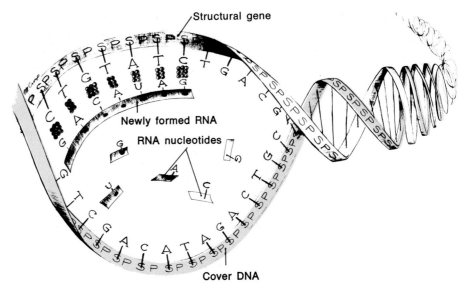

Fig. 10.10. *Transcription.* During the first stage of protein synthesis (transcription), individual RNA nucleotides base-pair on the chemical code of DNA to form an exact copy of the DNA nucleotide sequence.

Structural gene

Newly formed RNA

RNA nucleotides

Cover DNA

Table 10.2 *Amino Acids*

There are twenty common amino acids used in the protein synthesis operation of a cell. Each has a known chemical structure.

Amino acid	Abbreviation	Amino acid	Abbreviation
Alanine	Ala	Leucine	Leu
Arginine	Arg	Lysine	Lys
Asparagine	AspN	Methionine	Met
Aspartic Acid	Asp	Phenylalanine	Phe
Cystenine	Cys	Proline	Pro
Glutamic Acid	Glu	Serine	Ser
Glutamine	GluN	Threonine	Thr
Glycine	Gly	Tryptophan	Try
Histidine	His	Tyrosine	Tyr
Isoleucine	Ileu	Valine	Val

codon dictionary. Notice that more than one codon may code for the same amino acid. Some people have called this needlessly repetitive, but you might better consider these as synonyms. They can have survival value to the organism. If, for example, the gene or mRNA becomes damaged in a way that causes a particular nucleotide base to change to another type, the chances are still good that the proper amino acid will be read into its proper position (fig. 10.11). However, not all such changes can be compensated for by this codon system. Changes that would show up in very harmful ways can occur. Some damage is so extensive that the entire strand of DNA is broken, resulting in improper protein synthesis or a total lack of synthesis. This kind of change in DNA changes more than just a nucleotide base and is called a **chromosomal mutation.** A number of things are either known or are strongly suspected of causing DNA damage, and they are called **mutagenic agents.** Two agents known to cause damage to DNA are **x-radiation** and the chemical warfare agent **mustard gas.** Both have been experimented with extensively, and there is little doubt that they cause chromosomal mutations. In some cases the damage is so extensive that cells die. If a large enough number of cells are destroyed, the whole organism will die. The mutagenic agent LSD (lysergic acid-diethylamide) has been undergoing much research. A number of experiments indicate that this chemical causes the DNA to break into smaller pieces.

A single **chromosome** may have tens or hundreds of genes aligned end-to-end. Therefore, it is important to know where the blueprint for one protein molecule ends and the next begins. The codon table shows that such "punctuation marks" do exist in the nucleic acid language. These are also codons. The process of transcribing a mRNA from a particular gene will begin at one of these codons, called the **initiator codon.** The process will stop when the newly forming mRNA reaches the **terminator codon.** Both the initi-

Table 10.3 *Codon Dictionary: mRNA-Amino Acid Dictionary*
A dictionary can come in handy for learning any new language. This one can be used to translate mRNA language into protein language.

First letter		Second letter				Third letter
		U	C	A	G	
U	UUU UUC	Phe	UCU UCC		UAU UAC	Tyr	UGU UGC	Cys	U C
	UUA UUG	Leu	UCA UCG	Ser	UAA (terminator) UAG (terminator)		UGA (terminator) UGG Try		A G
C	CUU CUC CUA CUG	Leu	CCU CCC CCA CCG	Pro	CAU CAC	His	CGU CGC CGA CGG	Arg	U C A G
					CAA CAG	GluN			
A	AUU AUC AUA	Ileu	ACU ACC ACA	Thr	AAU AAC	AspN	AGU AGC	Ser	U C A
	AUG	Met (initiator)	ACG		AAA AAG	Lys	AGA AGG	Arg	G
G	GUU GUC GUA GUG	Val	GCU GCC GCA GCG	Ala	GAU GAC	Asp	GGU GGC GGA GGG	Gly	U C A G
					GAA GAG	Glu			

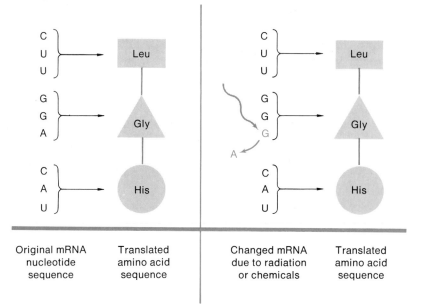

Fig. 10.11 *Noneffective Mutation.* Even though there may be a change in a nucleotide base of DNA, it is still possible that the correct amino acid will be positioned.

| Original mRNA nucleotide sequence | Translated amino acid sequence | Changed mRNA due to radiation or chemicals | Translated amino acid sequence |

ator and the terminator codons are often called **nonsense codons** (makes no sense) since they do not code for amino acids. In this way, the cell doesn't waste energy by copying unnecessary information or manufacturing unnecessary protein molecules (fig. 10.12).

The construction site of the protein molecules is outside the nucleus on the cell organelle called the ribosome. This organelle serves as the place at which mRNA and the amino acid building blocks come together. The mRNA molecule is placed on the ribosome two codons (six nucleotides) at a time (fig. 10.13).

The amino acids are transferred to the workbench by molecules that are so specific they are only capable of transferring one particular type of amino acid. These are hairpin-shaped RNA molecules called **transfer RNA,** or **tRNA.** There are twenty different types of amino acids and twenty different coding types of tRNA. It is the job of each tRNA to transfer a specific free amino acid to a site of protein synthesis. The tRNA properly aligns each amino acid so that it may be chemically bonded to another amino acid, forming a long chain. One end of a tRNA molecule is designed to attach to its particular amino acid, while the other has a unique triplet nucleotide sequence. This sequence is called an **anticodon,** since it can hydrogen-bond with a complementary mRNA codon as it sits on the ribosome (fig. 10.13).

The tRNA carrying an amino acid hydrogen-bonds with the mRNA only long enough to allow for certain reactions: (1) a dehydration synthesis reaction combines the amino acids to one another, (2) the first tRNA is released from the ribosome and its amino acid, and (3) the next mRNA codon is moved into position. In this way, the mRNA moves through the ribosome, and its specific codon sequence allows for the chemical bonding

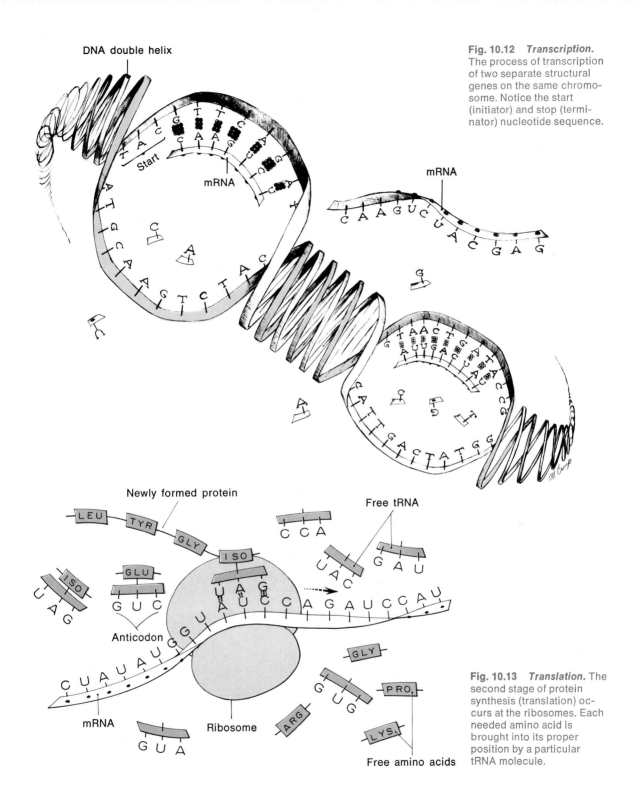

DNA double helix

Start

mRNA

Fig. 10.12 *Transcription.* The process of transcription of two separate structural genes on the same chromosome. Notice the start (initiator) and stop (terminator) nucleotide sequence.

mRNA

Newly formed protein

Free tRNA

Anticodon

mRNA

Ribosome

Free amino acids

Fig. 10.13 *Translation.* The second stage of protein synthesis (translation) occurs at the ribosomes. Each needed amino acid is brought into its proper position by a particular tRNA molecule.

of a specific sequence of amino acids. Remember that the sequence was originally determined by the DNA (fig. 10.14).

Each protein has a specific sequence of amino acids that determines its three-dimensional shape. The activity of a particular protein molecule is determined by its three-dimensional shape. The protein may be a structural component of a cell, or a tool (enzymes) that the cell uses in its chemical processes. Any changes in amino acids or their order changes the action of the protein molecule. The protein insulin, for example, has a different amino acid sequence than the digestive enzyme trypsin (fig. 10.15). Both proteins are essential to man's survival and must be produced constantly and accurately. The specific amino acid sequences of each is determined by a different gene. Each gene is a particular sequence of DNA nucleotides, and any alteration of that sequence can directly alter the protein structure, and therefore the survival of the organism. Another example of this structure-function relationship may be of value at this point.

Little Things Mean a Lot

Fig. 10.14 *Protein Synthesis.* Steps involved in protein synthesis.

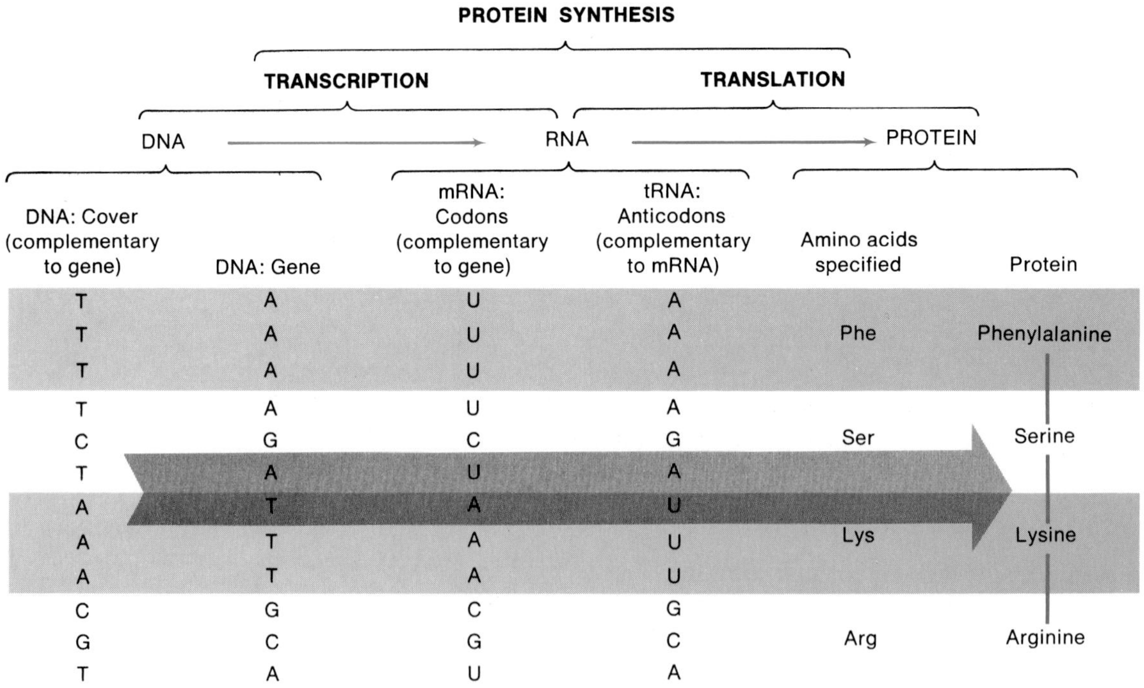

Human red blood cells contain the oxygen transport molecule hemoglobin. Normal hemoglobin molecules are composed of 150 amino acids in four chains, two alpha chains and two beta chains. The nucleotide sequence of

PROTEIN SYNTHESIS

DNA: Cover (complementary to gene)	DNA: Gene	mRNA: Codons (complementary to gene)	tRNA: Anticodons (complementary to mRNA)	Amino acids specified	Protein
T	A	U	A		
T	A	U	A	Phe	Phenylalanine
T	A	U	A		
T	A	U	A		
C	G	C	G	Ser	Serine
T	A	U	A		
A	T	A	U		
A	T	A	U	Lys	Lysine
A	T	A	U		
C	G	C	G		
G	C	G	C	Arg	Arginine
T	A	U	A		

TRANSCRIPTION — TRANSLATION

DNA → RNA → PROTEIN

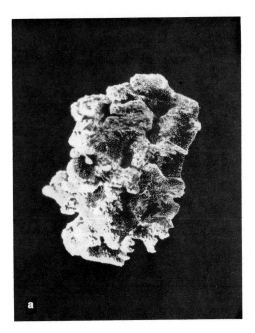

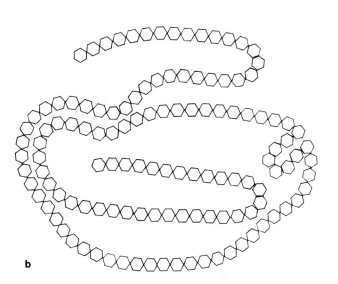

the gene for the beta chain is known, and the amino acid sequence of this chain has been identified. In normal individuals the sequence is:

Val-His-Leu-Thr-Pro-*Glu*-Glu-Lys- ....

In some persons, a single nucleotide of the gene controlling synthesis of the beta chain has been changed. This is called a **point mutation.** The result is a new amino acid sequence in all the red cells of this person's blood:

Val-His-Leu-Thr-Pro-*Val*-Glu-Lys- ....

This single nucleotide change, which causes a single amino acid to change, may seem to be of minor importance. However, it is the cause of **sickle-cell anemia,** a disease that affects the red blood cells by changing them from a circular to a sickle shape (fig. 10.16). When this sickling occurs, the red cells clog blood vessels and are unable to transport oxygen very well. A number of complicated physical disabilities may result. Some of these include physical weakness, brain damage, pain and stiffness of the joints, kidney damage, rheumatism, and in severe cases death.

There is no cure for this disease, since all of a person's cells contain the same wrong genetic information. The original unique blueprint for an entire individual is found in the fertilized egg of sexually reproducing organisms. This one cell reproduces itself thousands of times. If a nucleotide error such as sickle-cell anemia is found in the original DNA blueprint, all descendents of that cell will show that error.

Fig. 10.15 *Protein Structure.* The particular sequence of amino acids in a protein is determined by a structural gene. This sequence will determine the 3-D shape of the protein and the function it can perform. The protein enzyme trypsin is illustrated in *(a).* Insulin is illustrated in *(b).* In both cases, the exact sequence of amino acids is known. (Courtesy of John Wiley & Sons, Inc.)

Fig. 10.16 *Normal and Abnormal Red Blood Cells.* Normal red blood cells *(a)* are shown in comparison to cells showing the sickle shape *(b)*. This sickling is the result of a single amino acid change in the molecule hemoglobin.

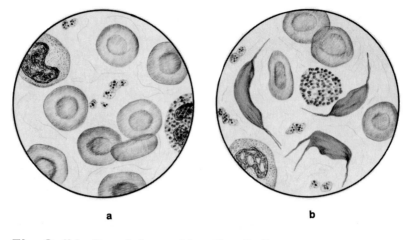

a   b

The Cell Is Dead, Long Live the Cell

When a cell divides into two new cells, each must have a complete set of genetic information. Since the original cell had only one set, there must be a doubling of this DNA information if the two new cells are to have a complete set. The process of **DNA duplication** is the second major function of DNA. The accuracy of duplication is essential to guarantee the continued existence of the correct nucleotide sequence in all future generations.

The DNA duplication process begins much the same as protein synthesis. An enzyme breaks the hydrogen bonds between the bases of the genes and the DNA covers. It begins at one end and proceeds to the opposite end of the DNA molecule. It "unzips" the halves of the DNA double helix (fig. 10.17). As this enzyme proceeds down the length of the DNA, new individual DNA nucleotides are moved into position. The complementary bases pair with both exposed DNA strands by forming new hydrogen bonds. Once properly aligned, a covalent bond occurs between the newly positioned nucleotides to form the strong backbone of sugar and phosphate molecules (fig. 10.18). A new cover DNA is formed on the old DNA genes, and new genes are formed on the old cover DNA. In this way the original DNA serves as **templates,** or patterns, for the formation of the new DNA. As the new DNA is completed, it grows in length, twisting into its protective double helix shape. The completion of the process yields two double helices, identical in their nucleotide sequences. Now the cell contains twice the amount of genetic information (fig. 10.19).

The DNA duplication process cannot continue indefinitely in the same cell. The results would be chemical chaos with the cell wasting energy by producing excess blueprints and excess proteins from these blueprints. Cells respond to this problem by redistributing this doubled genetic information to a new generation of cells. This involves the splitting of the cell and the distribution of the same genetic information to the new daughter cells. In this way each new cell has the necessary information to control its activities. The

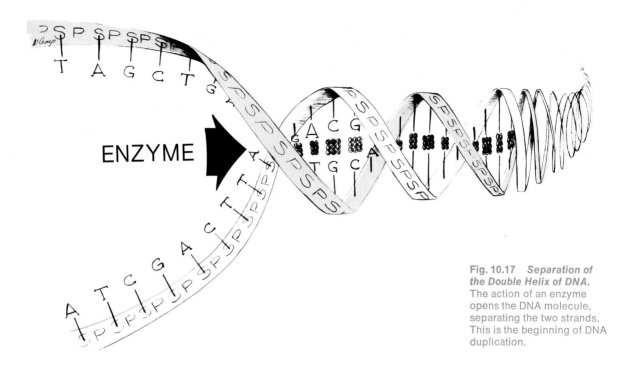

ENZYME

Fig. 10.17 *Separation of the Double Helix of DNA.* The action of an enzyme opens the DNA molecule, separating the two strands. This is the beginning of DNA duplication.

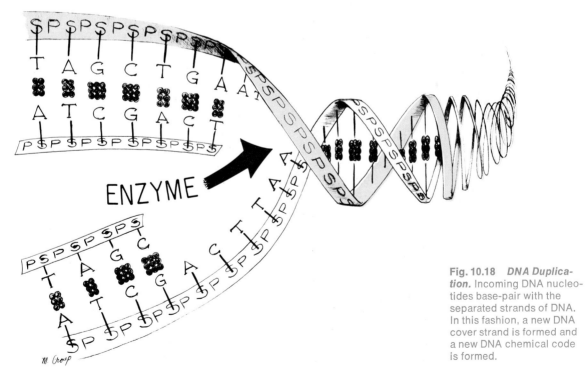

ENZYME

Fig. 10.18 *DNA Duplication.* Incoming DNA nucleotides base-pair with the separated strands of DNA. In this fashion, a new DNA cover strand is formed and a new DNA chemical code is formed.

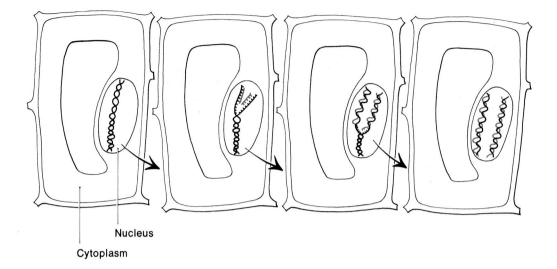

Nucleus

Cytoplasm

Fig. 10.19 *Process of DNA Duplication.* These are the generalized events in the nucleus of a cell during the process of DNA duplication. Notice that the final cell has two double helices; each is identical to each other and to the original strand.

mother cell does not die, but ceases to exist, since it divides its contents between the smaller daughter cells.

This means that the young daughter cells can use "fresh" building materials to cope with environmental changes and reproduce themselves. In this way, cell types continue to exist unless they are killed. A cell doesn't really die when it reproduces itself; it merely starts over again. This is called the **life cycle** of a cell.

There are a number of ways that a cell may divide and redistribute its genetic information to the next generation. These processes will be dealt with in detail in chapters eleven and twelve, but be sure to return to this chapter to review the particular DNA-associated events that make cell division possible and necessary.

Summary

The successful operation of a living cell depends on its ability to control chemical reactions. This is done directly by the enzymes, but the production of protein molecules is under the control of the nucleic acids, the primary control molecules of the cell. It is the structure of the nucleic acids, DNA and RNA, that determines the structure of the proteins. And it is the structure of the proteins that determines their function in the cell's life cycle. The process of protein synthesis is a decoding of the DNA into specific protein molecules and involves the use of the intermediate molecules mRNA and tRNA at the ribosome. Errors in any of the codons of these molecules may produce observable changes in the cell's functioning and lead to the death of the cell.

The process of DNA duplication results in the exact doubling of the genetic material. This occurs in a way that to a high degree guarantees identical strands of DNA being passed on to the next generation of cells.

Today Dr. Fritz Von Adelhoff, III, announced the discovery of a new
cellular organelle. He described this structure as being composed entirely
of protein. It is shaped like a doughnut and is slightly smaller than a
ribosome. As yet no function is known for this organelle. However, Von
Adelhoff speculates that it may be responsible for epoxy glue, which
holds the cells together. Further information on the possible origins and
functioning of this organelle will be looked into by Von Adelhoff's able
assistant *(fill in your name)*. He has extensive research experience in the
areas of organic chemistry, cell structure and function, and exceptional
knowledge of DNA and protein synthesis.

Go ahead doctor, write the follow-up article!

Questions

1. What is the difference between a nucleotide, a nitrogenous base, and a codon?
2. What are the differences between DNA and RNA?
3. List the sequence of events involved in translating a DNA message into a protein.
4. Chromosomal and point mutations both occur in DNA, but differ in what ways?
5. Why is the duplication of DNA necessary?
6. What are nonsense codons, and how might they function?
7. How does DNA duplication differ from the manufacture of an RNA molecule?
8. If a DNA nucleotide sequence is CATAAAGCA, what is the mRNA nucleotide sequence that would base-pair with it?
9. What amino acids would occur in the protein chemically coded by the above sequence of nucleotides?
10. How do tRNA and mRNA differ in their function?

Chapter Glossary

adenine   A double-ring nitrogenous base molecule found in DNA and RNA. It is the complementary base of thymine or uracil.

anticodon   A sequence of three nitrogenous bases on a tRNA molecule capable of hydrogen-bonding with three complementary bases of a mRNA codon during translation of protein synthesis.

chromosomal mutation   A change in the gene arrangement in a cell, as a result of breaks in the backbone of the DNA molecule.

chromosome   A term used to refer to a double strand of DNA when it is in a highly coiled, shortened state, and dyed to make it more visible under the microscope.

codon   A sequence of three nucleotides on a mRNA molecule that directs the placement of a particular amino acid during the process of protein synthesis.

complementary base The base that can form hydrogen bonds with the base of a specific nucleotide. Adenine is said to be complementary to thymine, since two hydrogen bonds can form between them in a DNA helix. Guanine is complementary to cytosine, and cytosine is complementary to guanine.

cytosine A single-ring nitrogenous base molecule found in DNA and RNA, which is the complementary base of guanine.

deoxyribose A five-carbon sugar component of deoxyribonucleic acid (DNA).

deoxyribonucleic acid (DNA) Molecule in the nucleus of a cell that functions as a blueprint for the synthesis of proteins.

DNA duplication The process by which the genetic material (DNA) of the cell reproduces itself prior to its distribution to the next generation of cells.

double helix Two regularly twisted strands of DNA that are parallel to each other.

guanine A double-ring nitrogenous base molecule found in DNA and RNA, which is the complementary base of cytosine.

initiator codon A nonsense codon that indicates to the cell the beginning of a gene.

life cycle (of the cell) The events in the life of a cell.

messenger RNA (mRNA) A molecule composed of ribonucleotides. The sequence of nucleotides is determined by the sequence of nucleotides in a piece of DNA. This molecule functions as a copy of the gene and is used in the cytoplasm of the cell.

mustard gas Used in the past as a chemical warfare material, it is known to cause chromosomal mutations. This nitrogen-containing compound is an example of a mutagenic agent.

mutagenic agent Anything that causes permanent change in DNA.

nitrogenous base A category of organic molecules found as components of the nucleic acids. There are five common types: thymine, guanine, cytosine, adenine, and uracil.

nonsense codon A three nucleotide sequence that is not translated. It can be used by the cell to indicate the beginning or end of a gene.

nucleotide The basic building block of the nucleic acids; each is composed of a five-carbon sugar, a phosphate, and a nitrogenous base.

phosphate A group of atoms composed of phosphorus, oxygen, and hydrogen atoms. This group is part of the backbone of a nucleotide.

point mutation A change in the DNA of a cell as a result of a loss or change in a nitrogenous base sequence.

protein synthesis The process whereby the tRNA utilizes the mRNA as a guide to arrange the amino acids in their proper sequence.

ribonucleic acid (RNA) A molecule that is similar to DNA and functions in the decoding of the hereditary information as it is used in the cell.

ribose A five-carbon sugar component of ribonucleic acid (RNA).

sickle-cell anemia A disease of an individual caused by a point mutation. This misformation produces sickle-shaped red blood cells.

structural gene A sequence of DNA nucleotides that specifies the structure of a particular protein (enzyme).

template   A model from which a new structure can be made; this term has special reference to DNA as a model for both DNA duplication and synthesis of RNA.

terminator codon   A nonsense codon that indicates to the cell the end of a gene.

thymine   A single-ring nitrogenous base molecule found only in DNA and not in RNA. It is the complement of adenine.

transcription   The first of two stages in protein synthesis; it involves the formation of mRNA from a template of a structural gene in the DNA.

transfer RNA (tRNA)   A molecule composed of ribonucleic acid. One end of the tRNA serves as the attachment point to mRNA, while the other end is the attachment point for a particular amino acid. The tRNA molecules function as an amino acid carrier in the process of translation.

translation   The second of the two stages in protein synthesis; it involves the pairing of mRNA codons with tRNA anticodons and results in alignment of the proper amino acids as determined by a structural gene.

uracil   A single-ring nitrogenous base molecule found only in RNA and not in DNA. It is the complement of adenine.

x-radiation   A high-energy beam capable of causing mutations in DNA.

Purpose   In the previous chapter we saw how the molecule DNA copies itself. Once this process is complete, doubled DNA is distributed to newly dividing cells. We will learn how this cell-splitting process determines that all future generations of cells have the same genetic message. It is also important to understand how cells with identical genetic messages may become different in the way they are built and the specific roles they perform. The relationships among DNA, genes, and chromosomes are concepts for later consideration of genetics, evolution, and sex cell formation.

Mitosis—The Cell Copying Process

11

A Cell's Life Goes On and On and On and . . .

Not quite! A cell does not live forever. Cells may die, but during the lifetime of an organism, the process of **mitosis** assures that the genetic information of the first cell is passed on to each new cell that is formed. Let us consider the life of the first cell of a new organism, starting from the time just after the sperm has joined with the egg. This cell may die or reproduce itself depending on surrounding conditions. If it divides it must first duplicate its DNA. This occurs by the process described in a previous chapter in which DNA strands separate and two new complementary strands are formed. The two identical sets of DNA molecules will move to opposite ends of the cell. The cell then splits in two, packaging the DNA into a new generation of cells. This process repeats itself many times resulting in a mass of cells that are all descended from the original **mother cell.** After a large number of cells are produced, we discover that some of the cells will not divide again, but will become **differentiated.** That is, they will change in such a way that they become specialized to perform a special job. For example, some may become muscle cells while others may become nerve cells. Since all cells are descended from a single **zygote** (fertilized egg), all cells of an individual have identical DNA molecules. However, some cells can still specialize for one job and some for another because there is a way to allow only certain genes to act while the others do not. For example, all human cells have genes for eye color, but only a relatively small number of the cells will ever have that gene working.

As a cell becomes specialized for a particular function, it may lose the ability to divide. Nerve and muscle cells specialize to the point that they can no longer divide. Consequently, damage to muscles and nerves is permanent. On the other hand, some cells of an organism do not lose the ability to divide. Cells in the deeper layers of the skin retain this ability, which allows for replacement of cells lost as a result of scrapes, bathing, or minor burns. The healing of a skin wound involves both the mitotic process and differentiation.

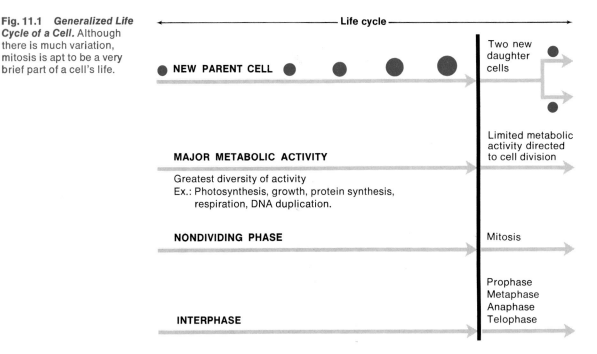

Fig. 11.1 *Generalized Life Cycle of a Cell.* Although there is much variation, mitosis is apt to be a very brief part of a cell's life.

Life cycle

NEW PARENT CELL

Two new daughter cells

MAJOR METABOLIC ACTIVITY

Limited metabolic activity directed to cell division

Greatest diversity of activity
Ex.: Photosynthesis, growth, protein synthesis, respiration, DNA duplication.

NONDIVIDING PHASE

Mitosis

Prophase
Metaphase
Anaphase
Telophase

INTERPHASE

All cells go through this basic life cycle, but they may vary in the amount of time they spend in the different stages. A generalized picture of a cell's life cycle may help you to understand it better (fig. 11.1).

The majority of the time the cell is highly active, performing all the various chemical reactions we discussed in previous chapters. It is during this period that the cell takes on the appearance of the "typical cell" as described in chapter six. If it is a plant cell, both photosynthesis and respiration will be occurring, as well as the protein-synthesis reactions. It is during this time that the DNA will duplicate in the nucleus of the cell. This portion of the life cycle is called the **interphase** (fig. 11.2).

Stages of Mitosis

During mitosis, the appearance of the nucleus changes; the nucleus splits into two smaller **daughter nuclei.** As nuclear division is being completed, the cytoplasm of the cell also splits. During both interphase and mitosis, the cell is active; however, the interphase activity is primarily metabolic while the mitotic activity is directed toward the equal distribution of nuclear and other cell components. Although the cell is metabolically active in interphase, you cannot see the changes that are occurring. The nucleus has a distinct shape because of a stable nuclear membrane. The contained DNA is spread out and not easily seen, although it has been duplicated earlier in interphase. In animal cells the **centrioles** have been reproduced and are nestled close to the nucleus. Most plant cells lack centrioles.

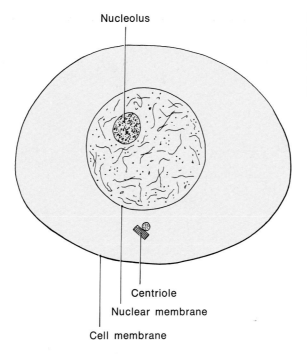

Nucleolus

Centriole

Nuclear membrane

Cell membrane

Fig. 11.2 *Interphase.* It is during interphase that DNA duplication occurs. The individual chromosomes are not visible, but a distinct nuclear membrane and nucleolus are present.

Prophase

It is not until prophase that we begin to see a tangled threadlike mass in the nucleus. These threads will gradually become more distinct as they twist and coil (fig. 11.3). They then appear to shorten and thicken. These threads are called **chromosomes** and are made up of DNA and protein molecules. Since the genes are composed of DNA, the chromosomes carry genes that are arranged in a specific order along the length of the chromosomes. Each chromosome carries its own set of genes, which is different from the sets of genes on other chromosomes. In the diagrams that follow, a few genes are shown as they might occur on the chromosomes of man. However, the diagrams show fewer chromosomes and fewer genes on each chromosome than are normally present in man (46 is normal in man). This is done to make the process easier to follow, since it would be very difficult to follow all forty-six chromosomes.

As prophase proceeds (fig. 11.4) and as chromosomes become more visible, we recognize that each chromosome is made of two parallel, threadlike parts lying side by side. These two parallel threads, called **chromatids,** were made earlier during interphase when the DNA molecules were duplicated. Each of these chromatid pairs is held together at a point called a **centromere.** Besides the appearance of the chromosomes, another event that identifies prophase is the migration of the centrioles. These little cylindrical bodies are present in animal cells, but not in plants. During interphase the

Fig. 11.3 *Early Prophase.* Chromosomes begin to appear as thin, tangled threads.

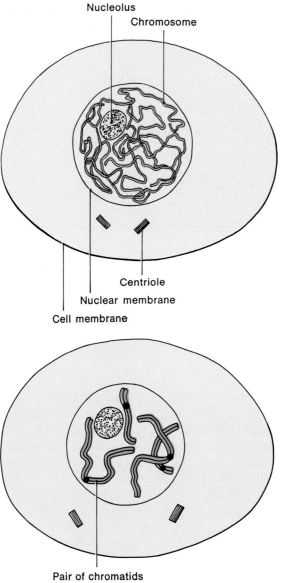

Nucleolus

Chromosome

Centriole

Nuclear membrane

Cell membrane

Fig. 11.4 *Late Prophase.* Each chromosome is now visible. The chromosomes are made up of a pair of chromatids.

Pair of chromatids for each chromosome

centrioles were close together outside the nuclear membrane, **but now** during prophase they move apart to take up positions opposite one another outside the nuclear membrane. Very small fibers, called **spindle fibers,** become visible as the centrioles move around the outside of the nucleus. Eventually these fibers will connect to the centromeres. This array of fibers is called the **spindle.** The final two events marking the close of prophase are the disappearance of each **nucleolus** (nucleoli, plural) and the loss of the nuclear membrane. The nucleoli and nuclear membrane are broken down into smaller parts, which are no longer visible. This loss sets the chromosomes free in the cytoplasm.

Metaphase

With the nuclear membrane gone, the chromosomes are free to move and arrange themselves on the spindle (fig. 11.5). They are arranged roughly in a circle at the equator of the cell. This lining up of chromosomes marks the line along which the cell will divide. In the lengthwise slices of the root tips of onions, commonly used to show mitosis in plants, we see only the edge view of this arrangement of chromosomes. The chromosomes appear to be in a single line at the center of the cell. If we were to scatter several books to form a rough circle on top of a table and then get down so that the table is at eye level, the books would appear to be in a line. We would expect to see the circular pattern only if we looked directly down at the tabletop. In the cells of the whitefish, commonly used to show mitosis in animals, we can see both views. The view of the chromosomes as a line is called the **equatorial view,** while the more or less circular pattern of chromosomes is known as the **polar view** (fig. 11.6). The lining up of the chromosomes in this way assures that the daughter cells will receive one of each type of gene.

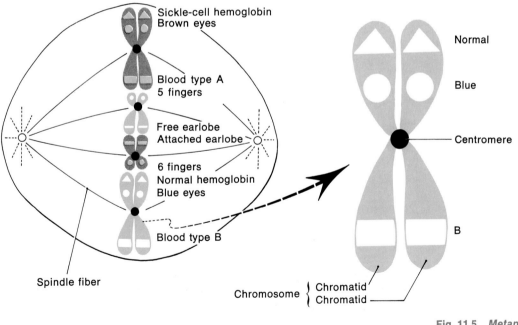

Fig. 11.5 *Metaphase.* Chromosomes line up on an equatorial plane. Note the arrangement of the genes on the chromosomes.

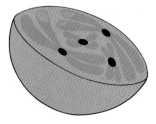

Fig. 11.6 *Polar View of Metaphase.* The polar view shows the chromosomes spread out on a plane.

Anaphase

After the chromosomes are aligned on the cell's equator during metaphase, the centromeres split. The chromatids now separate and begin to move away from one another. Because the chromatids are no longer connected at the centromere, they are sometimes called **daughter chromosomes.** They follow the spindle fibers toward the poles of the cell. Even though this movement of chromosomes has been observed repeatedly, no one knows the exact mechanism of this action (fig. 11.7).

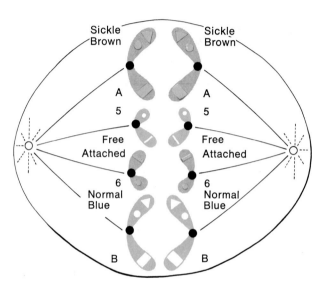

Fig. 11.7 *Anaphase.* The pairs of chromatids separate as the centromeres divide. The chromatids, now called chromosomes, are separating and moving toward the poles.

Telophase

The process of mitosis has resulted in two identical sets of daughter chromosomes (chromatids) moving away from the equator. Division of the cytoplasm begins in telophase as the two sets of daughter chromosomes finish their journey to the poles. In a plant cell, this cytoplasmic division is marked by the appearance of a **cell plate,** which begins as a faint line at the equatorial plane of the cell (fig. 11.8). As the plate gradually becomes more distinct and develops into the new cell wall, it divides the original cell into two daughter cells. Animal cells separate into two **daughter cells** by a pinching-in process, as if a string were tightened around its middle. This groove is called a **cleavage furrow** (fig. 11.9). As this daughter cell formation proceeds, the chromosomal threads become less visible. The nuclear membranes reappear along with the nucleoli, and the spindle disappears as the cells regain their original interphase appearance. These two daughter cells will begin to grow and carry on normal **metabolic activities** as each enters interphase. At some point during interphase, the DNA of the chromosomes duplicates, and unless the cells have become differentiated, they will eventually divide again.

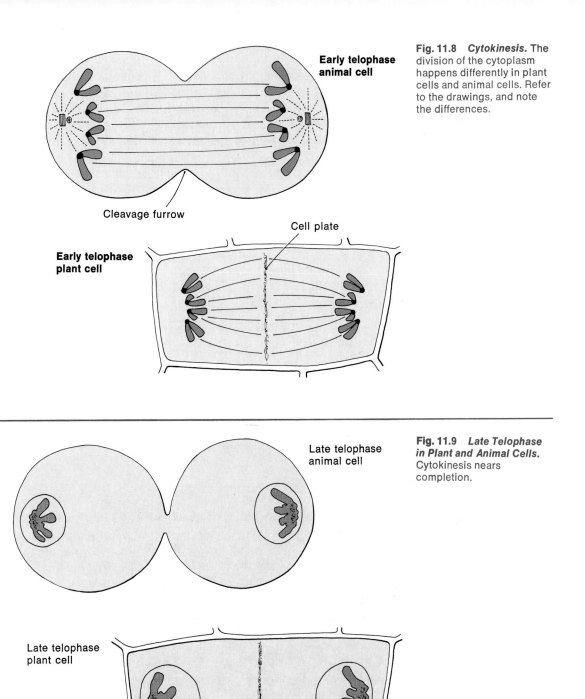

Early telophase animal cell

Fig. 11.8 *Cytokinesis.* The division of the cytoplasm happens differently in plant cells and animal cells. Refer to the drawings, and note the differences.

Cleavage furrow

Cell plate

Early telophase plant cell

Late telophase animal cell

Fig. 11.9 *Late Telophase in Plant and Animal Cells.* Cytokinesis nears completion.

Late telophase plant cell

Speed Kills

Understanding this process can help you to better grasp certain biological problems and to know how to solve them. All cells don't divide at the same rate, but each kind of cell has its division rhythm regulated. Regulation of the cycle can come from inside or outside the cell. When human white blood cells are grown outside the body under special conditions, they develop a regular cell division cycle. The cycle is determined by the DNA of the cells. However, white blood cells in a person may increase their rate of mitosis as a result of outside influences. Disease organisms entering the body, tissue damage, and change in cell DNA may all alter the rate at which white blood cells divide and grow. If an increase in white blood cells is due to the invasion of disease organisms, it is valuable since these white blood cells are capable of destroying them.

On the other hand, an uncontrolled increase in the rate of mitosis of white blood cells will cause a kind of cancer known as **leukemia.** This condi-

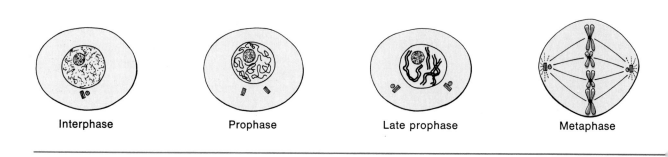

| Interphase | Prophase | Late prophase | Metaphase |

tion causes a general weakening of the body, because the excess number of white cells diverts necessary nutrients from other cells of the body. Leukemia may be controlled by taking advantage of the fact that these cells are undergoing an unusually rapid mitosis. Dividing cells are likely to be damaged by x-radiation because the radiation can more easily destroy the essential molecules, DNA, of the cell. Since cancer cells are dividing more rapidly than normal cells, they have an even greater chance of being killed by radiation. The doctor takes advantage of this when he prescribes that certain cancer patients take cobalt therapy. The cobalt is radioactive and releases radiation.

Radiation can also be dangerous to man for the same reasons that it can benefit him. In cases of extreme exposure to radiation, people develop what is called **radiation sickness.** The symptoms of this disease include loss of hair, bloody vomiting and diarrhea, and a reduced white-blood-cell count. These symptoms occur in parts of the body where normally the mitosis taking place is at a rapid rate. The lining of the intestine is constantly being lost as foods travel through and must be replaced by the process of mitosis. Hair growth is the result of the continuous division of cells at the roots, and white blood cells are continuously reproduced in the bone marrow. When radiation strikes these rapidly dividing cells and kills them, the hair falls out, the lining of the intestine is worn away and bleeds, and few new white blood cells are produced to defend the body from infection.

Summary

Mitosis is a basically simple process in which two daughter cells are formed from one parent cell. Both daughter cells have identical sets of chromosomes and genes that are exact copies of those in the parent cell. Although the process of mitosis has been presented as a series of stages, it should be realized that it is a continuously flowing process from interphase through telophase and back to the interphase condition again. For this reason, all of the diagrams (presented here together) give us "separate flash pictures" of different times during the process of mitosis (fig. 11.10).

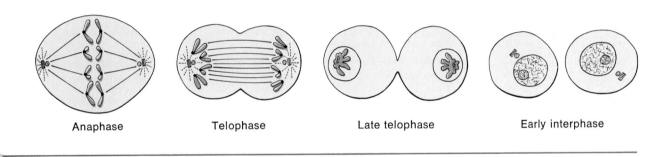

Anaphase   Telophase   Late telophase   Early interphase

Regulation of mitosis is important if organisms are to remain in balance. Regular divisions are necessary to replace lost cells and allow for growth. Unusually rapid cell division may result in cancer, and disruption in the total organism's well-being.

Fig. 11.10 *The Stages of Mitosis.* Mitosis is an on-going process, each stage as identified by a biologist grades into the next stage.

A chemical known as colchicine is extracted from the seeds of a small crocuslike plant. This chemical is used in biological laboratories because it can prevent the formation of the spindle fibers. Which parts of the cell cycle would proceed normally, and which parts would be altered if this chemical were used on cells? If you know that the cells are not killed by colchicine and they begin mitosis normally, what changes might occur in the numbers of chromosomes of the next cell generation, and how might this change the metabolism of the cell?

Consider This

Questions

1. Name the four stages of mitosis and describe the events that occur in each stage.
2. What is meant by the phrase "cell life cycle"?
3. During which phase of a cell's life does DNA duplication occur?
4. At what point in the division process is the DNA most visible?
5. What are the differences between plant and animal mitosis?
6. Why can cobalt treatment be used to control cancer?
7. What is the purpose of mitosis?
8. What is the difference between a cell plate and a cell wall?
9. What type of activities occur during interphase?
10. List five differences between an interphase cell and a cell in mitosis.

Chapter Glossary

anaphase   A stage in mitosis identified by the separation of chromatids (daughter chromosomes) and movement toward the poles.

cell plate   The first indication of the formation of a cell wall during plant mitosis.

centriole   A tubular organelle located just outside the nucleus, which functions in cell division.

centromere   A region of a chromosome where chromatids are joined.

chromatid   One of a pair of duplicate genetic strands. This pair makes up the chromosome in the early stages of mitosis.

chromosome   Coiled up chromatin material containing a package of genetic information. The number of chromosomes in the cells of a species is consistent. The threadlike structure appearing in mitosis that contains the genetic instructions (DNA) controlling the cell's characteristics.

cleavage furrow   The indentation of a cell membrane of an animal cell that finally pinches the cytoplasm into two parts.

daughter cells   Those two cells that are the result of cell division.

daughter chromosome   A separate chromatid, moving to one of the poles during anaphase.

daughter nuclei   The two nuclei that are the result of mitosis.

differentiation   The process of development that results in cells with structures and functions that are different from other cells in the same body.

equatorial view   The view of a cell during metaphase that presents the chromosomes arranged in a line across the middle of the cell.

interphase   The action stage in the growth of a cell. The between division stage. DNA duplication occurs during interphase.

leukemia   A disease of the mitotic process of white blood cells. Its symptoms include an abnormally large number of white blood cells.

metabolic activity   Those processes such as photosynthesis, respiration, and protein synthesis that are a part of normal cell activities.

metaphase   A stage of mitosis marked by the arrival of the chromosomes at the equatorial plane.

mitosis   The total process of cell division, which results in both the distribution of copies of the genetic information from the parent cell to the two daughter cells and cytoplasmic division.

mother cell   A cell that produces two daughter cells by the process of mitosis.

nucleolus   A lump of RNA that is located in the nucleus and disappears during cell division. Its function is unknown.

polar view   The view of a cell during metaphase, which presents the chromosomes arranged roughly in a circular pattern.

prophase   A stage at the beginning of mitosis in which the chromosomes become visible.

radiation sickness   Disease of the mitotic process that is linked to an over-exposure of high energy radiation. This radiation interferes with the normal ability of a cell to divide.

spindle   The group of spindle fibers collectively called the spindle.

spindle fibers   A series of fibers that are formed between the poles of a cell. Centromere of each chromosome attaches at the midpoint of a spindle fiber.

telophase   The last phase of mitosis, characterized by the division of the cytoplasm and the reorganization of the daughter nuclei.

zygote   A cell formed by the union of a sperm cell and an egg cell.

Purpose   How can the chromosome number in humans remain forty-six generation after generation if both parents contribute equally to the genetic information of the child? In this chapter, we will discuss the mechanics of the process of *meiosis*. Meiosis is a specialized cell division resulting in the formation of *sex cells*. A knowledge of the mechanics of this process is essential to understanding how genetic variety can occur in sex cells. This variety in sex cells ultimately shows up as differences in offspring, which are produced through sexual reproduction.

Meiosis—Sex Cell Formation

12

Meiosis, the Whys and Wherefores

In the previous chapter, you saw that a cell can divide to form two equal daughter cells. These daughter cells each contain a complete set of genetic information. Suppose we arbitrarily say that a particular parent cell has eight chromosomes. After division, the daughter cells produced from this original cell would still have eight chromosomes. This equal division of chromosomes and cytoplasm is called mitosis.

However, something was left unsaid before. Each parent cell with its eight chromosomes really has two complete sets of genetic data; one set of four chromosomes from its mother, and one set of four chromosomes from its father. Why is this so? An examination of part of a typical life cycle of an organism may help you to understand this.

Figure 12.1 shows that a **sperm cell** and an **egg cell** join to produce a single cell. This cell is called a **zygote** and the process of joining sperm and egg is called **fertilization.** Note that the zygote, resulting from the union of sperm and egg, contains a combination of four chromosomes from the father (sperm cell) and four from the mother (egg cell). The zygote contains a set of chromosomes from each parent, and more importantly, it also has a combination of genes different from that found in either parent.

The zygote then divides by mitosis. This results in cells having the same mixture of chromosomes and genes as in the zygote. The questions brought to mind are: how were the sperm and egg cells formed, and how did they get only one half of the set of eight chromosomes? The answers lie in the process of meiosis. One of the major functions of the process of meiosis is to produce cells that have one half the total amount of genetic information. Therefore, when fertilization occurs, the zygote will still have the same number of chromosomes as found in each parent, since each sex cell provides four of the eight chromosomes.

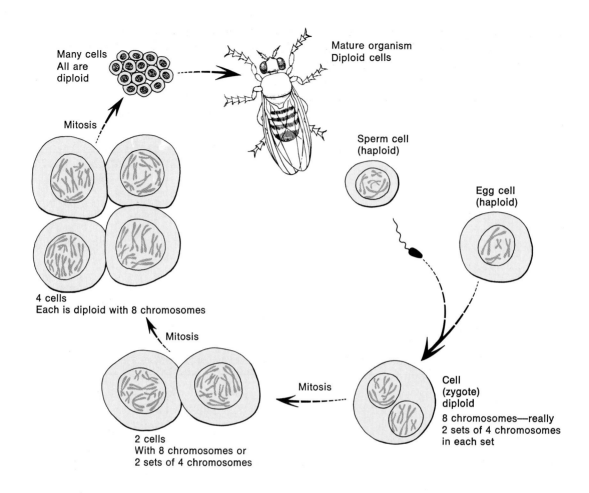

Many cells All are diploid

Mitosis

Mature organism
Diploid cells

Sperm cell
(haploid)

Egg cell
(haploid)

4 cells
Each is diploid with 8 chromosomes

Mitosis

Cell
(zygote)
diploid

8 chromosomes—really
2 sets of 4 chromosomes
in each set

Mitosis

2 cells
With 8 chromosomes or
2 sets of 4 chromosomes

Fig. 12.1 *Life Cycle.* Cells of a particular type of organism have a particular number of chromosomes in their nuclei. In preparation for sexual reproduction, the number of chromosomes must be halved so that fertilization will restore this particular number.

The two terms **diploid** and **haploid** are used to indicate the number of chromosomes present. A sperm cell or egg cell has only one set of four chromosomes and therefore only one set of genetic data. It is said to be haploid, or it has the haploid number of chromosomes. However, the fertilized cell, or zygote, which has both sets of genetic data, one from the sperm and one from the egg, is called diploid. For example, adult human cells are diploid. They have the information from both the sperm and egg cells. All the cells of the adult result from mitosis of the original fertilized egg (zygote). Therefore, they have the same set of genetic information. The adult human also produces cells that are haploid; these are the sperm or egg cells. In the life cycle shown previously (fig. 12.1), the diploid (2N) number of chromosomes is eight, and the haploid number (N) is four.

Not every animal cell goes through the process of meiosis, only special organs **(ovaries** and **testes)** contain cells capable of meiosis. In plants, there are also special structures that produce haploid cells. These haploid cells are also called eggs and sperm. Figure 12.2 compares the diploid parts of plants and animals with their haploid parts. We can now include this additional information in a life cycle diagram (fig. 12.3).

Earlier in this chapter we arbitrarily selected, as an example, cells that had a diploid number of eight. The haploid number of chromosomes of this organism is four, and these haploid cells contain only one complete set of four chromosomes. In figure 12.4, these chromosomes are drawn out to provide a clearer idea of the relationships of chromosomes to one another.

Fig. 12.2 *Haploid and Diploid Cells.* Both plants and animals produce cells that have the haploid number of chromosomes. The organs that produce the male haploid cells are called the anthers and the testes. The ovary produces haploid female cells.

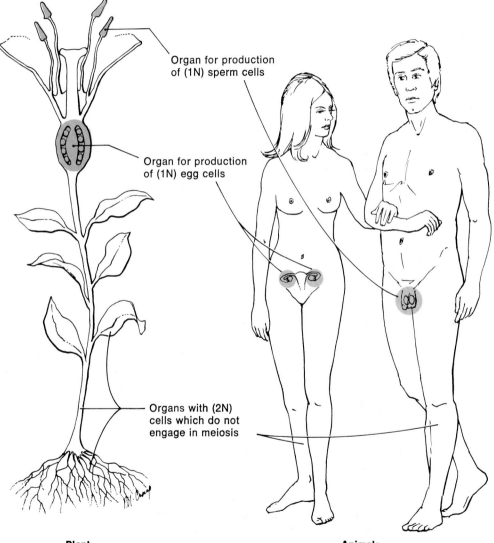

Organ for production of (1N) sperm cells

Organ for production of (1N) egg cells

Organs with (2N) cells which do not engage in meiosis

Plant

Animals

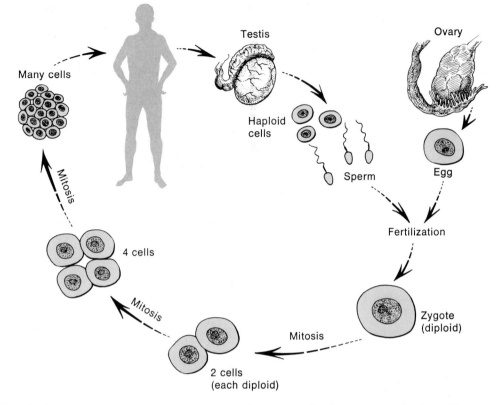

Fig. 12.3 *Life Cycle.* Notice that meiosis is the process whereby haploid cells are produced. Fertilization restores the diploid number. The cell division that results in increased numbers of cells is mitosis.

You can see that there are eight chromosomes in this cell. A closer look at figure 12.4 shows you that there are only four different types of chromosomes, but two of each type:

1. long chromosomes that consist of chromatids attached near the center
2. long chromosomes that consist of chromatids attached near one end
3. shorter chromosomes that consist of chromatids attached near one end
4. very short chromosomes that consist of chromatids attached near the center

Remember, a chromosome is composed of two chromatids, each containing DNA. These two chromatids are attached to each other at a point called the centromere. Any two chromosomes (fig. 12.4) that are similarly shaped are said to be a **homologous pair of chromosomes.** A homologous pair of chromosomes is defined as the two chromosomes in a diploid nucleus that look alike, and carry the same types of genes. One of the chromosomes of a homologous pair was donated by the father and the other by the mother (fig. 12.5). We can therefore talk about the number of chromosomes in two different ways. We might say that our hypothetical diploid cell has eight chromosomes, or we could say that it has four pairs of homologous chromosomes.

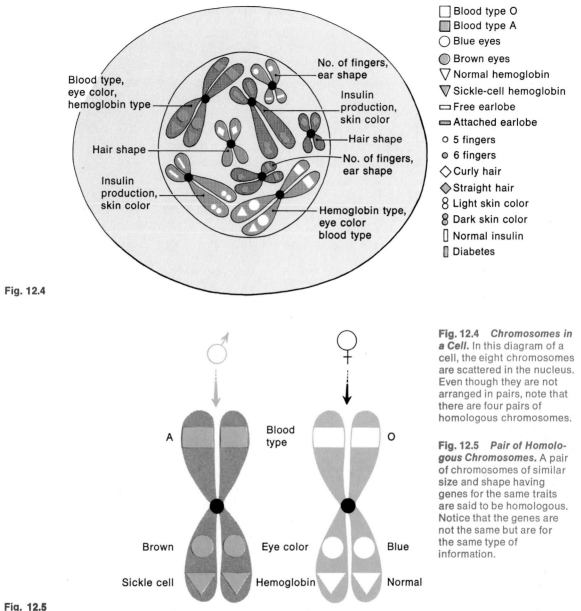

Blood type O
Blood type A
○ Blue eyes
◐ Brown eyes
▽ Normal hemoglobin
▼ Sickle-cell hemoglobin
▭ Free earlobe
▭ Attached earlobe
○ 5 fingers
◉ 6 fingers
◇ Curly hair
◆ Straight hair
8 Light skin color
8 Dark skin color
▯ Normal insulin
▮ Diabetes

Blood type,
eye color,
hemoglobin type

No. of fingers,
ear shape

Insulin
production,
skin color

Hair shape

Hair shape

Insulin
production,
skin color

No. of fingers,
ear shape

Hemoglobin type,
eye color
blood type

Fig. 12.4

A Blood type O

Brown Eye color Blue

Sickle cell Hemoglobin Normal

Fig. 12.5

Fig. 12.4 *Chromosomes in a Cell.* In this diagram of a cell, the eight chromosomes are scattered in the nucleus. Even though they are not arranged in pairs, note that there are four pairs of homologous chromosomes.

Fig. 12.5 *Pair of Homologous Chromosomes.* A pair of chromosomes of similar size and shape having genes for the same traits are said to be homologous. Notice that the genes are not the same but are for the same type of information.

Haploid cells, on the other hand, do not have homologous chromosomes, they have only one of each type of chromosome. The whole point of meiosis is to distribute the chromosomes and genes they carry, so that one daughter cell gets one member of each homologous pair, the other daughter cell gets the other member. In this way, each daughter cell gets half of the genes; and it is a complete genetic set, one gene for each characteristic.

Mechanics of Meiosis: Meiosis I

The division of members of homologous pairs of chromosomes into two complete sets occurs in a sequence of events called meiosis I. This is sometimes called a reduction division since the daughter cells will get only half the chromosomes from the parent cell. Meiosis I is preceded by an interphase stage during which DNA duplication has occurred. There are two sets of DNA molecules, and therefore, the division will begin with chromosomes that have two chromatids. The sequence of events in meiosis I is artificially divided into four phases: prophase I, metaphase I, anaphase I, and telophase I. Figure 12.6 shows the events in meiosis I.

Fig. 12.6   Meiosis I.

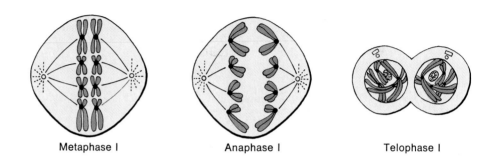

| Prophase I | Metaphase I | Anaphase I | Telophase I |

Prophase I

During this stage, the cell is preparing itself for division (fig. 12.7). Most of the events of mitosis and meiosis prophase stages are similar. The chromatin material coils and thickens into chromosomes, the nucleolus disappears, the nuclear membrane disintegrates, and the spindle apparatus is constructed. During prophase I, homologous chromosomes come to lie next to each other. This pairing of homologous chromosomes is called **synapsis.** An aligned pair of chromosomes are said to be synapsed (this pairing does not occur during the prophase of mitosis). It is while the chromosomes are synapsed that a process known as **crossing-over** can occur. This consists of an exchange of equal parts of chromatids. We will fit crossing-over into the whole picture later.

Metaphase I

The synapsed pair of homologous chromosomes move into position on the equatorial plane of the cell. There the centromeres of the pair of chromosomes attach to the spindle. The way they are arranged on the spindle (which one is on the left and which one is on the right) is determined only by chance (fig. 12.8).

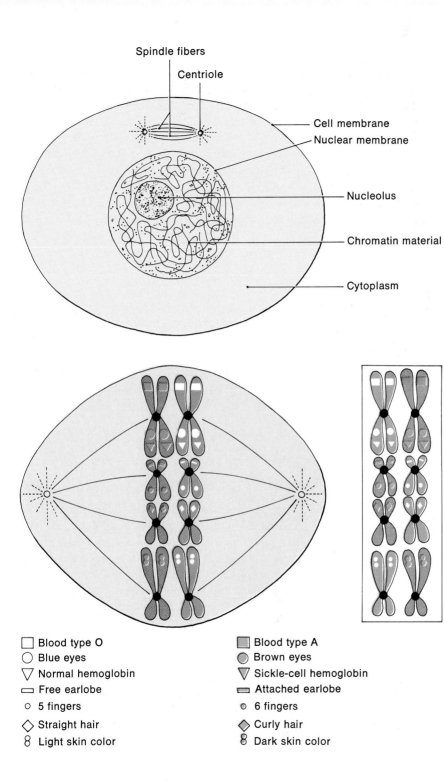

Spindle fibers

Centriole

Cell membrane
Nuclear membrane

Nucleolus

Chromatin material

Cytoplasm

Fig. 12.7 *Prophase I.* During prophase I, the cell is making its preparations for the division. List the events that you expect would happen when this cell is in prophase. The one unexpected thing that happens in prophase I is that the chromosomes are in synapsis.

Fig. 12.8 *Metaphase I.* Notice that the homologous chromosome pairs are arranged on the equatorial plane in the synapsed condition.

☐ Blood type O
◯ Blue eyes
▽ Normal hemoglobin
⬭ Free earlobe
∘ 5 fingers
◇ Straight hair
8 Light skin color

▩ Blood type A
⬤ Brown eyes
▼ Sickle-cell hemoglobin
▬ Attached earlobe
◉ 6 fingers
◆ Curly hair
8 Dark skin color

Anaphase I

Anaphase I is the stage during which separation of homologous chromosomes occurs (fig. 12.9). It is during this stage that reduction from diploid to haploid occurs. The two members of a pair of homologous chromosomes move away from each other toward opposite poles. The direction each moves is determined by how the pair was originally arranged on the spindle. Each chromosome is independently attached to a spindle fiber by its centromere. The separation of one pair of homologous chromosomes is not controlled by the separation of any other pair. This is known as the **independent assortment** of pairs of chromosomes. The isolation of the two members of a chromosome pair is called **segregation.** Notice that the centromeres do not divide during this stage.

Telophase I

Telophase I consists of changes that return the cell to an interphase condition (fig. 12.10). The chromosomes uncoil and become long thin threads, the nuclear membrane reforms around them and nucleoli reappear. Also during telophase I, the cytoplasm divides producing two separate cells.

As a result of meiosis I, the total number of chromosomes has been divided equally between the two daughter cells. Each daughter cell has one member of each homologous chromosome pair. Each member is still composed of two chromatids joined at the centromere, and the chromosome number has been reduced from diploid to haploid.

Mechanics of Meiosis: Meiosis II

Meiosis II is composed of several stages: prophase II, metaphase II, anaphase II, and telophase II. This division takes place in both daughter cells formed as a result of meiosis I, so that eventually four cells will result from the two divisions. The events of meiosis II are summarized in figure 12.11.

There may or may not be a period of time following telophase I during which a cell engages in normal metabolic activity which corresponds to an interphase stage. However, the chromosomes do not duplicate as they did prior to prophase I.

Prophase II

The activities of this stage are similar to prophase in mitosis: the nuclear membrane disintegrates, nucleoli disappear, and the spindle apparatus forms. However, it differs from prophase I in that these cells are haploid, not diploid (fig. 12.12).

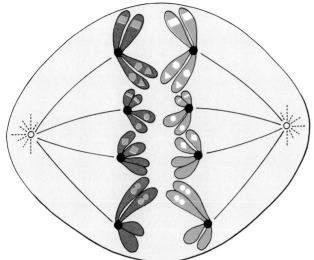

Blood type O
Blood type A
Blue eyes
Brown eyes
Normal hemoglobin
Sickle-cell hemoglobin
Free earlobe
Attached earlobe
5 fingers
6 fingers
Straight hair
Curly hair
Light skin color
Dark skin color

Fig. 12.9 *Anaphase I.* It is during this phase that one member of the homologous chromosome pair is segregated from the other member of the pair. Notice that the centromeres of the chromosomes do not split.

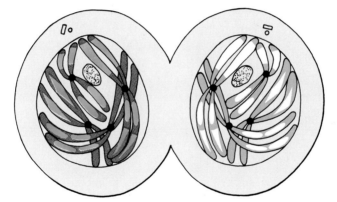

Fig. 12.10 *Telophase I.* What activities would you expect to occur during a telophase stage of cell division?

Fig. 12.11 *Meiosis II.*

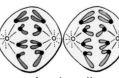 

Prophase II   Metaphase II   Anaphase II   Telophase II

Meiosis—Sex Cell Formation   199

Fig. 12.12 *Prophase II.*
The two daughter cells are
preparing for the second
division of meiosis.

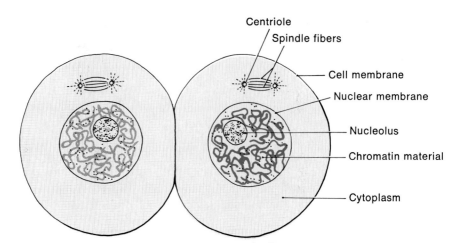

Centriole
Spindle fibers
Cell membrane
Nuclear membrane
Nucleolus
Chromatin material
Cytoplasm

Metaphase II

The metaphase II stage is typical in that the chromosomes attach by their centromeres to the spindle fibers at the equatorial plane of the cell. Since pairs of chromosomes are no longer together in the same cell, each chromosome attaches to a separate spindle fiber (fig. 12.13).

Anaphase II

Anaphase II differs from anaphase I in that the centromere divides. The centromere of each chromosome splits in two, and the chromatids move apart (fig. 12.14).

Telophase II

During this stage, the cell goes back into a nondividing condition. New nuclear membranes are formed, chromosomes uncoil, nucleoli reform, and spindle fibers disappear. This stage is followed by differentiation in which the four cells mature into **gametes** (i.e., egg or sperm) (fig. 12.15).

In many organisms, egg cell production occurs in such a manner that three of the four cells that result from meiosis disintegrate and only one remains. However, since the one that survives is randomly selected, this does not interfere with the likelihood of any one particular combination of genes being formed.

If you reread the statement of purpose of this chapter, you see that the whole point of learning the mechanism of meiosis is to see how variation can occur. Now we can look at this major topic of variation and how it comes about.

Chapter 12

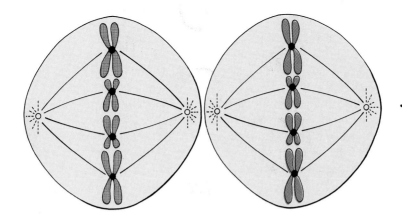

Fig. 12.13 *Metaphase II.*
During this metaphase, each chromosome lines up on the equatorial plane. Each chromosome is composed of two chromatids and a centromere.

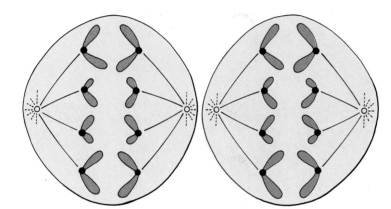

Fig. 12.14 *Anaphase II.*
This anaphase stage is very similar to the anaphase of mitosis. The centromere of each chromosome divides and one chromatid separates from the other. At this time, these chromatids are known as chromosomes.

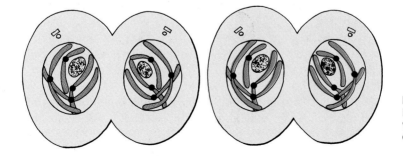

Fig. 12.15 *Telophase II.*
During the telophase stage, what events would you expect to occur?

Kinds of Variation

There are three things that influence this variation: segregation, independent assortment, and crossing-over. As a result of these three mechanisms, a greater variety of sex cells can be formed. Crossing-over occurs during meiosis I when homologous chromosomes are in synapsis. During this time, one part of a chromatid becomes detached, and the comparable part of a chromatid on the other homologous chromosome also detaches itself. The two pieces then switch places. Examine figures 12.16 and 12.17 carefully to note precisely what occurs during crossing-over. Figure 12.16 shows a pair of homologous chromosomes close to each other. Notice that the genes for each characteristic occupy a specific spot on the chromosome, and that homologous chromosomes contain an identical order of genes. It is important to realize that for simplicity, there are only a few genes labeled on these chromosomes. Actually, the chromosome contains hundreds or possibly thousands of genes.

What does crossing-over have to do with the possible kinds of cells which result from meiosis? Consider figure 12.17; note that without crossing-

Fig. 12.16 *Synapsis Allows Crossing-over to Occur.* While pairs of homologous chromosomes are in synapsis, one part of one chromatid can break off and be exchanged for an equivalent part of its homologous chromatid.

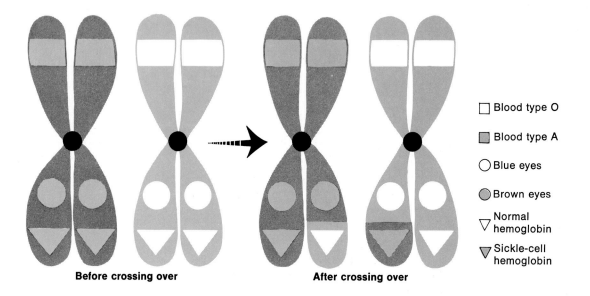

Before crossing over   **After crossing over**

☐ Blood type O

▦ Blood type A

◯ Blue eyes

◉ Brown eyes

▽ Normal hemoglobin

▼ Sickle-cell hemoglobin

over, only two different kinds of cells result. Two of the four cells have one type of chromosome, and the other two would have the other type of chromosome.

With just one crossover, we have doubled the kinds of cells possible from meiosis. Even greater variation is possible when one realizes that crossing-over can occur at almost any point along the length of the chromo-

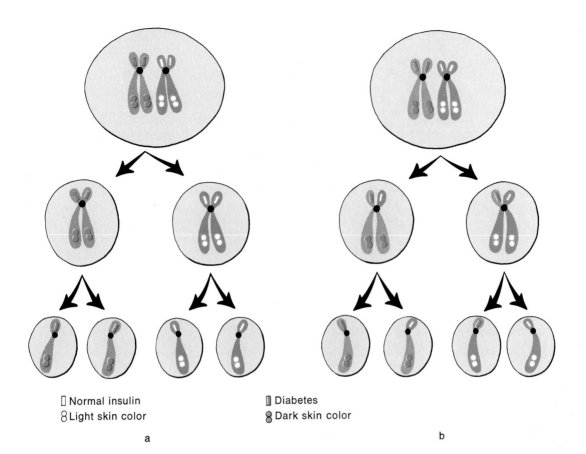

Normal insulin
Light skin color

Diabetes
Dark skin color

a

b

some. Not only is this true, but crossing-over may occur at a number of points on the same chromosome. That is, we are not limited to one cross-over per chromosome pair (fig. 12.18). Crossing-over helps to explain why a child can be a mixture of family characteristics. If the black chromosome was the chromosome which a mother received from her mother, the child could receive not only some genetic information from the mother's mother, but also some of the genetic information from the mother's father (fig. 12.19).

Sometimes it is valuable to think of the individual genes located on the chromosome rather than the total chromosome. Look at the diagram in figure 12.16. Notice that the genes for blood type, eye color, and hemoglobin are all located on the same chromosome. When this chromosome separates from its homologous member, it carries a particular group of genes. All of the genes on that chromosome go together into the new cell. Think of the chromosome as a package of genes. All of the genes in the package are said to be linked, or are called a **linkage group.** With this background, you can now see that the effect of crossing-over is to destroy old linkage groups and create new ones.

Fig. 12.17 *Variations Resulting from Crossing-over.* The cells shown in *a* resulted from meiosis without crossing-over. Those cells in *b* had one crossover. Compare the results of meiosis in both cases.

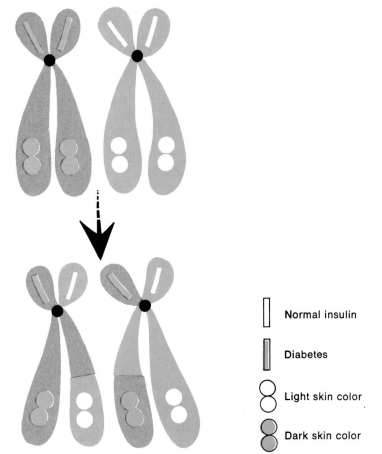

Normal insulin

Diabetes

Light skin color

Dark skin color

Variation Due to Segregation

Let's assume the genes in figure 12.17*b* represent information for the building of the protein insulin. Insulin is necessary for normal metabolism. When a person has one gene for normal insulin and one gene for abnormal insulin, he will produce enough insulin to be healthy. However, during meiosis half of the sex cells will contain the gene for normal insulin production, and the other half will contain the gene for abnormal insulin production. It is because these two genes segregate into different sex cells during meiosis that this normal appearing parent may produce offspring that will not be healthy. This can only occur if this sex cell fertilizes another sex cell which also carries the gene for abnormal insulin production. This child will produce abnormal insulin and be a diabetic.

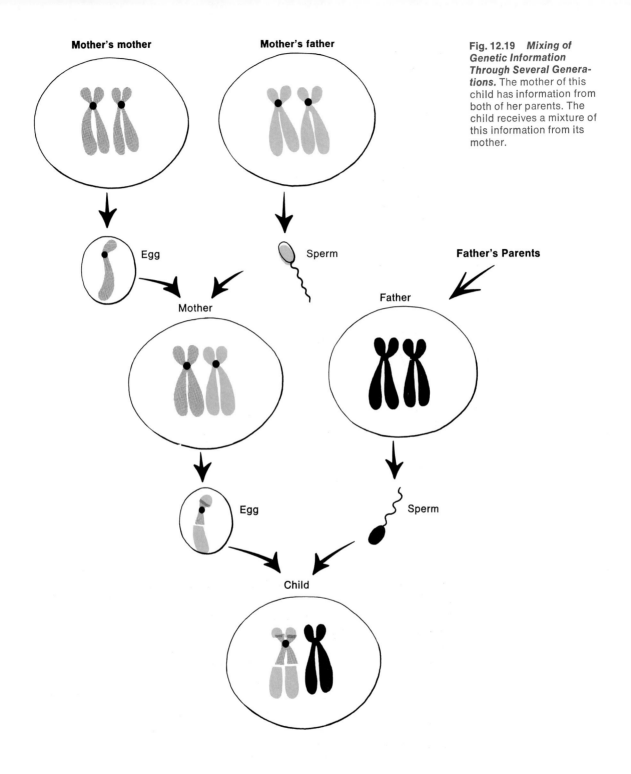

Mother's mother

Mother's father

Egg

Sperm

Father's Parents

Mother

Father

Egg

Sperm

Child

Fig. 12.19 *Mixing of Genetic Information Through Several Generations.* The mother of this child has information from both of her parents. The child receives a mixture of this information from its mother.

Variation Due to Independent Assortment

So far, we have dealt only with one pair of chromosomes. Let's see how variation in the combinations of genes in sex cells changes when we add a second or third pair of chromosomes (fig. 12.20).

Remember that during anaphase I, the pole to which a chromosome moves is controlled by chance. In the diagram below, chromosomes carrying blood-type information always separate from each other. The second pair of chromosomes with the finger number also separate. Since chance determines the pole a chromosome moves toward, you can see that half of the time the chromosomes would divide so that blood type A and six fingeredness would move in the same direction and blood type O and five fingeredness would move in the opposite direction. The other half of the time, blood type A and five fingeredness would go together and blood type O and six

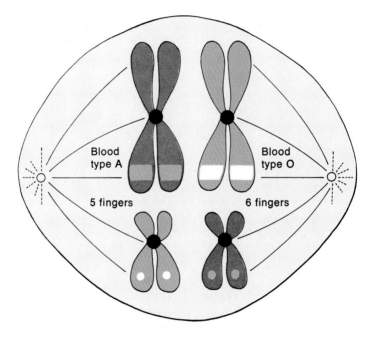

Fig. 12.20 *Independent Orientation of Homologous Chromosome Pairs.* The orientation of one pair of chromosomes on the equatorial plane does not affect the orientation of a second pair of chromosomes. This results in increased variety of the haploid cells.

Blood type A

Blood type O

5 fingers

6 fingers

fingeredness would go to the other pole. With four chromosomes (two pair) there are four possible kinds of cells. These four possibilities are shown in figure 12.21.

With three pairs of homologous chromosomes, there are eight possible kinds of cells with respect to gene combinations resulting from meiosis. See if you can list them. Because one pair of homologous chromosomes divides independently of the other pairs of homologous chromosomes, a greater

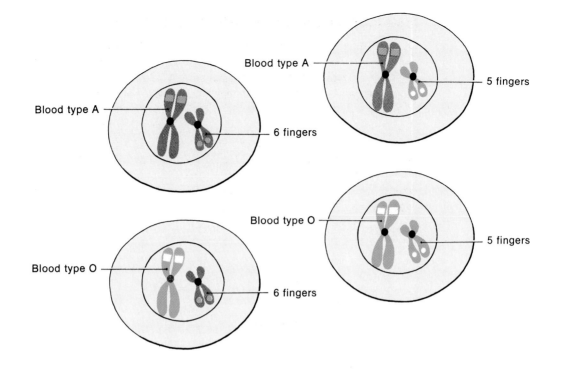

Blood type A — 6 fingers

Blood type A — 5 fingers

Blood type O — 6 fingers

Blood type O — 5 fingers

variety of gametes is produced. The concept that homologous chromosomes separate without regard to how the other pairs of homologous chromosomes separate is called independent assortment.

As a result of meiosis, a variety of haploid sex cells is formed. The variety of sex cells produced means that after sexual reproduction the next generation will get a shuffled set of genetic information. Just as every card player expects a "different hand" next time, biologically, we expect a "different combination of genes" in the next generation.

Fig. 12.21 *Variety Generated by Independent Assortment.* When a cell has two pairs of homologous chromosomes, four different kinds of haploid cells can result from independent assortment.

Summary

Meiosis is a specialized cell division process resulting in the production of four cells, each of which has the haploid number of chromosomes. The total process involves two sequential divisions, and as a result, one diploid cell is reduced to four haploid cells. Since the chromosomes act as carriers for genetic information, genes are separated into different sets during meiosis. Crossing-over allows hidden characteristics to be displayed and independent assortment allows characteristics donated by the mother and the father to be mixed in new combinations.

Together crossing-over, segregation, and independent assortment assure that all sex cells will be unique. Therefore, when any two sex cells unite to form a zygote, the zygote will also be one of a kind.

Assume that corn plants only have a diploid number of 2. Each plant's chromosomes are diagrammed below:

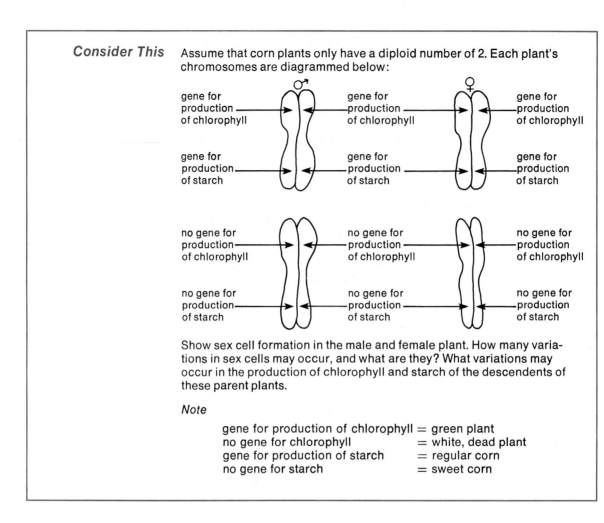

Show sex cell formation in the male and female plant. How many variations in sex cells may occur, and what are they? What variations may occur in the production of chlorophyll and starch of the descendents of these parent plants.

Note

gene for production of chlorophyll	= green plant
no gene for chlorophyll	= white, dead plant
gene for production of starch	= regular corn
no gene for starch	= sweet corn

Questions

1. List three differences between mitosis and meiosis.
2. How do haploid cells differ from diploid cells?
3. What are the major sources of variation that occur during meiosis?
4. Can a haploid cell undergo meiosis?
5. What is unique about prophase I?
6. Why is meiosis necessary in sexually reproducing organisms?
7. Define the terms zygote, fertilization, linkage group, and homologous chromosomes.
8. How much variation as a result of independent assortment can occur in cells with the following diploid numbers: 2, 4, 6, 8, and 22?
9. Diagram the metaphase I stage of a cell with the diploid number 8.
10. Diagram fertilization as it would occur between a sperm and an egg with the haploid number 3.

crossing-over The exchange of a part of a chromatid from one homologous chromosome with an equivalent part of a chromatid from the other homologous chromosome.

diploid Represented as 2N. This is the term given to a cell having both sets of chromosomes, one set from the maternal parent and one set from the paternal parent.

egg cells The haploid sex cells produced by sexually mature females.

fertilization The joining of haploid nuclei, usually from an egg cell and a sperm cell, resulting in a diploid cell called the zygote.

gamete Haploid sex cell.

haploid A single set of chromosomes. Represented as N. This haploid number results from the reduction division of meiosis.

homologous pair of chromosomes A pair of chromosomes in a diploid cell that contain similar pairs of genes throughout their length.

independent assortment The term that relates to the fact that the segregation, or assortment, of one pair of chromosomes is not dependent upon the segregation, or assortment, of a second, third, etc., pair of chromosomes.

linkage group A group of genes located on the same chromosome.

meiosis The specialized pair of cell divisions that reduce the chromosome number from diploid (2N) to haploid (N).

ovary Female sex organ responsible for the production of the haploid egg cells.

segregation Separation of homologous chromosomes during anaphase I.

sex cells The haploid cells, either sperm cells or egg cells, produced by sexually mature organisms.

sperm cells The haploid sex cells produced by sexually mature males.

synapsis The physical closeness of the two members of a pair of homologous chromosomes as they come together and line up on the equatorial plane.

testes Male sex organ responsible for the production of the haploid sperm cells.

zygote The diploid cell which results from the union of an egg cell and a sperm cell.

Purpose   In the previous chapter on meiosis, we discussed how haploid cells are formed. The process also results in the mixing of genes as they are repackaged into gametes. The uniting of two gametes brings together sets of genes in a single cell. This chapter will deal with reproduction and development—particularly human reproduction—and the various structures that are involved. The process will be followed from the production of gametes to the birth of a baby. Finally, there will be a discussion on some factors that can alter the developmental process.

Reproduction and Development

Where It Happens

Organisms that reproduce sexually have some special structures that are involved in producing gametes. In many organisms other additional structures are involved in the storage and transportation of gametes, such as sperm ducts and oviducts. Only mammals such as man, squirrels, and porcupines have other special structures used to care for the fertilized egg during its early development. The specific structures used in reproduction vary from one kind of organism to another. Three detailed examples are shown in figure 13.1. There are also many differences in the specific way in which gametes are formed. There are differences in gamete production between kinds of organisms and there are also differences in gamete production between males and females of the same kind. In animals, the process of meiosis leads to the production of gametes and is called **gametogenesis** (gamete generating) (fig. 13.2). Because of the many minor differences in gametogenesis between animals, the remainder of this chapter will deal primarily with humans.

The term **spermatogenesis** refers to the production of sperm, and the term **oögenesis** refers to the production of eggs. Spermatogenesis takes place in the **testes,** which are located in a saclike structure called the **scrotum.** The two testes are bean-shaped and are composed of many tubes held together by a thin covering membrane (fig. 13.3). All of the tubes join together to form a larger tube, which eventually leads out of the body through the **penis.** Before the beginning of meiosis in males, the tubes are packed solid with diploid cells. At the age of about eleven to thirteen years, these cells specialize and begin the process of meiosis. The tubes become hollow and can transport the sperm. Each cell that begins meiosis results in four smaller round haploid cells. These cells lose most of their cytoplasm and become "stripped down" for action. They develop a long thin tail, which drives the sperm toward the egg. The sperm have only a small amount of food reserves.

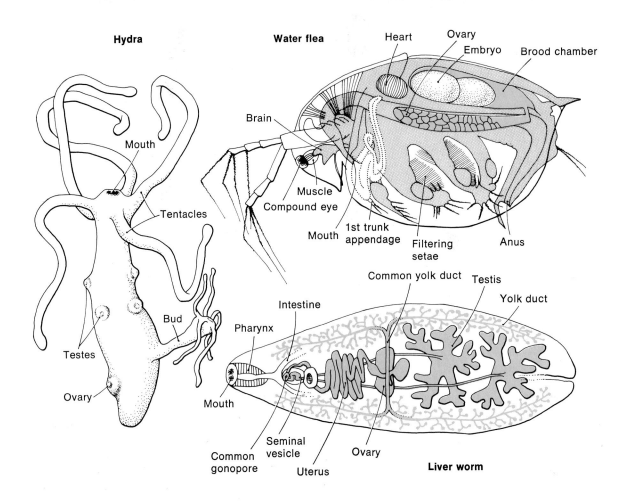

Hydra

Mouth

Tentacles

Bud

Testes

Ovary

Water flea

Heart

Ovary

Embryo

Brood chamber

Brain

Muscle

Compound eye

Mouth

1st trunk appendage

Filtering setae

Anus

Common yolk duct

Testis

Yolk duct

Intestine

Pharynx

Mouth

Common gonopore

Seminal vesicle

Uterus

Ovary

Liver worm

Fig. 13.1 *Sexual Reproductive Organs.* Each of these animals has the ability to reproduce sexually, but all differ in the complexity of their reproductive structures. Notice that the *Hydra* and the liver worm have both male and female structures in the same individual. The water flea is a female.

Therefore, once they are released and have become active swimmers, they only live a few hours. Human sperm usually live no more than seventy-two hours after they are released. However, the life of a sperm may be increased in some cases. If the temperature is lowered drastically by using special equipment, the sperm become deactivated and may live for years outside the testes. This has led to the development of sperm banks. Although human sperm banks have been formed, these banks are going out of business because there have been few depositors. The most successful use of sperm banks is in cattle breeding, where the sperm from selected animals is stored and used to fertilize cows. As a result, a particular animal may continue to reproduce his own kind for years after his own death. No one has ever asked cows how they felt about this procedure, but this method of fertilization has certainly lead to improvements in the quality of many animals.

Spermatogenesis in the human male takes place continuously; new gametes are produced throughout a male's reproductive life. The number

GAMETOGENESIS

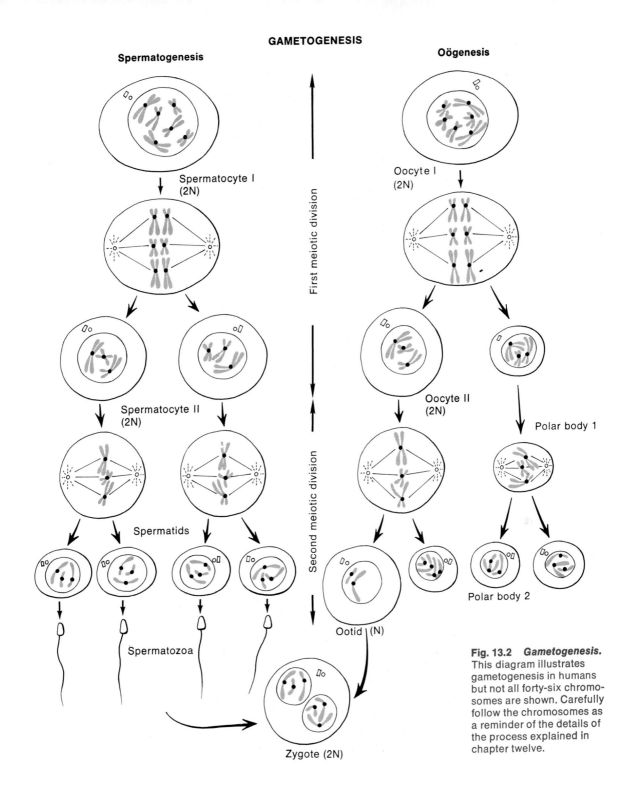

Spermatogenesis

Spermatocyte I (2N)

Spermatocyte II (2N)

Spermatids

Spermatozoa

First meiotic division

Second meiotic division

Oögenesis

Oocyte I (2N)

Oocyte II (2N)

Polar body 1

Polar body 2

Ootid (N)

Zygote (2N)

Fig. 13.2 *Gametogenesis.* This diagram illustrates gametogenesis in humans but not all forty-six chromosomes are shown. Carefully follow the chromosomes as a reminder of the details of the process explained in chapter twelve.

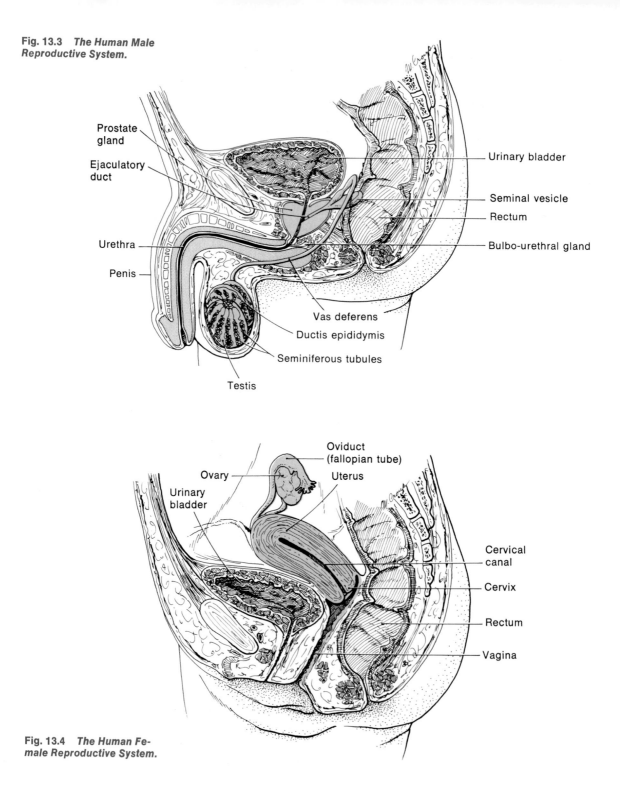

Fig. 13.3 *The Human Male Reproductive System.*

Prostate gland

Ejaculatory duct

Urethra

Penis

Testis

Seminiferous tubules

Ductis epididymis

Vas deferens

Urinary bladder

Seminal vesicle

Rectum

Bulbo-urethral gland

Oviduct (fallopian tube)

Ovary

Urinary bladder

Uterus

Cervical canal

Cervix

Rectum

Vagina

Fig. 13.4 *The Human Female Reproductive System.*

of sperm produced is great. Sperm counts can be taken and used to determine the probability of successful fertilization. For reasons not really understood, a man must be able to release at least one hundred million sperm at one time to be fertile. A healthy male probably releases about one billion sperm during each act of **sexual intercourse.**

While men produce many billions of gametes each year, this is not true for women. Just below the surface of the **ovary,** a single diploid cell begins to undergo meiosis in the normal manner. But when telophase I occurs, the two cells that form get unequal portions of cytoplasm; one cell gets only a small portion, while the other gets most of the cytoplasm. You might think of it as a lopsided division (fig. 13.2). The smaller of the two cells is called a **polar body.** During the second meiotic division, the large cell again divides unevenly so that another polar body is formed. None of the polar bodies survive to become eggs. As a result, only one large egg is produced by oögenesis.

Oögenesis begins before the female is born. The DNA is duplicated and the first meiotic division begins in about forty thousand cells of the ovaries. Oögenesis is halted before birth and does not resume again until she is eleven to thirteen years old. At this time, one of these cells completes the process of oögenesis approximately every twenty-eight days. The other cells remain in the ovary. As oögenesis is completed, the egg becomes encased in a saclike structure on the ovary, and a high water pressure is built up around it. When the pressure is great enough, the covering of the ovary splits, and the egg is shot off the surface. The egg then begins its travel through the tubes of the reproductive system (fig. 13.4). Thus, during a female's lifetime, she can release about three-hundred to five-hundred eggs. Fortunately, few of these eggs become fertilized.

One of the most important differences to note here is the age of the cell. In males, meiosis is continuous and occurs each time a new sperm is manufactured. Sperm do not remain in the tubes of the male reproductive system for very long. They are either released shortly after they are formed or they die and are absorbed. In females, meiosis begins before birth but the oögenesis process is not completed and the egg will not be released for many years. An egg released when a woman is thirty-seven began meiosis thirty-seven years before! During that time interval, the cell was exposed to many changes, a number of which may be damaging to the molecules of DNA or may interfere with the meiosis II process. Such alterations are less likely to occur in males.

Nondisjunction—Wrong Way on a One-Way Street

In chapter twelve, we described the normal process of reducing diploid cells to haploid cells. This involved segregating homologous chromosomes into separate cells during the first meiotic division. Occasionally a pair of homologous chromosomes does not divide properly during gametogenesis, and both chromosomes of the pair end up in the same egg. This abnormal kind of division is known as **nondisjunction.** As you can see in figure 13.5, one cell is missing a chromosome and the genes that were carried on it. This usually results in the death of the cell. The other cell has a double dose of one chromosome. Ordinarily, you wouldn't think this too drastic, but it appears that the genes of an organism are balanced against one another. A double dose of some genes and a single dose of others will result in abnormalities that may lead to the death of the cell. However, some of these abnormal cells do live and develop into sperm or eggs. If an abnormal sperm or egg happens to result in a zygote, the offspring will have an abnormal number of chromosomes. All the cells that develop from this zygote will also be abnormal.

Fig. 13.5 *Nondisjunction in Oögenesis.* Notice that the egg (the large cell) has lost a chromosome because of an error in separation in meiosis II.

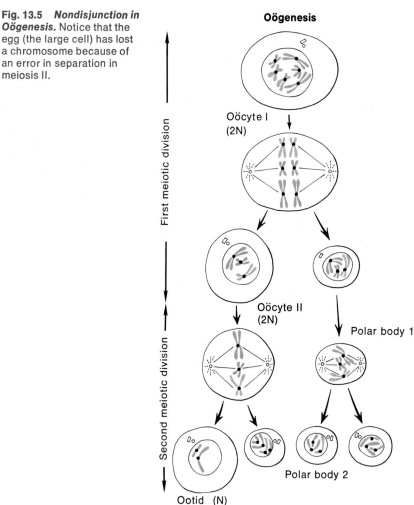

Oögenesis

First meiotic division

Oöcyte I (2N)

Oöcyte II (2N)

Polar body 1

Second meiotic division

Polar body 2

Ootid (N)

One example of the effects of nondisjunction is the condition known as **Down's syndrome** (mongolism), (fig. 13.6). The genetic difference between downics and normal individuals is the presence of an extra chromosome.

Knowing what we do about the time of duplication of DNA and the time of meiosis I, it would seem likely that the chances of having a mongoloid child would increase as the age of the mother increases. Figure 13.7 illustrates the frequency of occurrence of nondisjunction at different ages in women. Notice that the frequency of such a problem begins to increase very rapidly after age thirty-seven. It is for this reason that many doctors encourage couples to have their children in their early to mid-twenties, and not in their late thirties or early forties.

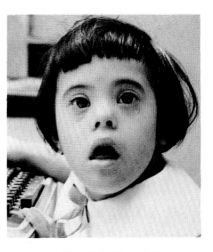

Fig. 13.6 *Down's Syndrome.* Every cell in this child's body has one extra chromosome. With special care and training, persons with this syndrome may be taught to do many things, but cannot reach full potential. (Photo courtesy of March of Dimes.)

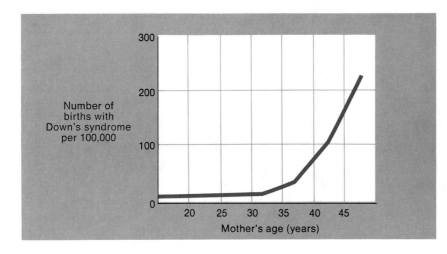

Fig. 13.7 *Age of the Mother and Nondisjunction.* Notice as the age of the female increases, there is only a slight increase in the rate of nondisjunction until the age of about 37. From that point on, the rate increases drastically.

Another case of nondisjunction can be seen in persons demonstrating the condition known as **Turner's syndrome.** Nondisjunction in these individuals has resulted in the loss of one of the chromosomes. They only have forty-five chromosomes. These persons are usually short, have low intelligence, are sterile, and have a very wide neck (fig. 13.8).

Fig. 13.8 *Turner's Syndrome.* This illustration shows one of the typical symptoms of Turner's syndrome. The person appears to have a very wide or webbed neck. Every cell of this person's body lacks one of the sex chromosomes. (Photo from M. Bartalos and T. A. Baramski, *Medical Cytogenetics*, 1967. The Williams & Wilkins Company.)

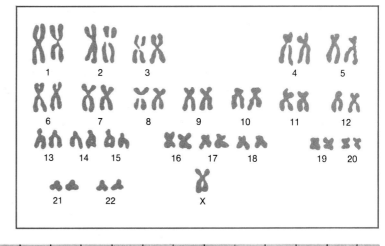

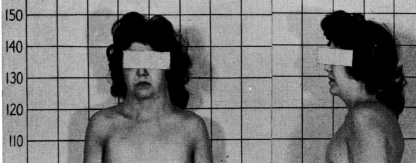

When Does Gametogenesis Occur?

From the point of view of energy, the production of gametes is an expensive process. It requires a good deal of energy to produce the millions of sperm and eggs needed to assure the continued existence of most species of plants and animals. Most organisms are seasonal in their breeding activities. They don't produce sperm and eggs all the time, but only during a portion of the year. The breeding period is usually timed so that the young are born or hatched when the environmental conditions are favorable and food is readily available. In parts of the world having a winter season, birds produce young in the spring and summer. Since the young develop rather rapidly, the eggs and sperm are produced in the early spring just prior to the mating and building of nests. Other animals such as deer also produce young in the spring when environmental conditions are most favorable. However, since deer remain in the uterus for about nine months, the production of eggs and sperm and the mating act must occur the previous fall.

Those plants and animals that live in areas without seasonal changes do not show the typical **seasonal reproductive patterns.** Although, there may still be periods of time when specific individuals are unable to produce sperm or eggs. Man is different from most other animals in that both sexes are continuously active in the production of eggs and sperm. As with most organisms, many more sperm than eggs are produced. This is probably related to the fact that the sperm must seek out the egg. Most of the sperm will never fertilize an egg. The release of sperm during the mating act is similar to shooting at a bird with a shotgun. With a large number of pellets flying through the air, there is a greater chance of hitting the target than if only one pellet were shot.

I Got Rhythm

We have just said that the production of gametes may be seasonal, but what controls the process? **Hormones** are involved in the control of the production of eggs and sperm. They are also involved in the control of other organs and the behavior associated with reproduction. A hormone is a chemical substance that is produced by one part of the body (usually a gland) and alters the activity of a different part of the body. Table 13.1 lists some hormones and their functions.

Table 13.1 *Human Hormones*
Listed here are a few hormones, their sites of production, and some of their functions.

Name of hormone	Production site	Function(s)
Adrenalin	Adrenal gland	Prepares body for emergency
Oxytocin	Pituitary gland	Causes uterus to contract and breasts to release milk
Thyroxine	Thyroid gland	Controls metabolism
Progesterone	Ovary	Controls female sex characteristics
Insulin	Pancreas	Controls sugar level in the blood
Testosterone	Testes	Controls male sex characteristics

In women certain hormones are involved in bringing about the release of an egg **(ovulation)** about every twenty-eight days. In addition to the regulation of egg release from the ovary, hormones control the cycle of changes in other organs. In particular, the breasts and the lining of the uterus are changed (fig. 13.9). The lining of the uterus becomes thicker and is filled with blood prior to the time that the egg is released. This assures that if the egg becomes fertilized, the new zygote will be able to attach itself to the wall of the uterus and receive nourishment. If the egg is not fertilized, the lining of the uterus will be shed. This is known as the **menstrual flow, menses,** or **period.** Once the wall of the uterus has been shed, it begins to build up again. This continual building and then shedding of the wall of the uterus is known as the **menstrual cycle.**

During the time that the hormones are regulating the release of eggs and the menstrual cycle, some changes are taking place in the breasts. The same hormones that prepare the uterus to receive the zygote also begin to prepare the breasts to produce milk. However, these changes in the breasts are relatively minor unless **pregnancy** occurs.

Fig. 13.9 *Ovarian Cycle in Human Females.* The cyclic release of eggs (ovulation) is timed to match the thickening of the uterus. The uterine cycle in mammals is the preparation of the uterine wall to receive the embryo if fertilization occurs. Knowing how these two cycles compare, it is possible to determine at what time pregnancy is most likely to occur.

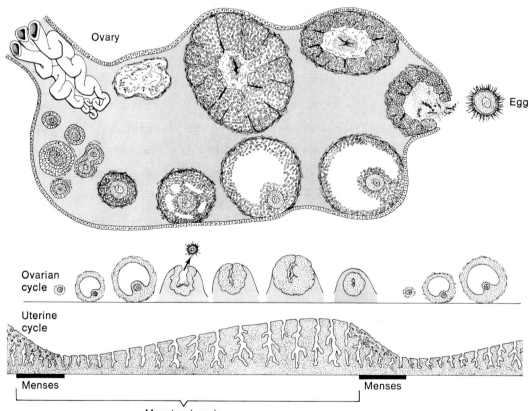

Ovary

Egg

Ovarian cycle

Uterine cycle

Menses

Menses

Menstrual cycle

Fooling the Body

An understanding of how various hormones regulate the menstrual cycle, egg release, milk production, and behavior patterns has led to the medical use of certain hormones. Some women are unable to have children because they do not release eggs from their ovaries or they release them at the wrong time. Doctors are able to use certain hormones (commonly called fertility drugs) to regulate the release of eggs from the ovary. Unfortunately, this often results in multiple births, since too many eggs are released at one time. A better understanding of hormone action may allow for a more controlled use of fertility drugs, so that the problem of multiple births can be eliminated. A second medical use of hormones is in the control of conception by the use of birth-control pills. Birth-control pills have the opposite effect of fertility drugs, since birth-control pills raise the hormone level to prevent the release of eggs from the ovary.

Hormonal control of fertility is not as easy to achieve in men because there is no comparable cycle of gamete release. One of the male hormones is called **testosterone** because it is produced in the testes. It controls such secondary sexual characteristics as beard growth, deepness of voice, and sexual drive. To further complicate matters, the growth of the testes and the production of sperm and testosterone are under the control of other hormones. Perhaps a better understanding of these hormone interactions in men may some day lead to the production of effective birth-control pills for them. One which was tested had an unusual side effect. It changed the color of the whites of a man's eyes to green. This side effect prevented it from becoming a popular birth-control method.

If a Body Meets a Body Coming Through the Tubes

In most women, an egg is released from the ovary at about the middle of the menstrual cycle. The cycle is usually said to begin on the first day of menstruation. If a woman has a regular twenty-eight day menstrual cycle, the egg will be released approximately on day fourteen. However, some women have very irregular menstrual cycles and it is very difficult to determine just when the egg will be released to become available for **fertilization.** Once the egg is released, it is swept into the **oviduct** (Fallopian tube) and moved toward the uterus. If it does not meet with sperm, the egg will die or be absorbed by the body. A few days later, menstruation will begin and the thick lining of the uterus will be shed. If sperm are present as a result of sexual intercourse, they will swim through the uterus and oviduct. Because of the possible irregularities in the time of ovulation and the fact that sperm can be active for up to three days, it is difficult to determine a specific period of time during which fertilization *cannot* occur (table 13.2).

If sperm are present, they will swarm around the egg as it passes through, but only one sperm will penetrate the outer layer of the egg to

Table 13.2 *Timing Fertilization*

Based on the varying uterine and ovarian cycles found in many women, this is one way to figure a woman's "safe days" (least likely days on which to become pregnant) and her "unsafe days" (most likely days on which to become pregnant). For example, if a woman has a twenty-eight-day menstrual cycle, she is most likely to become pregnant between the tenth and seventeenth day of her cycle.

Length of shortest cycle	First unsafe day after start of any period	Length of longest cycle	Last unsafe day after start of any period
22 Days	4th Day	22 Days	11th Day
23 Days	5th Day	23 Days	12th Day
24 Days	6th Day	24 Days	13th Day
25 Days	7th Day	25 Days	14th Day
26 Days	8th Day	26 Days	15th Day
27 Days	9th Day	27 Days	16th Day
28 Days	10th Day	28 Days	17th Day
29 Days	11th Day	29 Days	18th Day
30 Days	12th Day	30 Days	19th Day
31 Days	13th Day	31 Days	20th Day
32 Days	14th Day	32 Days	21st Day
33 Days	15th Day	33 Days	22nd Day
34 Days	16th Day	34 Days	23rd Day
35 Days	17th Day	35 Days	24th Day
36 Days	18th Day	36 Days	25th Day
37 Days	19th Day	37 Days	26th Day

fertilize it. This fertilized egg, which now has two complete sets of chromosomes, is known as the **zygote.** As the zygote continues to travel down the oviduct, it begins dividing by mitosis into smaller and smaller cells, forming what is called an **embryo.** As the embryo enters the uterus, it comes in contact with the thickened uterine wall. The embryo becomes buried in the uterine wall (fig. 13.10) and is covered over by the cells of the uterus. Some of the embryo's cells intermingle with the cells of the uterus and begin to function as a structure known as the **placenta.** Both the embryo and the placenta are able to produce hormones that prevent menstruation and ovulation during the nine months that the embryo is in the uterus.

As the embryo's cells divide and grow, some of them become specialized. Some become nerve cells, bone cells, blood cells, or other specialized cells. In order to divide and grow, cells must receive nourishment. This is provided by the mother through the placenta. The placenta is an amazing organ in which the circulatory system of the mother and the circulatory system of the embryo come in close contact, but do not join. This closeness allows for the exchange of materials between the two (fig. 13.11).

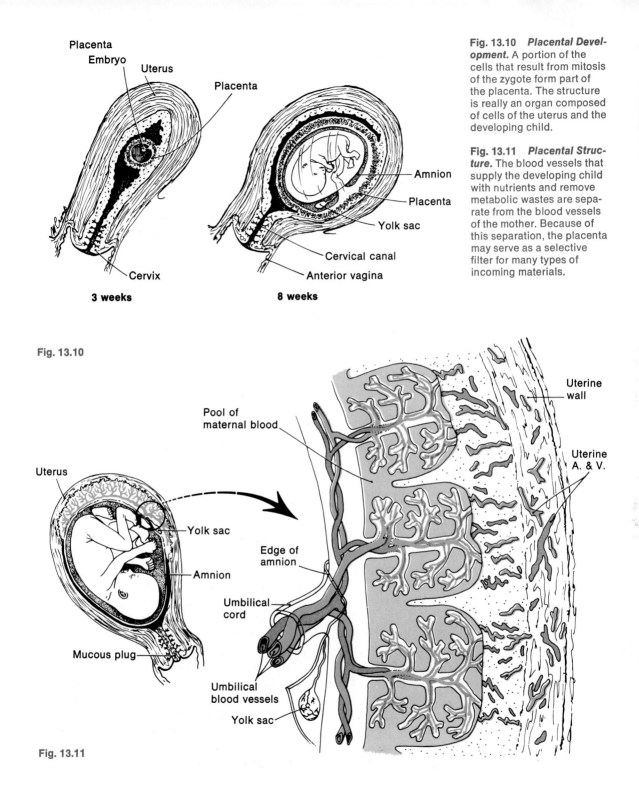

Placenta
Embryo
Uterus
Placenta

Cervix

3 weeks

Amnion
Placenta
Yolk sac
Cervical canal
Anterior vagina

8 weeks

Fig. 13.10 *Placental Development.* A portion of the cells that result from mitosis of the zygote form part of the placenta. The structure is really an organ composed of cells of the uterus and the developing child.

Fig. 13.11 *Placental Structure.* The blood vessels that supply the developing child with nutrients and remove metabolic wastes are separate from the blood vessels of the mother. Because of this separation, the placenta may serve as a selective filter for many types of incoming materials.

Fig. 13.10

Uterus

Yolk sac
Amnion

Mucous plug

Pool of maternal blood

Edge of amnion

Umbilical cord

Umbilical blood vessels

Yolk sac

Uterine wall

Uterine A. & V.

Fig. 13.11

The materials diffusing across the placenta include oxygen, carbon dioxide, nutrients, and a variety of waste products. The materials entering the embryo travel through blood vessels in the **umbilical cord.** Other cells from the embryo form a membrane which surrounds the embryo like a bag. It is filled with fluid that serves to keep the embryo moist and protect it by acting as a shock absorber. Some people have compared this life-support system to that of astronauts in a space capsule. The embryo is contained within the mother's body and relies upon her body to provide all its needs. Development of the major parts of the body occur by the tenth week of pregnancy (fig. 13.12). After this time, the embryo increases in size, and refinements are made in the structure of the body.

Fig. 13.12 *Early Development of the Embryo.* Even though *mom* may not *show* her pregnancy, many developments are occurring within the first few weeks of pregnancy.

4 weeks. Limb buds showing, lungs and stomach being formed, heart forming, nerves and brain just forming.

6 weeks. Face showing jaws, external ear forming, lungs obvious, blood being formed, eyes showing pigment.

7 weeks. Fingers beginning to appear, tail shortening, tongue forming, stomach almost in final shape, eyelids forming.

12 weeks. Head dominant, bridge of nose formed, cheeks formed, tooth buds formed, bile secreted, blood forming in bone marrow, bone becoming hard, brain cells becoming well defined.

15 weeks. Face looks "human," hair forming, muscles contracting spontaneously, tonsils beginning to form, kidneys showing typical shape, heart beginning to contract, sweat glands developing.

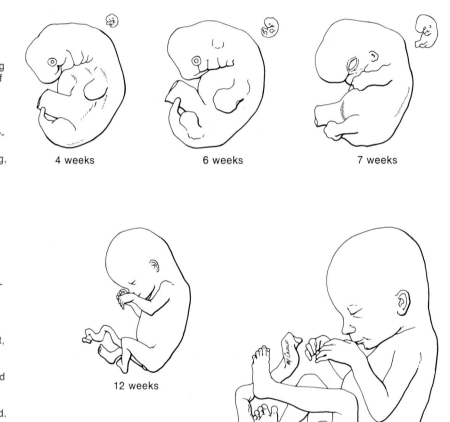

4 weeks

6 weeks

7 weeks

12 weeks

15 weeks

Hello Cruel World

At the end of about nine months, hormone changes in the mother's body stimulate contractions of the muscles of the uterus during a period prior to birth called **labor.** These contractions normally move the baby headfirst through the vagina, or birth canal. One of the first effects of these contractions is the bursting of the bag of waters surrounding the baby. Following this, the uterine contractions become stronger and shortly thereafter the baby is born. In some cases, the baby becomes turned in the uterus before labor. If this occurs, the head will not be born first. Such a birth is called a **breech birth.**

Following the birth of the baby, the placenta is born and is usually referred to as the **afterbirth.** Once born, the baby begins to function on its own. The umbilical cord collapses and the baby's lungs, kidneys, and digestive tract must now support all his bodily needs. This change is usually quite a shock, but the baby's loud protests fill the lungs with air and stimulate his breathing (fig. 13.13).

Fig. 13.13 *Changing Attitudes.* Many doctors and hospitals are changing their ideas with respect to fathers witnessing the birth of their children. (Courtesy of Leonard J. Ciblay.)

During pregnancy, both the expectant father and mother attend classes to prepare them for the birth.

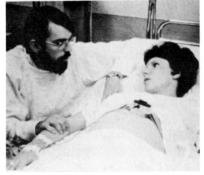

At the time of labor, the expectant father can be with his wife to provide emotional support.

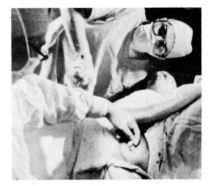

In the delivery room, the father is right there. Holding his wife's hand, he helps her during the delivery.

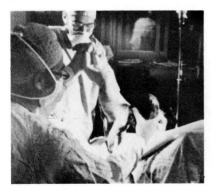

The presence of the father at birth allows the family to begin with a real feeling of togetherness.

This togetherness is continued at home with father and the other members of the family.

Over the next few weeks, the mother's body will begin to return to normal with one major exception. The breasts, which have also undergone changes during the period of pregnancy, have become prepared for the production of milk to feed the baby. Following birth, hormones stimulate the production and release of this milk. If the baby is breast-fed, the stimulus of the baby's sucking will prolong the time during which milk is produced. In some cultures, breast feeding continues for two-to-three years. The continued production of milk often delays the reestablishment of the normal cycles of ovulation and menstruation. Many people believe that a woman cannot become pregnant while she is nursing a baby, but because there is so much individual variation among women, relying on this as a natural birth-control method would be unrealistic. Lots of women have been surprised to find out that they will give birth to another baby ten or eleven months after their previous delivery.

On Not Becoming Pregnant

A great variety of conception-control methods have been tried (fig. 13.14) by man throughout history. In ancient times, conception control was encouraged during times of short food supply or when tribes were on the move from one area to another in search of a new home. Ancient writings as early as 1500 B.C. indicate that the Egyptians used a form of tampon, medicated with the ground powder of a shrub to prevent fertilization. This may sound "primitive," but we use the same basic principle today to destroy sperm in the vagina. Contraceptive jellies and foams change the environment of the vagina to a more acid condition, which makes the survival of sperm less likely. The aerosol foams are an effective method of conception control; but the pill is more effective (table 13.3). The spermicidal (sperm killing) foam or jelly is placed in the vagina before intercourse, and when the sperm make contact with the acidic environment, their movement is stopped and they soon die.

Death of the sperm is not the only method by which conception control may be achieved. Any barrier that prevents the sperm from reaching the egg can prevent conception. The two most commonly used are the **diaphragm** and **condom.** The diaphragm is inserted into the vagina and positioned so that it covers the opening of the uterus. The effectiveness of the diaphragm is increased if spermicidal foam or jelly is also used. Because of anatomical differences between females, diaphragms must be fitted by a doctor. The condom is probably the most popular contraceptive device. It is a thin, rubber sheath which is placed over the erect penis before intercourse. Not only does this physical barrier prevent sperm from reaching the egg, but the barrier can also prevent the transmission of the venereal diseases syphilis and gonorrhea. Because of the alarming increase in the number of cases of venereal diseases, many health authorities are recommending a return to the use of both the condom and the diaphragm to reduce transmission of these diseases through the population.

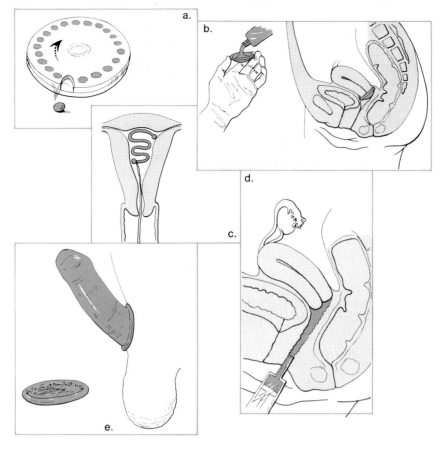

Fig. 13.14 *Contraceptive Methods.* These are the primary methods of conception control used today. *(a)* Oral contraceptive device. *(b)* Diaphragm and spermicidal jelly. *(c)* Intrauterine contraceptive device. *(d)* Spermicidal vaginal foam. *(e)* Condom.

Table 13.3 *Effectiveness of Contraceptive Methods*

Method	Pregnancies Per 100 Women Per Year[a]	
	High[b]	*Low*
No contraceptive[c]	80	40
Coitus interruptus	23	15
Condom[d]	17	8
Douche	61	34
Chemicals (spermicides)[e]	40	9
Diaphragm and jelly	28	11
Rhythm[f]	58	14
Pill	2	0.03
IUD	8	3
Sterilization	0.003	0

a Data describe the number of women per 100 who will become pregnant in a one-year period while using a given method.

b High and low values represent best and worst estimates from various demographic and clinical studies.

c In the complete absence of contraceptive practice, 8 out of 10 women can expect to become pregnant within one year.

d Effectiveness increases if spermicidal jelly or cream is used in addition.

e Aerosol foam is considered to be the best of the chemical barriers.

f Use of a clinical thermometer to record daily temperatures increases effectiveness.

From E. Peter Volpe, *Man, Nature, and Society* (Dubuque, Ia.: Wm. C. Brown Co. Publishers, 1975). Used by permission of the publisher.

The **intrauterine device (IUD)** is not a physical barrier that prevents the egg and the sperm from uniting. The exact method by which this contraceptive device works is not completely known. However, it may be that the device in some way interferes with the attachment of the embryo to the lining of the uterus. This device must also be fitted and inserted by the doctor. A doctor can remove the IUD if pregnancy is desired.

Two other contraceptive methods performed by doctors are tubal ligations and vasectomies. The tubal ligation requires hospitalization and involves the cutting and tying off of the two oviducts. Ovulation continues as usual, but the sperm and egg are prevented from uniting. In males, the vasectomy can be performed in a doctor's office and does not require hospitalization. A small opening is made in the scrotum and the sperm duct **(vas deferens)** is cut and tied. This prevents the sperm from moving through the ducts to the outside. Because the majority of the sperm-carrying fluid **(semen)** is produced by the **seminal vesicle, prostate,** and **bulbo-urethral glands,** a vasectomy does not interfere with normal ejaculation. The sperm that are still being produced die and are reabsorbed in the testes. Neither tubal ligation nor vasectomy interferes with the normal sex drive. However, these methods of conception control should be considered permanent, and only persons who do not wish to have more children should consider (*a*) tubal ligation and (*b*) vasectomy (fig. 13.15).

Fig. 13.15 *Tubal Ligation and Vasectomy.* Two very effective contraceptive methods that require surgery.

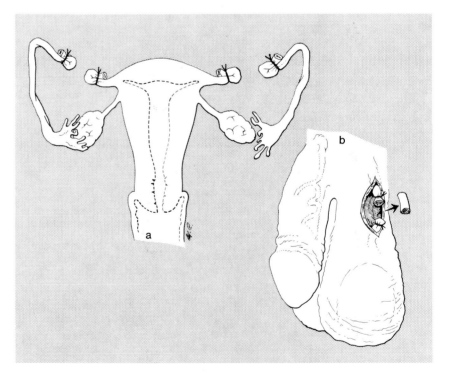

Surprises, Problems, and Changing Attitudes

What we have discussed so far is a description of what usually occurs during reproduction in humans. However, you need to recognize variations that are fairly common. One common side effect of pregnancy is known as **morning sickness.** The dizziness, nausea, and vomiting may be the result of hormone and other chemical changes that are taking place in the body. Once these changes are made, the morning sickness usually disappears. The changes occurring during pregnancy also affect the metabolic balance of the mother. As a result, she requires a greater amount of water, nutrients, and growth factors. This leads to more trips to the bathroom and the refrigerator. Both the developing embryo and the mother will suffer if the mother's diet is poor. Proteins are extremely important during pregnancy, since they are required by the mother and the embryo for the production of additional cells and enzymes. Without adequate protein, the baby will suffer both mentally and physically. In countries with high birthrates and a low protein diet, the population is caught in a cycle of mental and physical poverty, which can only be broken by increasing the protein available or reducing the population so that each individual receives enough of the proper foods. Three countries that are currently in this situation are India, Ghana, and Paraguay.

Mental and physical damage may result from other causes. For instance, drugs taken by the mother or diseases such as German measles or syphilis can also influence the development of the baby during pregnancy. A number of years ago in Europe, the drug thalidomide was given to pregnant women as a sedative. Unfortunately, the drug was able to cross the placenta and interfered with the normal development of arms and legs. As a result of birth abnormalities throughout the world, this drug was removed from the market. Mothers addicted to heroin have babies who are also addicted to the drug. After these babies are born and no longer have a constant supply of the drug coming to them through the placenta, they go through withdrawal symptoms. These are extreme cases in which drugs taken by a pregnant woman have a severe effect on her unborn child. Consequently, all medication is carefully controlled by the doctor during pregnancy. During routine examinations, the doctor listens for the heartbeat of the embryo. Occasionally more than one heartbeat may be heard and the doctor may inform the mother that she will have twins. Twins may be produced in two ways. **Identical twins** are of the same sex and have the same genes. When the zygote divides for the first time, the two cells may separate from one another and develop into two independent embryos. Since they both come from the same single fertilized egg they are genetically identical (fig. 13.16). **Fraternal twins** do not contain the same genetic information, and may be of different sexes. They result from the fertilization of two separate eggs by different sperm. Therefore, they are no more identical to one another than ordinary brothers and sisters.

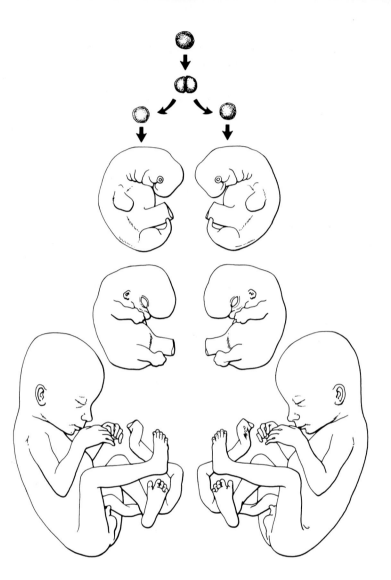

As attitudes toward sex have changed and people have become less inhibited, there have been changes in attitudes toward childbirth. In the past, fathers were prohibited from seeing the birth of their children. But today, an increasing number of doctors and hospitals are encouraging fathers to be present during the birth of their children. Many fathers want to see the birth of their child and to provide emotional support to the mother during childbirth (fig. 13.13).

The use of anesthetics during childbirth has been routine for many years. But today, many doctors encourage mothers to have their children with a minimum of drugs for relief of pain. Any drug which is given to the mother also reaches the child through the placenta and may slow his reactions at birth. A limited use of anesthetics also allows for a speedier recovery by the mother. Along with this trend toward natural childbirth, there has been an increase in the number of mothers who wish to breast-feed their babies. Breast feeding is less expensive, easier, and more fulfilling than bottle feeding for many mothers. In addition, the milk is designed to meet the needs of the human baby.

Summary

Sexual reproduction involves the production of gametes by meiosis in the ovaries and testes. The production and release of these gametes is controlled by the interaction of hormones. In males, four active sperm are the result of spermatogenesis; while in females, one egg and polar bodies result from oögenesis. Nondisjunction is an abnormal kind of meiosis which causes abnormal embryos as found in Down's and Turner's syndromes. Many organisms, including man, have specialized structures for the support of the developing embryo. Many factors influence the development of the embryo in the uterus. Successful sexual reproduction depends on proper hormone balance, proper meiotic division, fertilization, placenta formation, proper diet of the mother, and birth. Hormones are involved in the normal reproductive process by controlling ovulation and menstruation, and may also be used to encourage or discourage ovulation. Such control can be seen by the use of fertility drugs and "the pill." In addition to the pill, a number of other conception-control methods have been developed and include the diaphragm, condom, IUD, spermicidal jellies and foams, tubal ligation, and vasectomy. During pregnancy it is important that the mother receive proper nutrition and avoid unnecessary use of drugs since the developing embryo may be influenced. During labor, the contractions of the uterus move the baby through the birth canal headfirst. The placenta is born following this. Even though the process of sexual reproduction and birth have remained the same, many attitudes toward breast feeding, natural childbirth, and the father's participation during the birth have changed over the last few years.

Consider This

A great world adventurer discovered a tribe of women in the jungles of Brazil. After many years of very close study and experimentation, he found that sexual reproduction was not possible. He also discovered that the female children resemble their mothers to a great degree, and that all women had a gene which prevents meiosis from occurring. Ovulation occurs as usual, and pregnancy lasts nine months. The mothers nurse their children for three months after birth and become pregnant the next month. This cycle is repeated in all the women of the tribe.

Consider the topics of meiosis, mitosis, sexual reproduction and regular hormonal cycles in women, and explain in detail what may be happening in this tribe.

1. What structures are associated with the human female reproductive system? What are their functions?
2. What structures are associated with the human male reproductive system? What are their functions?
3. What are the differences between oögenesis and spermatogenesis in humans?
4. What is nondisjunction? Give an example.
5. How are ovulation and the menstruation cycle related to one another?
6. What changes occur in ovulation and menstruation during pregnancy?
7. What are the functions of the placenta?
8. If a woman begins to menstruate on the first of June and she has a regular twenty-eight day menstrual cycle, on what dates would sexual intercourse most likely result in pregnancy? What if the cycle lasted twenty-two days?
9. In which part of the female body is fertilization most likely to occur?
10. What are some advantages of breast feeding?

Chapter Glossary

afterbirth   Another name for the placenta, which is released from the uterus after the child is born.

breech birth   A birth in which the head is not born first. Example: an arm or the feet may appear first.

bulbo-urethral gland   A part of the male reproductive system that produces a portion of the semen.

condom   A mechanical conception-control device used by men to cover the erect penis.

diaphragm   A mechanical conception-control device used by women to cover the entrance to the uterus.

Down's syndrome   A genetic disease resulting from the presence of an extra chromosome; symptoms include thickened eyelids, low level of intelligence, faulty speech; sometimes called mongolism.

embryo   The early stage in the development of a sexually reproduced organism.

fertilization   The uniting of the male gamete (sperm) and the female gamete (egg) to form a zygote.

fraternal twins   Two offspring that are born at the same time, but are the result of the fertilization of two separate eggs.

gametogenesis   Gamete generating; the meiotic cell division process resulting in the production of sex cells.

hormone   Chemical substances that are released from glands in the body and have a regulating affect on other parts of the body.

identical twins   Two offspring that are born at the same time and are the result of the fertilization of one egg that has separated into two cells.

intrauterine device (IUD)   A mechanical conception-control device placed in the uterus to prevent embryo attachment.

labor   The contractions of the uterus which results in the birth of the young.

menses (period, menstrual flow)   The shedding of the lining of the uterus.

menstrual cycle   The continual building and then shedding of the lining of the uterus.

morning sickness   One of the symptoms of pregnancy characterized by nausea, vomiting, and dizziness.

nondisjunction   An abnormal meiotic division that results in sex cells that have too many or too few chromosomes.

oögenesis   The specific name given to the gametogenesis process that leads to the formation of eggs.

ovary   The female organ that produces eggs.

oviduct   The tube that carries the egg to the uterus; sometimes called the fallopian tube.

ovulation   The release of an egg from the ovary.

penis   A portion of the male reproductive system which deposits sperm in the female reproductive tract.

placenta   An organ made up of tissues from the embryo and the uterus of the mother that allows for the exchange of materials between the mother's bloodstream and the embryo's bloodstream; it also produces some hormones.

polar body   The smaller cell formed by an unequal meiotic division during oögenesis.

pregnancy   In mammals, the period of time during which the embryo is developing in the uterus of the mother.

prostate   A portion of the male reproductive system that produces a portion of the semen.

scrotum   A sac that contains the testes.

seasonal reproductive patterns   Most plants and animals reproduce at specific times of the year; their sexual behavior and ability to reproduce is restricted to a particular time of the year.

semen   The fluid, produced by the seminal vesicle, prostate, and bulbo-urethral glands of a male, that carries sperm.

seminal vesicle   A part of the male reproductive system that produces a portion of the semen.

sexual intercourse   The mating of male and female; the action of depositing sperm in the reproductive tract of the female.

spermatogenesis   The specific name given to the gametogenesis process that leads to the formation of sperm.

testes   The male organ that produces sperm.

testosterone   The male sex hormone produced in the testes that controls the secondary sex characteristics.

Turner's syndrome   A genetic disease resulting from the lack of one chromosome. Symptoms include lowered intelligence, thick neck, sterility, and usually shortness.

umbilical cord   The cord that contains the blood vessels that carry materials between the placenta and the embryo.

vas deferens   The portion of the sperm duct, which is cut and tied during a vasectomy.

zygote   The fertilized egg.

Purpose   This chapter will consider the fundamentals of inheritance. Previous chapters have introduced you to the basic concepts of sexual reproduction, meiosis, mitosis, and the importance of DNA as a molecule for storing the genetic information used to manufacture proteins. Throughout this chapter we will discuss how characteristics are passed from one generation to the next using many human characteristics to illustrate these patterns of inheritance.

Mendelian Genetics

Tying It All Together

Genetics is a relatively new field of biology, which has been revolutionized by the discovery that **genes** are really portions of DNA molecules arranged in a linear fashion on the chromosomes (somewhat like a single-line message written on a long strip of paper). The first person to formulate any laws about how characteristics are passed from one generation to the next was an Augustinian monk named Johann Gregor Mendel (1866) (fig. 14.1). However, his work was not generally accepted until 1900 when three men working independently rediscovered some of the ideas that Mendel had

Fig. 14.1 *Gregor Mendel.* Mendel raised peas in the monastery garden to help him determine how characteristics are inherited in plants. (From *Biology, The Living World,* by Francis D. Curtis and John Urban, © copyright 1958, by Ginn and Co. (Xerox Corp.). Used with permission.)

formulated over thirty years earlier. This kind of study is often called **Mendelian genetics.**

In order to understand this chapter, some fundamental terminology must be understood. One term that you encountered earlier is the word *gene*. Mendel thought of a gene as a "particle" that could be passed from the parents to the **offspring** (children, descendants). Today we know that genes are actually composed of specific sequences of DNA bases. However, this new understanding doesn't necessarily do away with the "particle" idea, since genes are located on specific portions of chromosomes.

Most organisms have two chromosomes of each kind, which occur in pairs (fig. 14.2). These organisms are diploid, since they have two genes for each characteristic. Other organisms that have only one chromosome of each kind are called haploid. The gametes (sex cells, eggs and sperm) are

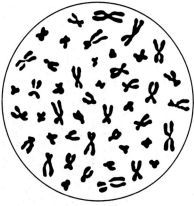

Fig. 14.2 *Human Male Chromosomes.* The human male chromosomes shown on the left are randomly arranged. Those on the right have been arranged into pairs of homologous chromosomes. (Adapted from Guide to Human Chromosome Defects (1968): Redding and Hirschhorn. In *Birth Defects:* Orig. Art. Ser., ed. D. Bergsma. Published by the National Foundation —March of Dimes, White Plains, N.Y. Vol. 4, no. 4, p. 2, 1968.)

also haploid in almost all cases. Since gametes are haploid and most organisms are diploid, the conversion of diploid cells to haploid cells during meiosis is a very important process. Diploid organisms usually inherit one gene of each type from each parent. For example, each of us has two genes for eye color; one was donated from our father's sperm and the other from our mother's egg.

How Genes Work Together to Produce Characteristics

Although each diploid organism has two genes for each characteristic, there may be a number of different alternative forms of each gene. Those genes that affect the same characteristic but produce different expressions of a characteristic are called **alleles.** In man, there are a number of different alleles for hair color, such as red, blond, and black. The color of a person's hair is determined by the kind of allele (gene) he received from each of his parents, and how the alleles interact with one another to produce such a characteristic. Alleles are always located on the members of a homologous pair of chromosomes (one allele on each chromosome). These alleles are always located at the same spot **(locus)** on the same type of chromosome in all individuals of a species (fig. 14.3).

The DNA that an organism has constitutes a catalog of genes known as the **genotype** of the organism. The expression of these genes will result in a certain collection of characteristics referred to as the **phenotype.** The phenotype of an organism consists of its observable characteristics. The genotype cannot be seen, since it is the DNA chemical code (formula) of an organism. There is not always a total expression of the genotype. Particular genes may not express themselves for a variety of reasons. In some cases the physical environment will determine if certain genes will have a chance to express themselves. For example, some cats have coat color genes that do not express themselves unless the temperature is below a certain point. Often the only parts of the cat that are cool enough to allow the genes to express themselves are the tips of the ears and feet, which will differ in color from the rest of their bodies. In humans the presence of a gene for freckles will not express itself fully unless the person's skin is exposed to sunlight (fig. 14.4).

The expression of some genes is directly influenced by the presence of other genes in the organism. For any particular pair of alleles in an individual organism, either the two alleles are identical or they are not. If the alleles are identical, the organism is said to be **homozygous** for that particular characteristic. But, if the two alleles are not identical, the organism is **heterozygous** for that characteristic. If the two alleles are identical, the characteristic will be expressed in a specific manner (i.e., two genes for blue eyes in man will result in a blue-eyed person). However, if the organism is heterozygous, which of the alleles will express itself, and how will these genes interact to determine the phenotype? Often one of the alleles will express itself and the other will not. The allele that expresses itself is the **dominant allele,** and the

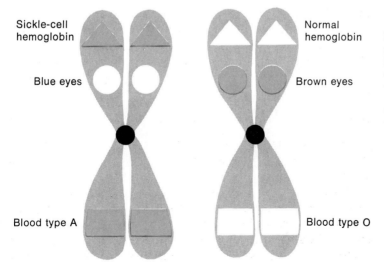

Sickle-cell hemoglobin

Blue eyes

Blood type A

Normal hemoglobin

Brown eyes

Blood type O

Fig. 14.3 *A Pair of Homologous Chromosomes.* Homologous chromosomes contain genes for the same characteristics at the same place. Note that the blue eye allele is located at the eye color locus on one chromosome, and the brown eye allele is located at the eye color locus on the other member of the homologous pair of chromosomes. (We really don't know on which chromosomes most human genes are located. The examples presented here are for illustrative purposes only.)

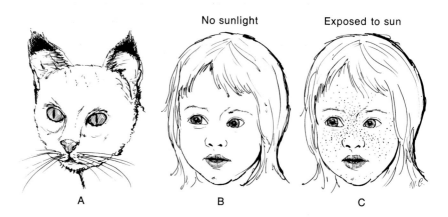

Fig. 14.4 *Environment and Gene Expression.* The expression of many genes is influenced by the environment. The gene for dark hair in the cat is sensitive to temperature and only expresses itself in the parts of the body that stay cool. The gene for freckles expresses itself more fully when the person is exposed to sunlight.

No sunlight   Exposed to sun

A   B   C

allele that does not express itself is the **recessive allele.** For example, if a person has one allele for blue eyes and one allele for brown eyes, he will have brown eyes. This happens because the allele for brown eyes is dominant over the allele for blue eyes; the blue eye allele is recessive. The fact that an allele is recessive in a particular combination does not in any way weaken or alter that allele, nor is a dominant gene more valuable than a recessive gene. Each gene can still be separated from the other allele during meiosis and be passed on to the next generation.

In describing genotypes it is traditional to use a shorthand notation to refer to the genes that an organism has. In the case of human eye color we usually denote the brown allele with the capital letter *B* since brown is dominant. The allele for blue eyes is denoted by the small letter *b*. The possible genotypes that could occur would be as follows:

Genotype		Phenotype
BB	(Homozygous for brown eyes)	Brown eyes
Bb	(Heterozygous for eye color)	Brown eyes
bb	(Homozygous for blue eyes)	Blue eyes

In each of these cases one of the alleles was originally present in the sperm donated by the father, and the other allele was contained within the egg. Since gametes are haploid, there is only one gene of each kind in each sex cell. (Note: the example of human eye color, used a number of times in this chapter, is much more complex than we have presented. There are other factors that influence eye color and they are not as yet clearly understood by scientists.)

Question 1

If a husband and wife both have brown eyes, is it possible for them to have blue-eyed children? The answer is yes if both parents are heterozygous for eye color. See figure 14.5 for a complete explanation.

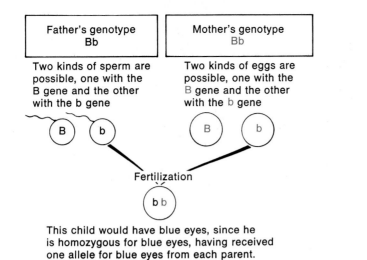

Fig. 14.5 *Inheritance of Eye Color in Humans.* Two brown-eyed parents can have a blue-eyed child.

This child would have blue eyes, since he is homozygous for blue eyes, having received one allele for blue eyes from each parent.

We have just seen that it is possible for two brown-eyed parents to have a blue-eyed child if both parents are heterozygous for eye color. Another question we could ask is how probable is it that they will have blue-eyed children. There is a considerable difference between possibility and probability. A statement of **probability** is more precise than simply saying something is possible. For example, it is possible to flip a coin and have it come up heads. The probability that it will come up heads is one chance in two (½, or 0.5, probability). It is also possible to flip two coins at the same time and have both show heads, however, the probablity of this happening is ½ × ½ = ¼, or 0.25. These situations are possible, but each has a different probability.

Question 2

If both parents are heterozygous for eye color, what is the probability that they will have a blue-eyed child? The probability or likelihood of them having a blue-eyed child is one out of four. See figure 14.6 for an explanation.

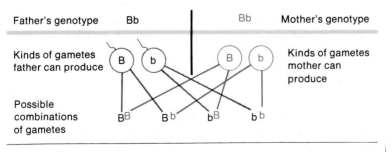

Fig. 14.6 *Probability and Gamete Production.* You can see that there are four possible combinations of gametes. They are all equally probable (0.25 or ¼). Only one of the combinations will produce a blue-eyed child. Therefore, the probability of these parents having a blue-eyed child is one chance in four or 0.25.

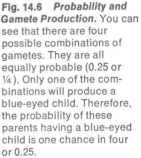

Mendelian Genetics

Often it is convenient to use the following Punnett Square method to determine probabilities of gene combinations in the zygote produced by the union of the egg and the sperm.

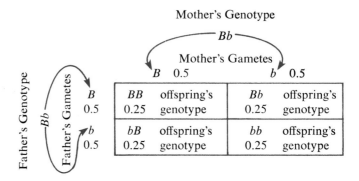

What we have just considered is usually referred to as a **monohybrid cross** (single hybrid), since only one characteristic (eye color) is being followed from one generation to the next. The term **hybrid** is often used to refer to organisms descended from parents who have different genotypes.

The Dihybrid Cross

When two characteristics are being studied at the same time this is referred to as a **dihybrid cross.** Let's examine a situation in which this occurs. In humans, eye color is determined by a dominant allele for brown eyes and a recessive allele for blue eyes. Earlobes may be free or attached. Free earlobes are dominant over attached earlobes.

Question 3

If a man and woman are heterozygous both for eye color and for the condition of earlobes, what could they expect their children to be like (fig. 14.7)?

Any of the combinations of genes that have a *B* and an *E* will be brown-eyed and have free earlobes. Nine of the sixteen possibilities have this condition. These are marked with an asterisk (*). Three of the possible combinations would have two alleles for blue eyes (*bb*) and at least one allele for free earlobes (*E*). These individuals would be blue-eyed with free earlobes. These are marked with a dot (·). Three of the combinations would yield brown eyes and attached earlobes. These are marked with a square (■). The remaining compartment has the genotype (*bbee*) for blue-eyedness and attached earlobes.

This information allows us to make some predictions about what the offspring of these two parents will be like. They may have children with any one of four possible phenotypes: there are nine chances out of sixteen that

Fig. 14.7 *Dihybrid Cross.*
A dihybrid cross studies the inheritance of two characteristics at the same time.

Symbols for the 4 alleles

B = brown eye allele
b = blue eye allele
E = free earlobes
e = attached earlobes

Appearance of the parents

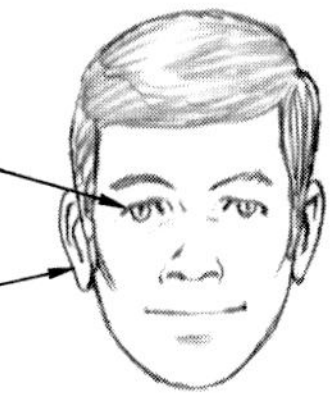

brown eyes
free earlobes

brown eyes
free earlobes

Genotypes of parents

BbEe

BbEe

Possible gametes produced

(BE) (Be) (bE) (be)
0.25 0.25 0.25 0.25

(BE) (Be) (bE) (be)
0.25 0.25 0.25 0.25

Possible combinations of gametes

Mother's gametes

Father's gametes	BE	Be	bE	be
BE	BBEE *	BBEe *	BbEE *	BbEe *
Be	BBeE *	BBee ■	BbeE *	Bbee ■
bE	bBEE *	bBEe *	bbEE •	bbEe •
be	bBeE *	bBee ■	bbeE •	bbee

the child will have brown eyes with free earlobes; three chances out of sixteen that the child will have brown eyes and attached earlobes; three chances out of sixteen that the child will have blue eyes and free earlobes; and one chance out of sixteen that the child will have blue eyes and attached earlobes. All four phenotypes are possible, but some are more probable than others.

Question 4

If a blue-eyed man is heterozygous for free earlobes, and his wife is homozygous for brown eyes and attached earlobes, what could they expect their offspring to be like (fig. 14.8)?

Fig. 14.8 _Genotypes Resulting from a Dihybrid Cross._ In this case, there are only two genotypes possible for the children. Therefore, these parents should expect all of their children to have brown eyes and about half to have free earlobes and half to have attached earlobes.

	Father	Mother
Genotype of parents	bbEe	BBee
Gametes	bE & be — Two gametes possible and equally probable	Be — Only one type of gamete possible
Possible genotypes in the offspring	bBEe	bBee
Phenotypes of the offspring	Brown eyes with free earlobes	Brown eyes with attached earlobes

There are only two different genotypes possible for the children. This couple should expect all of their children to have brown eyes. Half of them will have attached earlobes and half will have free earlobes.

Some More-Complicated Situations

So far we have considered a few simple cases in which a characteristic is determined by simple dominance and recessiveness. There are, however, other situations that don't fit these patterns.

Lack of Dominance

All of the cases that we have considered so far have involved pairs of alleles in which one was clearly dominant over the other. Although this is quite common, it is not always true. In some combinations of alleles, there will be a **lack of dominance** and both alleles will express themselves to some extent. One of the classical examples involves the color of the petals of snapdragons.

There are two alleles for color of these flowers; one for white petals (F^w) and one for red (F^r) petals. There are three possible combinations of these two alleles:

Genotype	Phenotype
F^wF^w	White flowers
F^rF^r	Red flowers
F^rF^w	Pink flowers

Both the red flower allele and the white flower allele express themselves to some extent when they are both present.

Multiple Alleles

Although only two specific alleles can influence a characteristic in a single organism, it is possible that there may be a large number of different alleles that influence the same characteristic in the many organisms of a population. These are referred to as **multiple alleles.** The larger the number of different kinds of alleles there are, the larger the possible combinations of pairs of alleles and the more variable the characteristic will be within the population. For example, in humans there are three different alleles that determine blood type. Let's denote them as follows:

$$I^A$$
$$I^B$$
$$i$$

There are six different possible combinations of two of these three alleles.

Genotype	Phenotype
I^AI^A	Blood type A
I^BI^B	Blood type B
I^AI^B	Blood type AB
I^Ai	Blood type A
I^Bi	Blood type B
$i\ i$	Blood type O

When we have two nonidentical alleles in a pair it is possible to determine whether one is dominant to the other. When the I^A and I^B alleles are present, they both express themselves (i.e., there is lack of dominance) and we have a blood type called AB. However, when I^B and i are combined or I^A and i are combined, the i allele is always recessive to the I^B or I^A allele.

Polygenic Inheritance

Thus far we have considered characteristics that have been determined by alleles located at a specific single place on homologous chromosomes. However, there are some characteristics that are determined by genes located at a number of different loci (on different chromosomes or different places on a single chromosome); this is referred to as **polygenic inheritance.** Skin color in humans is a good example of this inheritance pattern. According to some experts, there are at least three different loci where genes for skin color are located. The allele for dark skin is dominant over the allele for light skin at each of these loci. Therefore, it is possible to have a wide variety of skin colors depending on how many dark skin alleles are present (fig. 14.9). Polygenic inheritance is very common. Just as in the skin color example, there are many other characteristics that cannot be categorized as either black or white. People show great variations in tallness. There aren't just tall and short people. Likewise there are not just smart and dumb people, but a whole range of levels of intelligence. These are just three examples of polygenic inheritance patterns.

Pleiotropy

Often a gene may have a variety of effects on the phenotype of the organism. As a matter of fact, each gene probably affects many different characteristics or phenotypes shown by the organism. This ability of a gene to influence many aspects of the phenotype of the organism is referred to as **pleiotropy.** For example, the gene that causes sickle-cell anemia also has the effect of making individuals somewhat immune to the disease of malaria. So this particular gene has both a good and a bad side. Those persons who are heterozygous have both normal hemoglobin and resistance to malaria.

Genotype	Phenotype
HH	Normal hemoglobin, nonresistance to malaria
H^SH^S	Resistance to malaria but die of sickle-cell anemia
HH^S	Normal hemoglobin and resistance to malaria

Pleiotropy is probably best explained by seeing how a single gene may affect many different chemical reactions that occur in a cell's metabolism (fig. 14.10). People normally have a gene for the production of an enzyme that converts the amino acid phenylalanine to tryptophan. If this gene is functioning properly, the tryptophan will be available for conversion by other enzymes into a variety of products seen in the biochemical pathway. These products are important in the proper development of the phenotypic characteristics of skin pigmentation, thyroid gland functioning, and nerve cell development. We know that this one gene may result in changes of one or more of these characteristics.

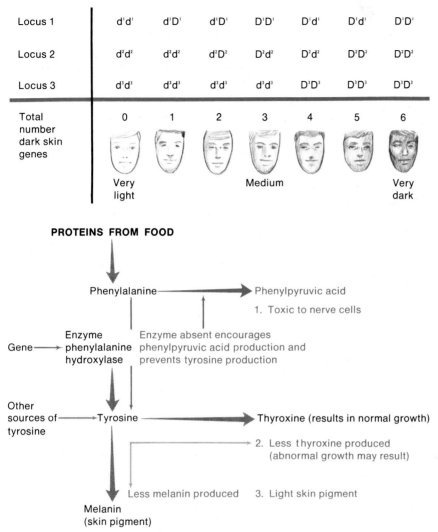

Locus 1	d^1d^1	d^1D^1	d^1D^1	D^1D^1	D^1d^1	D^1d^1	D^1D^1
Locus 2	d^2d^2	d^2d^2	d^2D^2	D^2d^2	D^2d^2	D^2D^2	D^2D^2
Locus 3	d^3d^3	d^3d^3	d^3d^3	d^3d^3	D^3D^3	D^3D^3	D^3D^3
Total number dark skin genes	0	1	2	3	4	5	6
	Very light			Medium			Very dark

Fig. 14.9 *Polygenic Inheritance.* Skin color in humans is an example of polygenic inheritance. The darkness of the skin is determined by the number of dark skin genes a person inherits from his parents.

PROTEINS FROM FOOD

Phenylalanine ⟶ Phenylpyruvic acid

1. Toxic to nerve cells

Enzyme absent encourages phenylpyruvic acid production and prevents tyrosine production

Gene ⟶ Enzyme phenylalanine hydroxylase

Other sources of tyrosine ⟶ Tyrosine ⟶ Thyroxine (results in normal growth)

2. Less thyroxine produced (abnormal growth may result)

Less melanin produced   3. Light skin pigment

Melanin (skin pigment)

Fig. 14.10 *Pleiotropy.* Pleiotropy is a condition in which a single gene has more than one effect on the phenotype. This diagram shows how the normal metabolic pathways work (these are shown in black). If the enzyme phenylalanine hydroxylase is not produced because of an abnormal gene, there are three major results: (1) mental retardation, because phenylpyruvic acid kills nerve cells; (2) abnormal body growth, since less of the growth hormone thyroxine is produced; and (3) pale skin pigmentation, because less melanin is produced (abnormalities shown in color).

Linkage

Genes located on nonhomologous chromosomes are divided up at random during the process of meiosis when the chromosomes are separated into sex cells. Since each chromosome has many genes on it, these genes on a chromosome tend to be inherited in a group. These genes are linked to one another forming a **linkage group.** The closer two genes are to one another on a chromosome, the more likely it is that they will be inherited together. The process of crossing-over, which occurs during prophase I of meiosis, may split up these linkage groups. Crossing-over occurs between the chromosome donated by the mother and the chromosome donated by the father, and results in a mixing of genes.

Sex-Linked Characteristics

Many organisms have genetic methods for determining what sex the organism will be. In man and some other animals, there is one pair of chromosomes that is not identical in shape or in the genes present. These two chromosomes are called the X and Y chromosomes. Females are produced when there are two X chromosomes present. The presence of one X chromosome and one Y chromosome results in the development of a male individual. The Y chromosome is smaller and contains fewer genes than the X chromosome. This means that male individuals will have some genes on the X chromosome that will not have a matching gene on the Y chromosome. Therefore, male organisms will show recessive characteristics more frequently. A female could have a dominant gene on one X chromosome that would mask the effects of the recessive allele on the other X chromosome, while there is no other such gene on the Y chromosome in males. Since such characteristics show up more frequently in males than in females, they are called **sex-linked** characteristics. Consider this example: In man, red-green color blindness is determined by a recessive gene found on the X chromosome but not on the Y chromosome. People who are red-green color blind can't tell red from green. In order for a woman to be red-green color blind, she must have the recessive gene on both of her X chromosomes. However, a male with only one color-blind gene on his X chromosome will show the characteristic.

Question 5

If a color-blind man has a wife who is homozygous for normal color vision, would any of their offspring be color blind?

To answer this question we need to understand how the genes are passed to the next generation. In the case illustrated in figure 14.11, the sons would not be color blind, nor could they pass the gene on, since they don't have it. The daughters would also have normal vision but could pass the color-blind gene on to their offspring (fig. 14.12). If a female carrier mates with a male who has normal vision, they can expect half of their male children to be color blind. All of their daughters would have normal color vision, but half of the daughters would be carriers of the color-blind gene.

Environmental Influences on Characteristics

The specific phenotype an organism exhibits is determined by the interplay of the genotype of the individual and the conditions the organism encounters as it develops. Therefore, it is possible for two organisms having identical genotypes (identical twins) to have differences in their phenotypes. This is possible because all genes must express themselves through the manufacture of proteins. These proteins may be structural or enzymatic, and the enzyme may be more or less effective depending on the specific biochemical condi-

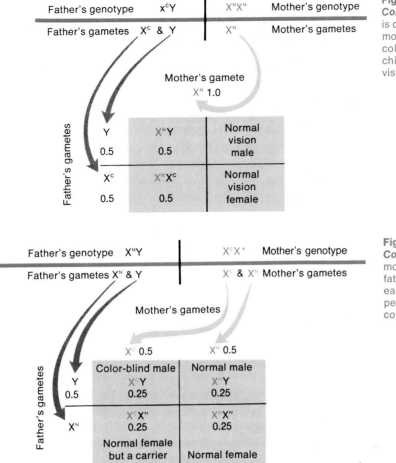

Father's genotype   X^{C}Y | X^{N}X^N Mother's genotype

Father's gametes   X^C & Y | X^N Mother's gametes

Mother's gamete
X^N 1.0

Father's gametes		X^{N}Y	Normal vision male
Y 0.5		0.5	
X^C 0.5		X^{N}X^C 0.5	Normal vision female

Fig. 14.11 Inheritance of Color Blindness. If the father is color blind and the mother is not a carrier of a color-blind gene, all the children will have normal vision.

Father's genotype   X^{N}Y | X^{C}X^N Mother's genotype

Father's gametes X^N & Y | X^C & X^N Mother's gametes

Mother's gametes

X^C 0.5   X^N 0.5

Father's gametes	Color-blind male X^{C}Y 0.25	Normal male X^{N}Y 0.25
Y 0.5		
X^N	X^{C}X^N 0.25 Normal female but a carrier	X^{N}X^N 0.25 Normal female

Fig. 14.12 Inheritance of Color Blindness. If the mother is a carrier and the father has normal vision, each male child has a 50 percent probability of being color blind.

tions that exist when the enzyme is in operation. In other words, the expression of the genes will vary depending on the environmental conditions that exist while the gene is operating.

Summary

Genes are units of heredity composed of specific lengths of DNA, which determine the characteristics an organism will display. Specific genes are located at specific loci on specific chromosomes. The phenotype displayed by an organism is the result of the effect of the environment on the ability of the genes to express themselves. Diploid organisms have two genes for each characteristic. The alternative genes of a characteristic are called alleles and there may be many different alleles for a particular characteristic. Those organisms with two identical alleles are homozygous for a characteristic, and those with different alleles are heterozygous for a characteristic. Some alleles are dominant over other alleles that are said to be recessive.

You should understand that in some cases when two alleles are present they will both express themselves, and often a gene may have more than one recognizable effect on the phenotype of the organism. Some characteristics may be determined by a number of different pairs of alleles. In humans and some other animals, males have an X chromosome with a normal number of genes and a Y chromosome with fewer genes. Even though they are not identical, they behave as a pair of homologous chromosomes. Since the Y chromosome is shorter than the X chromosome and has fewer genes, many of the recessive characteristics present on the X chromosome show up more frequently in males than in females, which have two X chromosomes.

Genetics Problems

Genetics problems are sometimes difficult for students to figure out because often students do not follow a method when trying to answer the problems. We suggest that if you follow a few simple steps you will be able to answer most genetics problems.

Step 1

Determine the genotypes of the individuals in question. If you know one allele, but not the other, leave the one blank (i.e., if a person has blood type A there are two possible genotypes and you only know one of the alleles for sure I^A _).

Step 2

Determine the possible kinds of gametes each individual will produce and their relative probabilities.

Step 3

Combine the gametes in all the possible combinations. If there are a number of possible gametes, you may want to construct a Punnett Square.

Step 4

Interpret your findings to answer the specific questions asked. This is the hardest part. Good luck!

1. How many different kinds of gametes are possible with the following genotypes?

Genotypes	Answers
a. *Aa*	2—*A* & *a*
b. *AaBB*	2—*AB* & *aB*
c. *AaBb*	4—*AB, Ab, aB, ab*
d. *AaBbCc*	8—*ABC, ABc Abc, AbC, aBC, aBc, abC, abc*

2. What is the probability of getting the gametes *ab* from each of the following genotypes?

Genotypes	Answers
a. *aabb*	100%—only *ab* is possible
b. *Aabb*	50%—*Ab* and *ab* are possible
c. *AaBb*	25%—*AB, Ab, aB,* and *ab* are equally possible
d. *AABb*	0%—*ab* not possible

3. What is the probability of each of the following parents producing the stated genotypes in their offspring?

Parents	Offspring Genotype	Answer
$AA \times Aa$	Aa	1/2
$Aa \times Aa$	Aa	1/2
$Aa \times Aa$	aa	1/4
$AaBb \times AaBB$	$AABB$	1/8
$AaBb \times AaBB$	$AaBb$	1/4
$AaBb \times AaBb$	$AABB$	1/16

4. If an offspring has the genotype Aa, what possible combinations of parental genotypes could exist?

Answer

$AA \times aa$

$AA \times Aa$

$Aa \times Aa$

$Aa \times aa$

5. In humans, the gene for albinism is recessive to the gene for normal skin pigmentation. If two heterozygous individuals have children,

   a. What is the probability that a child will be an albino?
   b. If a child is normal, what is the probability that it is a carrier of the recessive albino gene.

Answers

   a. 1/4 or 25%
   b. 2/3 or 67%

6. In certain pea plants, the gene T for tallness is dominant over t for shortness.

   a. If a homozygous tall and homozygous short are crossed, what would the phenotype and genotype of the offspring be?
   b. If both individuals are heterozygous, what would the phenotypic and genotypic ratios of the offspring be?

Answers

   a. tall, Tt
   b. phenotypic ratio, 3 tall to 1 short
      genotypic ratio, 1 homozygous tall, 2 heterozygous tall,
      1 homozygous short

7. Smoos are strange animals that are always one of three shapes: round, cuboidal, or pyramidal. If two cuboidal smoos are mated, they always have cuboidal offspring. If two pyramidal smoos are mated, they always produce pyramidal offspring. If two round smoos are mated, they will produce all three kinds of offspring. Assume only one locus is involved.

   a. How is smoo shape determined?
   b. What would the phenotypic ratio be if a round and cuboidal smoo were mated?

Answers

   a. This is a case of lack of dominance. Two genes for pyramidal = pyramidal, two genes for cuboidal = cuboidal, one gene for pyramidal + one gene for cuboidal = round.
   b. 1/2 cuboidal and 1/2 round

8. What is the probability of a child having type AB blood if one of its parents is heterozygous for A blood, and the other is heterozygous for B? What other genotypes are possible?

   Answers
   1/4
   AO, BO, OO

9. A color-blind woman marries a normal man. They have ten children: six boys and four girls:
   a. How many would be normal?
   b. How many would be color blind?

   a. (4) All the girls would have the normal phenotype, but would be carriers.
   b. (6) All the boys would be color blind.

10. A blue-eyed man has blood type O, his wife has brown eyes and blood type AB, but her father had blue eyes.
    a. What is the probability that they will have a child who has brown eyes and blood type A?
    b. What is the probability that they would have a blue-eyed child with blood type B?
    c. How many different phenotypes could their children show?

    Answers
    a. 1/4
    b. 1/4
    c. 4

11. In certain kinds of cattle there are two genes for coat color: R = red, and r = white. When an individual is heterozygous, it is spotted with red and white (roan). When two red genes are present, it is red; and when two white genes are present, it is white. The gene H for the presence of horns is dominant over h for lack of horns.
    a. If a bull and a cow both have the genotype $RrHh$, how many possible phenotypes of offspring could they have?
    b. How likely is each phenotype?

    Answers
    a. six possible phenotypes
    b. red with horns—$RRHH$ or $RRHh$ = 3/16
       roan with horns—$RrHH$ or $RrHh$ = 6/16
       white with horns—$rrHH$ or $rrHh$ = 3/16
       red, hornless—$RRhh$ = 1/16
       roan, hornless—$Rrhh$ = 2/16
       white, hornless—$rrhh$ = 1/16

12. Hemophilia is a disease in which the blood does not clot normally. It is caused by a recessive gene that is located on the X chromosome. A boy has the disease, but neither his parents nor his grandparents have the disease. What are the genotypes of his parents and grandparents?

Answer		*Answer*	
Father	$X^N Y$	Mother's mother	$X^H X^N$
Mother	$X^H X^N$	Father's father	$X^N Y$
Mother's father	$X^N Y$	Father's mother	$X^N?$

alleles   Alternative forms of the genes for a particular characteristic (i.e., brown-eye genes and blue-eye genes are alternative alleles for eye color).

dihybrid cross   A genetic study in which two characteristics are followed from the parental generation to the offspring.

dominant allele   The gene that when present with its allele expresses itself and masks the effect of the other gene.

gene   A unit of heredity located on a chromosome and composed of a sequence of DNA nucleotides.

genetics   The study of genes, how genes produce characteristics, and how the characteristics are inherited.

genotype   The catalog of genes that an organism has, whether or not these genes are expressed.

heterozygous   A condition when a diploid organism has different allelic forms of a particular gene.

homozygous   A condition when a diploid organism has the same allelic forms of a particular gene.

hybrid   The offspring that result from a mixture of two different parental genotypes.

lack of dominance   The condition that exists when two unlike alleles are present and they both express themselves—neither is dominant.

linkage group   Genes that are located on the same chromosome and tend to be inherited together.

locus (loci)   The spot on a chromosome where an allele is located.

Mendelian genetics   The pattern of inheriting characteristics that follows the laws formulated by Johann Gregor Mendel.

monohybrid cross   A genetic study in which a single characteristic is followed from the parental generation to the offspring.

multiple alleles   The concept that there are several different forms of genes for a particular characteristic.

offspring   Descendants of a set of parents.

phenotype   The physical, chemical, and psychological expression of the genotypes possessed by an individual.

pleiotropy   The multiple effects that a pair of alleles may have in the phenotype of an organism.

polygenic inheritance   Concept that a number of different pairs of alleles may combine their efforts to determine a characteristic.

probability   Chance that something will happen. Often expressed as a ratio in percent or fraction.

recessive allele   The gene that when present with another allele does not express itself, and is masked by the effect of the other allele.

sex-linked   A gene located on one of the sex-determining chromosomes.

Purpose This chapter is designed to help you understand why plants and animals of the same kind vary slightly in different parts of the world, and how man artificially maintains certain groups of characteristics in his domesticated plants and animals. Future chapters on evolution will build on this information. You will notice that there will be some overlap between this chapter and future chapters.

Population Genetics

15

Introduction

In chapter fourteen we concerned ourselves with small numbers of organisms having specific genotypes in order to understand the principles of genetics. However, plants and animals don't usually occur as isolated individuals, but as members of populations. Before we can go any further, we need to define two concepts that will be used throughout this chapter. These are the concepts of **species** and **population.**

A species is a group of organisms of the same kind that have the ability to mate and produce offspring that are also capable of reproducing. Usually the members of a species will look quite similar to each other, although there are some exceptions. For example all the dogs in the world are of the same species, but a Saint Bernard does not look very much like a Pekinese. Humans may also have very different appearances, but they too may reproduce offspring. It is possible for mating to occur between two quite different appearing organisms. If you examine the chromosomes of reproducing organisms, you will find that they are identical in number and size and usually carry very similar groups of genes (fig. 15.1). In the final analysis, the species concept is one that deals with the genetic similarity of organisms.

The concepts of population and species are interwoven, since a population is considered to be all the organisms of the same species found within a specified geographic region. Population, however, is primarily concerned with numbers of organisms. This chapter is going to mix these two ideas together; it will deal with populations and why differences in **gene frequencies** happen. For example, why are there more blue-eyed people in Scandinavia than in Spain?

Every Body in the Pool!

In the introduction, we related the species concept to genetic similarity; however, we don't want to give the impression that there are no differences. You know that any one organism has a specific genotype consisting of all the

Fig. 15.1 *Phenotypic Differences in Breeds of Dogs.* All of these dogs have the same number of chromosomes and have very similar arrangements of genes on the chromosomes, even though these dogs look quite different from one another.

genes that organism has in its DNA. It can have a maximum of two alleles for a characteristic (one on each homologous chromosome). In a group of organisms of the same kind, there may be more than two kinds of alleles for a specific characteristic. Since all organisms of a species are theoretically able to exchange genes, we can think of all the genes of all the individuals of the same species as a giant **gene pool.** Since each individual organism is simply a container of a set of genes, the gene pool consists of all the genes of all of the individuals of a species, and will contain many more kinds of genes than any one of the individuals. It is just as if you had a refrigerator full of cartons of different kinds of milk—chocolate, regular, skim, buttermilk, etc.—(fig. 15.2). If you were blindfolded and were to reach in with both hands, grabbing two cartons, you might end up with two chocolate, a skim and a regular, or a number of other possible combinations. The refrigerator contains a greater variety than any individual could determine by just taking out any two cartons of milk. Figure 15.3 illustrates how the gene pool and individuals are related to one another.

Individuals are usually found in clusters in the pool as a result of many different factors. Since we have these local collections of organisms, it is possible that there may be differences in the kinds of genes and the numbers of each kind of gene in each of the clusters. Gene clusters may be quite different from one place to another, and are called **demes.** Figure 15.3 also indicates the relationship of demes to individuals and the total species.

Since individuals tend to interbreed with other organisms located close by, there is a tendency for local collections of genes to be maintained unless there is a way of adding or subtracting genes from this local population. In a

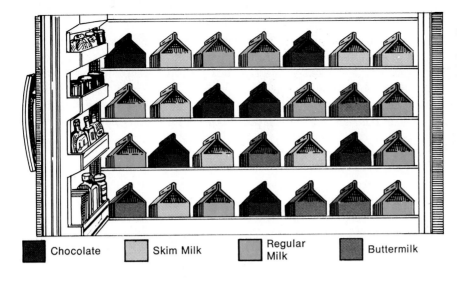

Fig. 15.2 Selection of Milk from a "Milk Pool." If you were blindfolded and reached into this refrigerator to remove two cartons of milk, there are a number of possible combinations that you could get.

■ Chocolate   ▢ Skim Milk   ▨ Regular Milk   ▨ Buttermilk

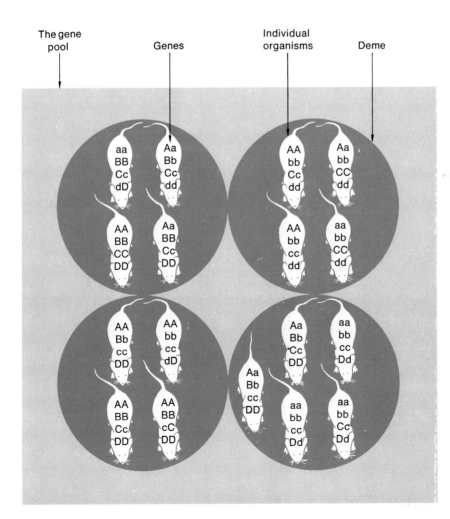

Fig. 15.3 Gene Pool. The gene pool consists of all the genes of all the individuals in the species. Notice that the four demes have different gene frequencies.

The gene pool

Genes

Individual organisms

Deme

sense, what is happening is that the genes are simply repackaged into new individuals from one generation to the next. Often there will be very little adding of new genes or subtracting of other genes from a deme, and a species will consist of a number of more or less separate groups (demes), which become known as **races, subspecies,** or **varieties.** When man artificially maintains certain demes, they are often known as **breeds.** Demes are really smaller portions of the gene pool, which might be called gene clusters.

Six of One, Half a Dozen of Another

When we talk about the gene pool and its demes, we often refer to the genetic differences between them as differences in gene frequency. Another way of stating this concept is to ask, "how common is this gene?" Usually it is stated in terms of a percentage or decimal fraction and is a mathematical statement of how frequently a particular gene will show up in the sex cells of that population (for example: 10%—0.1; 50%—0.5; etc.). It is possible for two demes to have all the same genes present, but with very different frequencies.

As an example, all humans are of the same species, and therefore constitute one large gene pool. However, many distinct local populations are scattered across the surface of the earth. These more localized populations (races) show many differences that have tended to be perpetuated from generation to generation. In Africa, the frequency of dark skin genes, tightly

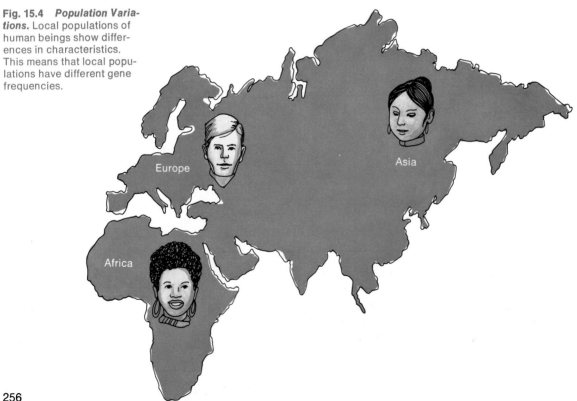

Fig. 15.4 *Population Variations.* Local populations of human beings show differences in characteristics. This means that local populations have different gene frequencies.

Europe

Asia

Africa

curled hair genes, and flat nose genes have very high frequencies. In Europe the frequencies of light skin genes, straight hair genes and narrow nose genes are the highest. Countries such as China tend to have moderately colored skin, straight hair, and broad noses. All three of these populations would have genes for dark skin and light skin, straight hair and curly hair, narrow noses and broad noses. However, the three differ in the frequencies of these genes (fig. 15.4). There are many other genes that show differences in frequency from one race to another, but these three characteristics are easy to see. Once a particular mixture of genes is present in a population, there is a tendency for that mixture to maintain itself unless something is operating to change the frequencies. In other words, gene frequencies are not going to change without reason. There will usually be a cause for any change in gene frequency. As transportation has become better developed, more individuals have moved from one geographic area to another, and gene frequencies in man have begun to change. Ultimately, as barriers to intermarriage (both geographic and sociological) between races are destroyed, the human gene pool will begin to show fewer and fewer racial differences. But it may be thousands of years before significant changes are seen.

For some reason, people tend to think that gene frequency has something to do with the dominance or recessiveness of genes. This is wrong. Often in a population, recessive genes are more frequent than dominate genes. Straight hair, blue eyes, and light skin are all recessive characteristics, yet they are quite common in populations of certain European countries. See table 15.1 for examples.

Table 15.1 *Recessive Traits with a High Frequency of Expression*
Many recessive characteristics are extremely common in some human populations. The corresponding dominant characteristic is also shown here.

Recessive	Dominant
Light skin color	Dark skin color
Straight hair	Curly hair
Five fingers	Six fingers
Type O blood gene	Type A or B blood type
Normal hip joints	Dislocated hip birth defect
Blue eyes	Brown eyes
Normal eyelids	Drooping eyelids
No tumor of the retina	Tumor of the retina
Normal fingers	Short fingers
Normal thumb	Extra joint in the thumb
Normal fingers	Webbed fingers
Ability to smell	Inability to smell
Normal tooth number	Extra teeth
Presence of molars	Absence of molars
Normal palate	Cleft palate

What really determines the frequency of a gene is the value that the gene has to the individual possessing it. The dark skin genes may be very valuable to a person living under the bright sun in tropical Africa, while light skin may be more valuable to someone living in less intense sunlight of the cooler European countries. This idea of value and what it can do to gene frequencies will be dealt with more fully later.

Why Do Demes Exist?

Since organisms are not genetically identical, it is possible that some individuals may possess combinations of genes that are more valuable than other combinations of genes. As a result, some individuals would find the environment to be more hostile than would others. This would mean that individuals having bad combinations of genes would leave the population more often by death or migration.

Since different demes will occupy different environments, the environments may select different combinations of genes as being good or bad. For example, a blind fish living in a lake would be at a severe disadvantage. However, a blind fish living in a cave where there is no light would not be at a disadvantage. Thus these two environments might allow or encourage different genes to be present in the two populations (fig. 15.5).

A second mechanism that tends to create small demes with gene frequencies different from other demes involves the founding of a population that was not there before. The collection of genes from a small founding

Fig. 15.5 *Blind Cave Fish.* This fish lives in caves where there is no light. The eyes do not function, and the animal has very little color in its skin. (Courtesy of the National Park Service.)

Chapter 15

population is likely to be different from the genes present in the larger parent population. Once a small founding population has established itself, it will tend to maintain the same collection of genes, since the organisms of the same local population tend to mate amongst themselves. This results in a reshuffling of genes from generation to generation, but does not allow for the introduction of new genes into the population. Many species of plants and animals are divided up into quite distinct demes by the presence of barriers to movement. Animals and plants that live in lakes tend to be divided into small separate populations by barriers of land. Whenever such barriers exist, there is a very strong likelihood that small differences will occur in the gene frequencies from lake to lake, since each lake was colonized separately and their environments are not identical. If the differences in gene frequencies are great enough, the local group of organisms may be called a subspecies, race, or variety. Other species of organisms experience few barriers and therefore subspecies are quite rare.

A population of organisms in which there is little genetic variety is likely to be on the verge of **extinction.** Such a stagnant gene pool will not provide new combinations of genes to prevent the death of the species as the environment changes. A large gene pool with a great variety of genes is more likely to contain some genes that will better adapt the organisms to a new environment. A number of mechanisms introduce this necessary variety into a population.

Mutations

Mutation is a method of introducing new genes into a population. Gene changes occur rather slowly. All alleles have originated as a result of mutation that occurred sometime in the past, and these changed genes have been maintained within the gene pool of the species. If a mutation produces a bad gene, that gene will remain rare in the population. While most mutations are bad, occasionally one occurs that is very valuable to the organism. For example, at some time in the past, mutations occurred in the populations of certain insects that made them tolerant to DDT. These alleles had been very rare in these insect populations until DDT was invented. Then, these genes became very valuable to the insect species. Since insects that lacked this gene died when they came in contact with DDT, more of the DDT-tolerant insects were left to reproduce the species, and therefore the DDT-tolerant gene became much more common within these populations.

Sexual Reproduction

The process of **sexual reproduction** also tends to generate new genotypes (collections of genes) when the genes from two individuals are mixed during fertilization to generate a unique individual. This doesn't directly change the gene pool, but the new individual may have a new combination of characteristics so superior to that of other individuals in the population that the new individual will be much more successful in producing offspring. In a corn population, genes may be present for resistance to corn blight (a fungus disease) and resistance to attack by insects. Corn plants that possess both of these genes are going to be more successful than corn plants that have only one of these genes. They will probably produce more offspring (corn seeds) than the others, and will tend to pass on this same combination of resistant genes to their offspring (fig. 15.6).

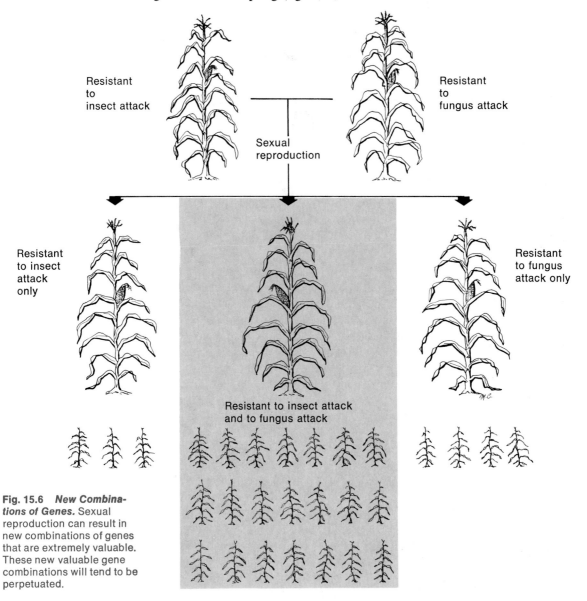

Resistant to insect attack

Sexual reproduction

Resistant to fungus attack

Resistant to insect attack only

Resistant to fungus attack only

Resistant to insect attack and to fungus attack

Fig. 15.6 *New Combinations of Genes.* Sexual reproduction can result in new combinations of genes that are extremely valuable. These new valuable gene combinations will tend to be perpetuated.

Migration

Migration of individuals from one deme to another is also an important way for genes to be added to or subtracted from a population. The extent of migration need not be great. As long as genes are entering or leaving a population, a change will occur in the gene pool.

The size of a population is going to have a lot to do with how effective any of these mechanisms are at generating variety. The smaller the population, the less genetic variety it can contain. Therefore, happenings such as migrations, mutations, and accidental death can have great effects on the genetic mixtures in small populations. For example, if a town had a population of twenty people and only two had blue eyes, what happens to those blue-eyed people would be more critical than if the town had twenty thousand people and two thousand had blue eyes. While the ratio of blue eyes to brown eyes is the same in both cases, even a small change in a population of twenty could change the gene pool significantly.

Man Sticks His Finger in the Gene Pool

Man often works with small select populations of plants and animals in order to artificially construct specific gene combinations that are useful or desirable from his point of view. This is particularly true with the plants and animals he uses for food. If he can collect together domesticated animals and plants with genes for resistance to disease, rapid growth, high reproductive capacity, and other similar characteristics, he will be better able to supply himself with energy in the form of food. Plants are particularly easy to work with in this manner since it is often possible to increase the numbers of specific organisms by **asexual reproduction.** Potatoes, apple trees, strawberries, and many other plants can be reproduced by simply cutting the original plant into a number of parts and allowing these parts to sprout roots, stems, and leaves. If a single potato has certain desirable characteristics, it may be reproduced asexually. All of these individual plants will have exactly the same genes and are usually referred to as a **clone.** Figure 15.7 shows how a clone may be developed.

Man can also collect together specific combinations of genes by selective breeding. This is usually not as easy as cloning. Since sexual reproduction is involved, this tends to mix up genes rather than preserve desirable combinations of genes. However, if two different demes of the same species each have particular desirable characteristics, they may be crossed to produce a heterozygous **hybrid** having the desirable characteristics of both demes. It is important that the desirable characteristic in each of the two demes have homozygous genotypes if hybridization is going to be of any value. It is possible to sexually reproduce a small population until specific characteristics are homozygous. To make two characteristics homozygous in the same individual is more difficult; therefore, hybrids are developed by crossing two

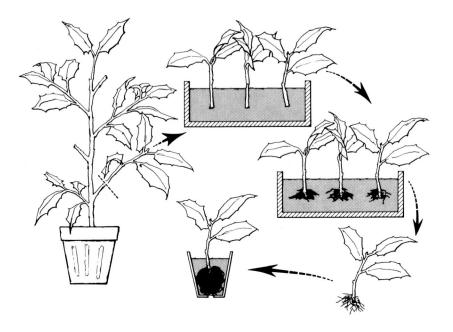

Fig. 15.7 *Clones.* The rooting of cuttings is one of the methods used to make clones of plants. All of the individuals in a clone have the same genotype.

different populations to collect together in one organism all of the desirable characteristics (fig. 15.8).

A serious side effect occurs as a result of maintaining specific gene combinations in domesticated plants and animals. What man is doing with these organisms is reducing the genetic variety within the population. Whether we are talking about a clone or a hybrid population, there is danger that the environment will change. Since these organisms are so similar, most of them will be affected in the same way. If the environmental change is a new variety of disease to which the organism is susceptible, the whole population may be killed or severely damaged. Since new diseases do come along, there is constant activity among plant and animal breeders to develop new clones, strains, or hybrids that will be resistant to the new diseases.

When man selects certain specific good characteristics, he often gets bad ones along with them. This requires constant attention by man to his "special" plants and animals. Insecticides, herbicides, cultivation, and irrigation practices are all used to aid the plants and animals that man needs to maintain himself as the number one animal in the world.

Another related problem in plant and animal breeding is the tendency for heterozygous organisms to mate and reassemble new combinations of genes by chance from the original heterozygotes. Thus hybrid organisms must be carefully managed to prevent the formation of gene combinations that would be unacceptable to man. Since most economically important animals cannot be propagated asexually, the development and maintenance of specific gene combinations in animals is a more difficult undertaking.

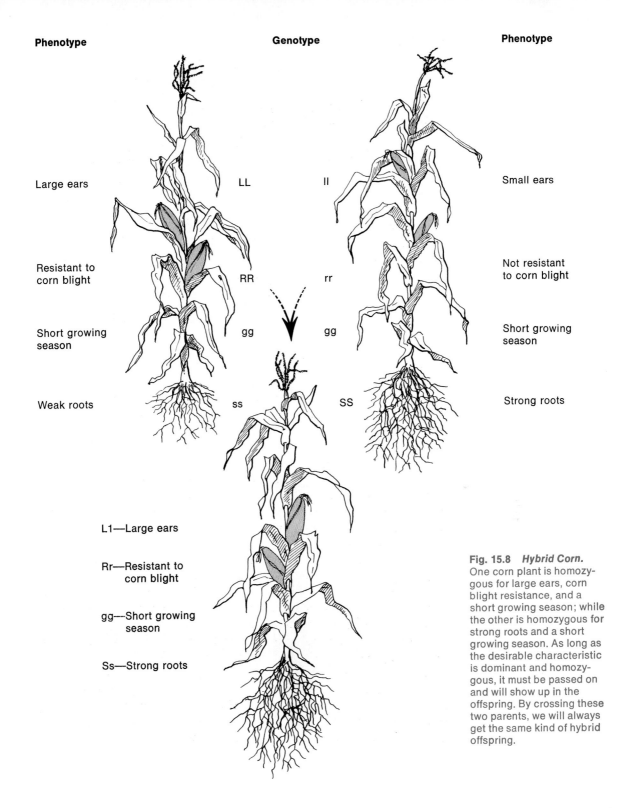

Phenotype   **Genotype**   **Phenotype**

Large ears   LL   ll   Small ears

Resistant to
corn blight   RR   rr   Not resistant
                                                        to corn blight

Short growing   gg   gg   Short growing
season   season

Weak roots   ss   SS   Strong roots

L1—Large ears

Rr—Resistant to
corn blight

gg—-Short growing
season

Ss—Strong roots

Fig. 15.8 *Hybrid Corn.*
One corn plant is homozy-
gous for large ears, corn
blight resistance, and a
short growing season; while
the other is homozygous for
strong roots and a short
growing season. As long as
the desirable characteristic
is dominant and homozy-
gous, it must be passed on
and will show up in the
offspring. By crossing these
two parents, we will always
get the same kind of hybrid
offspring.

Human Genetics Is Related to Populations

At the beginning of this chapter, it was pointed out that the human gene pool consists of a number of categories called races. The particular characteristics that set one race apart from another originated many thousands of years ago before travel was as common as it is today. And yet we still associate certain racial types with certain geographic areas. Even though there is much more movement of people and a mixing of racial types, a strong tendency still remains for people to marry others of their same social, racial, and economic background. This nonrandom mate selection can sometimes bring together genes that are relatively rare because they may have been common in the ancestral gene pool from which specific racial groups of modern people are descended. An understanding of the gene frequencies within specific human subpopulations can be very important to anyone who wishes to know the probability of having children with particular combinations of genes. This is particularly true if the gene combinaton is bad. Tay-Sachs disease causes degeneration of the nervous system and early death of children (fig. 15.9). Since it is caused by a recessive gene, both

Fig. 15.9 *Frequency of Tay Sachs Genes.* The frequency of a gene may vary from one population to another. Genetics counselors can make use of this information to advise people as to their chances of having these specific genes and of passing these genes to their children.

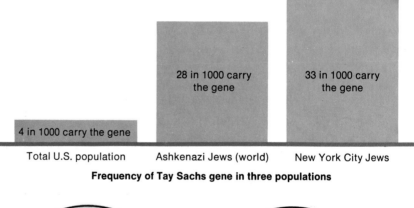

4 in 1000 carry the gene | 28 in 1000 carry the gene | 33 in 1000 carry the gene

Total U.S. population | Ashkenazi Jews (world) | New York City Jews

Frequency of Tay Sachs gene in three populations

Fig. 15.10 *Normal and Abnormal Red Blood Cells.* Sickle-cell anemia is caused by a recessive allele that slightly changes the hemoglobin molecule of the red blood cells. As a result, the red blood cells will become sickle shaped if they are deprived of oxygen.

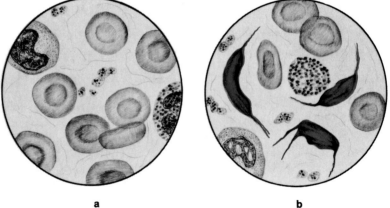

a

b

parents must pass the gene to their child in order for the child to have the disease. By knowing the frequency of the gene in the background of both parents, it is possible to determine how likely it will be for them to have a child of this genotype. It is known that individuals of the Ashkenazy Jewish background have a higher gene frequency of this recessive gene than do any other group of racial or social origin. It is logical, therefore, that people of this particular background be aware of the probability that they will have children who develop this disease. Likewise, sickle-cell anemia is more common in people of specific African ancestry than in any other human deme, and these people should be aware of the fact that they might be carrying this recessive gene (fig. 15.10). If they are, they might want to ask themselves the question, how likely is it that I will have a child with this disease? These and other cases make it very important that trained **genetic counselors** have information about the frequencies of genes in specific human demes if they are going to be able to help couples with problems.

Summary

The gene pool is the collection of all of the genes of a population. Those individuals that can reproduce sexually are members of the same species. Subpopulations (demes) may have different frequencies even though they are members of the same gene pool. The gene frequencies of a deme will stay the same if mutation does not occur, if the population is large, if random mating occurs, and if no organism migrates into or out of the deme. New variety in the gene pool can be generated by mutation, selective reproduction, and migration of organisms into or out of the population. Knowledge of population genetics is useful for the plant and animal breeder as well as people who specialize in genetic counseling. Breeders can maintain certain desirable gene frequencies in populations if they understand the factors that control changes in gene frequencies. The development of clones and hybrid organisms are two examples of how population genetics is used. The genetic counselor cannot control human populations the way plant and animal breeders do, but can make use of gene frequency information to determine the probability of abnormal children being born. This helps couples make decisions about whether or not to have children.

Consider This

Albinism is a recessive gene. Is it possible that this gene could be eliminated from the human gene pool? Include in your consideration: causes of mutations, how genes result in characteristics, gene frequency, and inheritance patterns.

1. How does the size of a population affect the gene pool?
2. List three different factors that change gene frequencies in a population.
3. Why do races or subspecies develop?
4. Give an example of a gene pool containing a number of separate demes.
5. How is a clone developed? What are its benefits?
6. How is a hybrid formed? What are its benefits?
7. What forces act to maintain racial differences in the human gene pool?
8. How do the concepts of species, deme, and population differ?
9. What is meant by the term *gene frequency?*
10. How do the gene frequencies in clones and normal reproducing populations differ?

Chapter Glossary

asexual reproduction   Propagation of an organism without the union of sex cells.

breed   A deme that differs significantly from others of the same species. Usually used to refer to man-made demes of animals.

clone   A line of genetically identical organisms that are maintained by asexual reproduction.

deme   A local, recognizable population that differs in gene frequencies from other local populations of the same species.

extinction   The nonsurvival of a particular species. Usually results from the inability of the species to cope with environmental change.

gene frequency   The percentage of sex cells that contain a particular allele.

gene pool   All of the genes of all of the individuals of the same species.

genetic counselor   A professional biologist with specific training in human genetics and gene frequencies.

hybrid   The offspring that results from a mixture of the two parental genotypes.

mutation   Any change in the genetic information.

population   All of the organisms of the same species within a specified geographic region.

race   Demes that differ significantly from others of the same species.

sexual reproduction   Propagation of organisms that involves the union of gametes from two parents.

species   A group of organisms of the same kind that can mate and produce fertile offspring.

subspecies   Local demes that differ from others of the same species.

variety   A deme that differs significantly from others of the same species. Usually used to refer to man-made demes of plants.

Purpose   Previous chapters have presented background in the areas of chemistry, information systems (DNA), sexual reproduction, heredity, and populations. These are all highly related to one another and are also related to the surroundings of organisms. Since the surroundings are always changing, the survival of living things is dependent on their ability to adjust their processes to the changing surroundings. These changes that assure survival can occur to any individual in the population, but unless they are genetically (DNA) determined and transmitted to the next generation, they will be of little value to the survival of the species. It is the purpose of this chapter to identify the ways in which differences come about and how these differences may change a sexually reproducing species over thousands of generations.

Variation and Selection

16

Sex and the Single Mutation

Each individual born into a population carries with it a unique set of genetic information. It is unique for two reasons. First, natural changes called **spontaneous mutations** have occurred in the DNA of its parents. The cells in which mutations have the greatest importance are the sex cells, since they will provide the genetic information for the next generation. The causes of these mutations have not been pinpointed, but are most likely due to naturally occurring cosmic radiation from the sun and natural sources here on earth. Spontaneous mutations occur at random, at an estimated rate in humans of one gene in one hundred thousand. It is reasonable to estimate the total number of genes within the forty-six human chromosomes at approximately two hundred thousand. This would mean that each person is likely to be carrying two new genes that were generated within himself and were not transmitted to him from his parents. However, these two new genes may "show themselves" in the offspring. Mutations are known to be caused by a variety of factors. Certain chemicals and man-made radiation increase the mutation rate to above that of the spontaneous rate. If a person is exposed to such mutagenic agents, he may be carrying more than two new genes. For this reason, special safeguards are taken to protect persons who are working in close contact with mutagenic agents. The safeguards may include radiation badges to record exposure to radiation, or special training in handling chemical mutagens (fig. 16.1).

The second reason for the genetic uniqueness of each individual has to do with the processes of meiosis and fertilization. You will recall from chapter twelve that during meiosis variety may be generated in gametes as a result of crossing-over and independent assortment of chromosomes. Both of these processes result in a reshuffling of genes prior to their being dealt to the sperm or egg. The exact combination of genes going into the offspring (next generation) at fertilization will differ from that found in the parent.

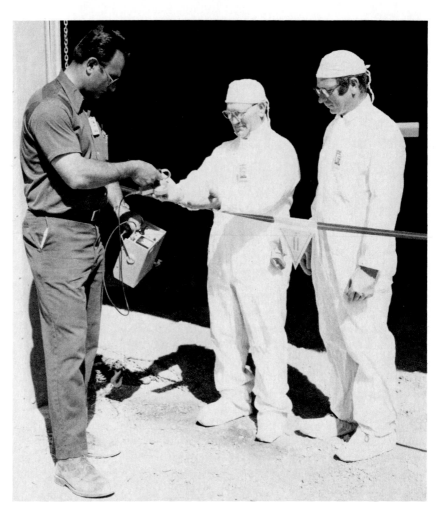

Fig. 16.1 *Monitoring Radioactive Contamination.* Radiation is known to cause mutations. Consequently, those people who work with radioactive material take special precautions. Here a health physicist monitors two workers before they leave an area having potential radiation contamination at the Atomic Energy Commission's Reactor Testing Station in Idaho. (Courtesy of the Energy Research and Development Administration.)

Thousands of unique gene packages in the form of gametes may be produced by any one individual during meiosis as a result of crossing-over and independent assortment.

When fertilization occurs, genes donated by each of the parents are recombined into a single cell—the zygote. Since unique genes (due to mutation) and gene packages (due to crossing-over and independent assortment) are brought together in a single cell **(genetic recombination),** this new individual will have gene combinations (genotypes) not found in either parent.

"We Hold These Truths to be Self-Evident"

Observations made by scientists and laymen throughout history have confirmed the uniqueness of each individual. Another basic truth is that sexually reproducing organisms tend to overreproduce. They have the potential of reproducing far more offspring than is necessary to replace the parents. For example, it is estimated that robins have a life span of ten years and that a single pair may raise two broods of four young each year. If these two parent birds and all their young were to survive and reproduce for a ten-year period, there would be a total of 19,531,250 birds in the family (fig. 16.2)!

It is also true that the size of populations remains relatively constant over long periods of time. Minor changes in number may occur, but if the species is living in harmony with its environment, the total reproductive potential is not reached. This is because the population is reproducing individuals at the same rate at which death is occurring. Don't be fooled by the idea of a "static population." Just because the total number of organisms of the species remains relatively constant doesn't mean that the makeup of the population does not change. In fact, the maintenance of a long-lived population in an everchanging environment can only occur if the species is changing in ways that better suit it for the new environment. In order for this to occur, members of the population must be eliminated in a nonrandom manner. Those that survive are those that are, for the most part, better suited to the environment. They have a better opportunity to reproduce their kind by transmitting their genes to the next generation. Those less suited to the environment will have fewer offspring.

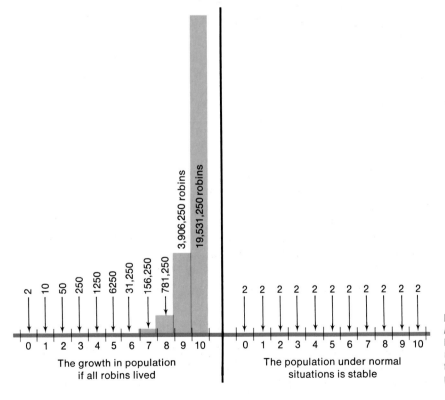

Fig. 16.2 *Overproduction in Organisms.* All organisms have the ability to over-reproduce. Usually many of the organisms die, and the population remains stable.

You've Got to Show Your Genes to Play the Game!

It is the changing environment that results in the elimination of organisms from the population. It also results in a change in the characteristics of the group. Not all surviving organisms contribute equally to this creative change in the gene pool. Simply because an organism has a good gene doesn't necessarily mean that it will survive to reproduce. Genes do not always show themselves, but may remain concealed within the individual. This concealment may occur because the gene does not express itself during the life of the individual, or because its effects are overshadowed by another more powerful gene (fig. 16.3). The latter case is an example of a recessive gene in a heterozygous individual (chap. 14). During sex cell formation, this recessive gene will be separated, and it could be recombined with another of its type at fertilization. This newly-formed homozygous offspring may then show the recessive characteristic, and the environment may recognize the feature as being a suitable one. In this way, many genes can be carried unseen within individuals of a population. They show up in later generations, allowing certain individuals to survive and reproduce a population better able to cope with the changed environment. In some cases "good" genes occur in

Fig. 16.3 Gene Expression. Genes must be expressed to allow the environment to select for or against them. The recessive gene *l* brings about superior characteristics in those individuals that have a homozygous genotype. The superior characteristic is hidden in heterozygous individuals.

Genotype	LL	Ll	ll
Phenotype	Normal individual	Normal individual	Superior individual

Fig. 16.4 *Acquired Characteristics.* The ability of this leader dog to guide his blind companion is a characteristic that is acquired through special training. This ability cannot be passed on to this dog's puppies. (Courtesy of Leader Dogs for the Blind, Rochester, Michigan.)

the population and show themselves to the environment but are lost because of random, accidental death.

Many organisms survive because they have characteristics that are not genetically determined, but are acquired during the life of the individual. Such **acquired characteristics** cannot be transmitted to the next generation, and therefore do not change the population. You might consider an excellent tennis player's skill, for example. This ability is acquired through practice, not genes. This tennis player's offspring will not "inherently" be excellent tennis players (fig. 16.4).

In a species population, we see the occurrence of different kinds of individuals, some of which have an advantage over others. These will survive better and reproduce greater numbers of offspring than those without the favorable characteristics. This is the **Theory of Natural Selection** proposed by Charles Darwin and Alfred Wallace. It was published in 1859 by Darwin in his book *On the Origin of Species by Means of Natural Selection, or the Preservation of Favored Races in the Struggle for Life.* This title needs clari-

Box VI

**The Voyage
of H.M.S. Beagle,
1831–1836 A.D.**

As with many people, Charles Darwin was influenced by a number of events that occurred during his early life and changed the course of the remainder of his life. Probably the most significant event was his appointment in 1831 as naturalist on a British survey ship, H.M.S. Beagle. Surveys were common at this time, since they helped to refine maps and chart hazards to shipping. Darwin was just twenty-two years old at the time and probably would not have gotten the appointment had not his uncle persuaded Darwin's father to allow him to go. The fact that Darwin's father was a wealthy man was probably influential in Darwin being assigned to the post of naturalist, a position that did not have any pay attached to it.

The voyage of the Beagle lasted nearly five years. During the trip, South America, the Galapagos Islands, Australia, and many Pacific islands were visited. Darwin's natural history notes served as a vast storehouse of information, which he used in his writings during the rest of his life. As a result of his experiences, he wrote books on the formation of coral reefs and volcanos, and finally the *Origin of Species*. This last book, written twenty-three years after his return from the voyage, changed biological thinking for all time.

The Voyage of H.M.S. Beagle, 1831–1836 A.D.

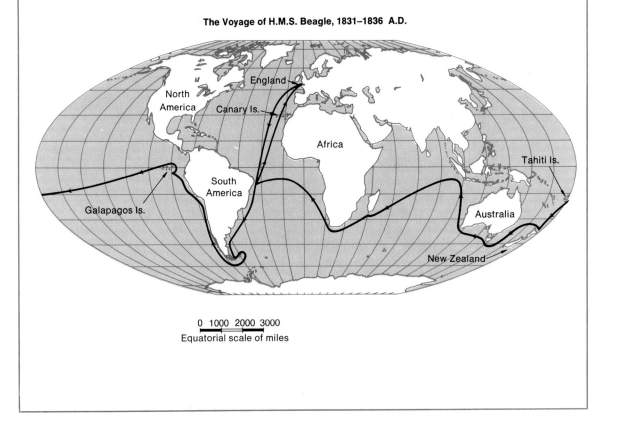

Fig. 16.5 *Favorable Genes with Multiple Effects.* There are many genetically different tomato plants in this field. Those with the genetic characteristic for tallness are better able to receive light and, therefore, are more likely to bear more fruit.

fication on two points. First, **natural selection** means the same as the phrase **differential reproduction,** and both mean that some organisms have more offspring than others. Therefore, a gene that better suits an individual to his environment is one that allows the individual to have more offspring than other organisms. This gene will become an increasingly important part of the gene pool in future populations. Secondly, the phrase *struggle for life* is not the same as the term *conflict*. Natural selection is a creative process in populations and results in a better gene pool. It is not necessary for fighting to occur during the natural selection process. We've never seen two tomato plants battle it out! However, they do **compete.** In an overcrowded tomato patch, all of the tomatoes will need sunlight. Those individuals with genes for tallness will receive more sunlight and will successfully bear more fruit (with offspring inside the seeds). The shorter plants will not be as successful in this competition and will leave fewer offspring (fig. 16.5).

When the Game Gets Dirty, We Change Our Genes!

The process of natural selection results in a slow, steady change in the frequency of occurrence of certain genes in a population. Thus, over generations of time, some genes will increase in number while others decrease. This can be seen if we return to the gene pool concept presented in chapter fifteen and deal with one pair of alleles as an example. By applying the Punnett Square method to the entire gene pool (not simply two mating individuals), we can determine the percentage of the population that is homozygous or heterozygous for a characteristic. Consider a gene pool composed of two alleles, *A* and *a*. In this hypothetical gene pool, we cannot know which individuals are male or female, nor can we know their genotypes. Therefore, we must guess as to which individuals will mate. For example, suppose that the A gene frequency was 60 percent (0.6), and that the a gene frequency was 40 percent (0.4). There are only two alleles and they make up 100 percent of the gene population. What possible genotypes could be produced in this gene pool? To find the answer, treat these genes and their frequencies as if they were individual genes being distributed into sperm or eggs. The males of the population could produce gametes with either A or a, and the females could produce gametes with either A or a. Set this up in a Punnett Square:

Possible female gametes:

	$A = 0.60$	$a = 0.40$
$A = 0.60$ Possible male gametes: $a = 0.40$	offspring genotype % $AA = 0.60 \times 0.60 = 0.36$	offspring genotype % $Aa = 0.40 \times 0.60 = 0.24$
	offspring genotype % $Aa = 0.40 \times 0.60 = 0.24$	offspring genotype % $aa = 0.40 \times 0.40 = 0.16$

Inside each of the boxes is the frequency of occurrence of each of the three possible genotypes that could exist in this population: $AA = 36$ percent, $Aa = 48$ percent, $aa = 16$ percent. What frequency of A and a in the population will result from sexual reproduction of this group? This can be determined by using the frequency figures for each of the genotypes in this parent population. Organisms with the homozygous dominant genotype, AA, make up 36 percent of the total gene pool. They would then contribute 36 percent of the A genes to the next generation in their gametes. Organisms with the homozygous recessive genotype, aa, make up 16 percent of the total gene pool, and they would contribute 16 percent of the a genes to the next generation in their gametes. Those with the heterozygous genotypes, Aa, make up 48 percent of the population and can contribute either the A or the a gene to the next generation. That means that half of the gametes produced by the heterozygotes (24%) would contain the A gene, and the other half (24%) would contain the a gene. The total frequency of each type of gene that is being donated to the next generation is: 36 percent A + 24 percent A = 60 percent A and 16 percent a + 24 percent a = 40 percent a. If fertilization occurs in the four possible ways indicated above, *the resultant genotypes in the next generation will occur in the exact same frequencies as in the parent generation.*

At least on paper, gene frequencies will not change generation after generation provided certain assumptions are true. On paper it is possible to (1) mate all organisms totally at random, (2) eliminate changes in frequencies due to mutations, (3) eliminate the gain or loss of genes due to in-migration or out-migration, and finally, (4) to deal with large enough numbers of genes so that the frequencies do not change by accident. These four conditions must occur in order to have gene frequencies remain unchanged.

What You See Isn't Always What You Get

It would appear that changes in populations would **not** occur (contrary to that proposed by Darwin and Wallace) if these factors were operating in real life. This statement of gene frequency balance is known as the **Hardy-Weinberg Law.** This law states that populations of organisms will maintain the same gene frequencies from generation to generation if mating is random, if the population is large, if mutation does not occur, and if there is no migration in or out of the population. It holds comparable status to Mendel's laws of independent assortment and segregation (see chap. 14). However, what happens on paper and what happens in real life are two different things! Both Hardy and Weinberg realized this, and therefore this law is used only as a base from which to develop an understanding of the reasons for gene frequency changes in gene pools (fig. 16.6).

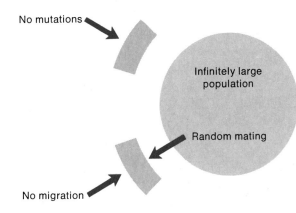

No mutations

Infinitely large population

Random mating

No migration

Fig. 16.6 *The Hardy-Weinberg Law.* This law only works on paper. The population in the circle must not have its gene frequencies change by mutations or migration. The infinitely large population must also mate randomly.

Return to the gene pool idea and you can understand why the four assumptions of the Hardy-Weinberg Law do not function in real populations. First of all, random mating does not occur. Many segments of a gene pool are isolated to some extent, and are prevented from mating with other segments during the lifetime of the individuals. In human populations, these isolations may be geographic, political, or social. Therefore, the Hardy-Weinberg Law becomes invalid because nonrandom mating is a factor and leads to natural selection or differential reproduction (fig. 16.7a). Secondly, you will recall that the DNA is constantly being changed (mutated) spontaneously. It is likely that the A and a genes will undergo other changes. They may change to totally new kinds such as a' or a''; or a may change back again to A. Both of these mutations would automatically change the gene frequencies in the gene pool (fig. 16.7b).

Fig. 16.7 *Changing Gene Frequencies.* Four factors operate in life to change to gene frequencies and allow for change in a population.

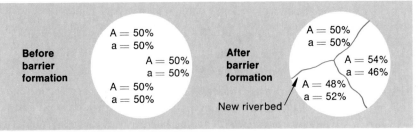

A. Natural divisions of a population prevent random mating and gene frequency changes:

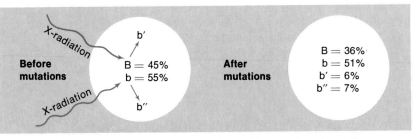

B. Various mutagenic agents cause genes to change from one form to another:

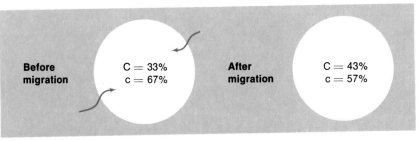

C. Migration of individuals may also change gene frequencies:

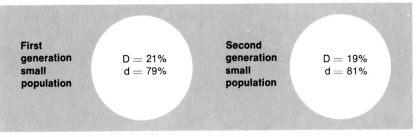

D. In small populations chance plays an important part in gene frequency changes:

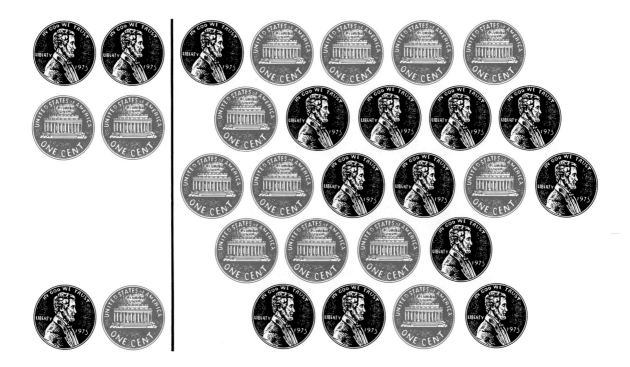

Thirdly, environmental changes themselves may lead to in-migration or out-migration of individuals, thus changing the frequencies of genes within that deme. This has been seen in many parts of the world when severe weather disturbances have lifted animals and plants and moved them over great distances, isolating them from their original gene pool (fig. 16.7c). The island of Krakatoa was blown to bits in 1883 by a volcanic explosion. For two months it remained so hot that the rain that fell on the remaining island turned into steam. This effectively eliminated all life on the island, and the nearest possible source of new organisms was twenty-five miles away on the island of Java. And yet, in only one year following this disaster, plants were found growing on Krakatoa, and by 1908, two hundred species of animals were identified.

The final assumption deals with population size and requires that the population be infinitely large. This requirement exists as a result of the statistical analysis involved. For example, if you flip a coin once, you say there is a fifty, fifty (50:50) chance that the coin will turn up heads. If you flip two coins, you may come up with two heads or two tails, or one head and one tail. In order to come closer to the 50 percent head, 50 percent tail probability in your coin flipping, you would want to flip many coins. In fact, the more coins you flip, the more likely it is that you would end up with 50 percent of all coins showing heads and the other 50 percent showing tails (fig. 16.8). The same is true of gene frequencies. Gene frequency differences

Fig. 16.8 *Probability.* The more coins you flip, the more likely it is that you will come close to the 50% heads/50% tails probability.

that result from chance are more likely to show up in small populations than in large populations (fig. 16.7d). An example of this kind of frequency change is seen in a Pennsylvania settlement of the German Baptist Brethren, or Dunkers. Because they are socially and biologically isolated from the rest of the American population, several of their genes appear at frequencies that differ greatly from the population of the whole country. One of these is called hitchhiker's thumb and is the ability to bend the thumb backwards so that it points toward the elbow. The normal condition is shown below (fig. 16.9 A).

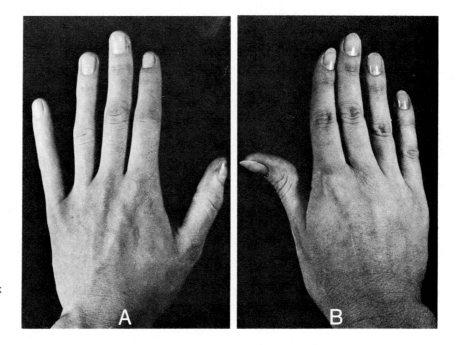

Fig. 16.9 *Hitchhiker's Thumb.* Persons with the normal gene *(A)* cannot bend the thumb as far back as persons with the gene for hitchhiker's thumb *(B).* (Courtesy of G. Gentner.)

All Genes Are Not Created Equal

Now we return to our original example of genes *A* and *a* to show how natural selection based on nonrandom mating can result in gene frequency changes in only one generation. Again, assume that the parent generation has the following genotype frequencies: *AA* = 36 percent, *Aa* = 48 percent, *aa* = 16 percent, with a total population of 100,000 individuals. Suppose that 50 percent of all the individuals having at least one *A* gene do not reproduce because they are more susceptible to disease. The parent population of 100,000 had 36,000 individuals with genotype *AA;* 48,000 with *Aa;* and 16,000 with *aa.* Because of the 50 percent loss, only 18,000 *AA* individuals and 24,000 *Aa* individuals will reproduce. However, all of the *aa* individuals will reproduce. This now makes a total reproducing population of not

100,000, but only 58,000. What percentage of A and a will go into the gametes of these reproducing individuals?:

$$\frac{18,000}{58,000} = 32 \text{ percent } AA \qquad \frac{24,000}{58,000} = 41 \text{ percent } Aa \qquad \frac{16,000}{58,000} = 27 \text{ percent } aa$$

The percentage of A containing gametes produced by these individuals will be 32 percent from the AA parents and 20.5 percent from the Aa parents (table 16.1). The total is 52.5 percent for the frequency of the A gene. The percentage of a containing gametes produced by these parents will be 20.5 percent from the Aa parents and 27 percent from the aa parents. A total of 47.5 percent for the frequency of the a gene. The original parental gene

Table 16.1 *Differential Mortality*
The percentage of each genotype in the original population becomes changed in the offspring as a result of differential reproduction.

Original gene frequencies and genotypes	Total number of persons within population of 100,000	Number lost due to 50% death	Total of each genotype in reproducing population of 58,000	New percentage of each genotype in population
AA = 36%	36,000	36,000 −18,000 —— 18,000	18,000	$\frac{18,000}{58,000} = 32\% \, AA$
Aa = 48%	48,000	48,000 −24,000 —— 24,000	24,000	$\frac{24,000}{58,000} = 41\% \, Aa$
aa = 16%	16,000	16,000 −0 —— 16,000	16,000	$\frac{16,000}{58,000} = 27\% \, aa$

frequencies were $A = 60$ percent and $a = 40$ percent. These have now changed to $A = 52.5$ percent and $a = 47.5$ percent. This gene frequency will show itself as more individuals in the population having the aa genotype and fewer having the AA and Aa genotypes. This is natural selection in action. Differential reproduction has changed the frequency of characteristics of this population of organisms.

The Environment Calls the Shots

Throughout this chapter we have stated that as the environment changes, it acts as a **selecting agent** on the gene pool of a species. As a result of natural selection, gene frequencies change and so do the frequencies of the pheno-

Fig. 16.10 *Peppered Moth.* The two variations of the peppered moth demonstrate that natural selection by the bird population will be greater against the light moth. However, before the lichen covered tree bark became darkened due to air pollution, the darker colored moth was more likely to be eaten. (Courtesy of the American Museum of Natural History.)

types produced. A classic example of this is found in the English peppered moth (fig. 16.10). Two forms of the moth are found in the population, light and dark-colored moths. These moths normally rest on the bark of trees during the day, where they may be eaten by birds. About 150 years ago, the most common were the light-colored moths. However, as the industrial revolution came upon England and the use of coal as an energy source increased, air pollution increased. The **fly ash** in the air settled on the trees changing the bark to a darker color. This allowed the birds to select the light-colored moths for their daily meals because the light moths were more easily seen against a dark background. The darker ones were not eaten as frequently, and therefore were more likely to reproduce. The light-colored moth, originally the most common of the two forms, is now the most rare. This change in gene frequency occurred within the short span of 50 years. Scientists, who have studied this situation, have estimated that the dark-colored moths have a 20 percent better chance of reproducing than do the light-colored moths. This study continues today. As England solves some of her air pollution problems, the light-colored form of the pepper moth is again increasing in frequency.

Another study of environmental effects of gene frequency involves the genes that control the height of clover plants (fig. 16.11). Scientists planted two identical fields and allowed animals to graze in one of them. The cows acted as a selecting agent by eating the taller plants first. These tall plants never reproduced; only the shorter plants flowered and produced seeds.

Fig. 16.11 *Selection.* The clover field is undergoing natural selection by the grazing cattle, and tall plants are less able to reproduce than the short plants. The other field is not subjected to this selection pressure, and the clover population will be genetically different.

After some time, the plants were sampled by collecting the seeds from both fields. They were then grown in the greenhouse under identical conditions. The heights of the plants from the grazed field were compared to the heights of the plants from the ungrazed field. It was found that the plants from the ungrazed field had some tall, some short, but mostly average height plants. The plants from the grazed field showed many more shorter plants and many fewer average and tall plants. The cows had selectively eaten the plants that had the genes for tallness, thus removing them from the reproducing population.

Summary

All sexually reproduced organisms possess natural differences as a result of mutations, meiosis, and genetic recombination. These differences are of prime importance in the survival and reproduction of the species, since they are the basis upon which the process of natural selection acts. Natural selection by the environment will allow better-suited individuals to reproduce their own kind. Selecting agents will act to change the gene frequencies of the population if the Hardy-Weinberg Law is violated. After generations of time, the favored individuals will make up a greater part of the gene pool than existed previously. As a result, the species will show changes in inherited characteristics. Natural selection can have no influence on the frequency of acquired characteristics. The entire process allows for the maintenance of a species in its environment, even as the surroundings change.

Questions

1. Why are acquired characteristics of little interest to evolutionary biologists?
2. What factors can contribute to variety in the gene pool?
3. Why is overreproduction necessary for evolving species?
4. What is natural selection, and how does it work?
5. The Hardy-Weinberg Law is only a theoretical law. What factors do *not* allow it to operate in a natural gene pool?
6. What will be the gene frequencies in the next generation of a gene pool that originally had equal numbers of the genes B and b, and half of the B genes mutated to b genes in this original generation?
7. The original gene frequencies in a gene pool are:

   $R = 50\%$, or 0.5
   $r = 50\%$, or 0.5

   If all the homozygous recessive individuals (rr) migrate from the population to another area, what will be the gene frequencies of R and r in the next generation?
8. How might a bad gene remain in a gene pool for generations without being removed by natural selection?
9. Give two examples of selecting agents.
10. The smaller the population, the more likely it is for random changes to influence the gene frequencies. Why is this true?

Chapter Glossary

acquired characteristic   A characteristic of an organism gained during its lifetime, which is not caused by its genes, and therefore, is not transmitted to the offspring. Example: cutting off the tail of a dog in a particular breed has to be done generation after generation.

compete   Two or more organisms attempting to acquire some substance necessary for their survival.

differential reproduction   Those organisms that have better genetic information for a particular environment out-reproduce the organisms that have less desirable information.

fly ash   Small particles released from industrial smoke stacks that settle out of the air onto houses, trees, cars, and other physical surfaces.

genetic recombination   The regrouping of parental genetic material at fertilization.

Hardy-Weinberg Law   Populations of organisms will maintain their gene frequencies from generation to generation as long as mating is random, the population is large, mutation does not occur, and no migration occurs in or out of the population.

natural selection   See Theory of Natural Selection.

selecting agent   A factor in the environment that chooses certain members of a population to reproduce better and/or faster than other members.

spontaneous mutation   A change in DNA caused by an unidentified environmental source.

Theory of Natural Selection   Genetically differing organisms of a species reproduce at different rates. This tends to transmit to the next generation the more favorable genes in conjunction with a changing environment.

Purpose   Populations have some unique features that make them special enough to justify a chapter in a book such as this. Some of these features will be introduced in this chapter and will allow you to see how populations grow and how this growth is controlled. While not specifically directed to the growth of the human population, much of the material covered in this chapter has specific relation to modern problems associated with the human *population explosion.*

Populations

17

Populations—What Are They?

A **population** is most acceptably defined as a group of individuals of the same species within a specified area who are able to reproduce with each other. With this definition in mind, you may think about a population of dandelions in your lawn, a population of rats in a metropolitan area, or the human population of a country or of the world.

Members of a population can reproduce with other members of the population, and the result is offspring with a reshuffled set of genetic data. This definition of population is a valuable one, since it allows one to consider the flow of genes through a population during sexual reproduction. **Gene flow** is the movement of genes within a population from place to place as a result of migration; and from generation to generation as a result of gene duplication and sexual reproduction (fig. 17.1).

In chapter fifteen you were introduced to the concept of gene frequency, which is a measure of how often a specific gene shows up in the gametes of a population. Gene frequencies within a population have a tendency to remain the same generation after generation, unless a gene is particularly advantageous; then the frequency tends to increase. On the other hand, if a gene is disadvantageous, there is a tendency for it to decrease in frequency. The frequency of a particular gene is unique to that population and is related to how that species functions in its environment.

Another feature of a population is its **age distribution.** Not all members of a population are of the same age. Some will be prereproductive juveniles, some will be reproducing adults, and some will be postreproductive senior citizens. A stable population will have these three age groups in some sort of balance. If the majority of the population were postreproductive, then few new combinations of genes would be produced for the next generation. If the majority of the population were reproducing adults, then we could expect a "baby boom." You should not conclude that each population is divided into equal thirds. In some situations, a population may be made up

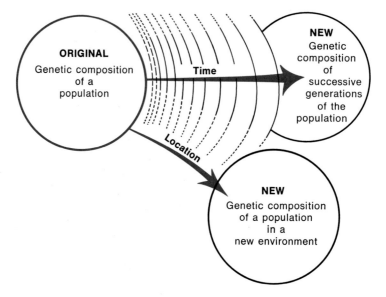

Fig. 17.1 Gene Flow.
Genetic composition of a population is continually being changed over a period of time (successive generations) and as a result of a changing environment. These changes are called gene flow.

ORIGINAL Genetic composition of a population

Time

Location

NEW Genetic composition of successive generations of the population

NEW Genetic composition of a population in a new environment

of a majority of one age group. Too many reproducing adults will overcrowd an area. This overcrowding might be an important factor that causes exploration and migration into different areas by many individuals of the population. This dispersal of organisms will relieve the overcrowded conditions in the home area, and at the same time lead to the establishment of new population. This dispersal of organisms will relieve the overcrowded condireproduces, the juvenile individuals relieve the overcrowding by leaving the home area and dispersing the population into a wider geographic area.

One feature of a sexually active population, which has been ignored so far, is that of sex ratio. A **sex ratio** is the relative number of males and females in a population. In a strongly paired bird population, where each male is strongly attached to a female, the ratio of male birds to female birds is nearly one to one. If we take as an example a plant population, we frequently find that flowers have fewer female reproductive structures (pistils) than male reproductive structures, stamens (fig. 17.2). The opposite extreme exists when one male services a harem of females such as in a population of bison or horses (fig. 17.3).

Reproduce—and Multiply

Sex ratios and age distributions within a population have a direct bearing on the rate of reproduction within a population. Each species has an inherent **reproductive capacity,** that is, an ability to produce offspring. Generally, this reproductive capacity is many times greater than the number of offspring that actually survive to become reproducing members of the population.

In plants and animals, there are many mechanisms that insure the overreproduction of their species. Some of these are physical adaptations and

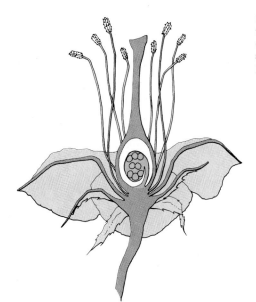

Fig. 17.2 *Flower.* The flower is the structure that contains the organs for sexual reproduction in some plants.

Fig. 17.3 *Sex Ratio in Elk.* Note that there is only one male in this herd with many females. (Courtesy of Michigan Department of Natural Resources.)

Fig. 17.4 *Adaptations for Pollination.* Adaptations in certain animals have resulted in their ability to carry out cross-pollination in certain plant species.

Bird

Bee

Bat

some are behavioral adaptations. Many flowering plants rely on bees or other insects to carry the pollen from one flower to another. The flowers must have adaptive features that will direct the activities of the insects toward the reproductive parts of the plant. Some of these are specific colors and patterns of color as in clover and orchid petals. The presence of nectar and odors also attract insects to specific flowers. These mechanisms insure that the insects will visit the flowers and bring about sexual reproduction (fig. 17.4). Behavior patterns such as courtship and nest building in birds also insure that mating will occur and that young will be protected while they are helpless (fig. 17.5).

Overreproduction is valuable to a species, since some of the reproductive events will fail to produce offspring, and some of the offspring produced will not survive. The reproductive event and survival of offspring can be insured in two ways. First, some organisms expend their energy producing millions of gametes and spend no energy caring for the offspring. Most of these offspring will die, but enough will survive to continue the species.

Fig. 17.5 *Courtship Ritual.* The elaborate dance that is a part of the courtship behavior in certain species is an essential part of the sexual reproductive process.

Male

Female

Oysters produce a million fertilized eggs when they reproduce, but few young reach maturity. An alternative method is to expend relatively little energy in producing gametes, but expend much energy in the care of the few young that are produced. Humans generally produce a single offspring during each pregnancy, but most of them survive.

Nature Throws a Curve

Whether the species produces a million offspring at a time or only one at a time, there is a high enough success rate such that the population will be carried on. As a result of this high reproductive potential, populations grow in size. For example, two mice produce four, which then produce eight, and then sixteen, and so on. Figure 17.6 shows a typical **growth curve** of a

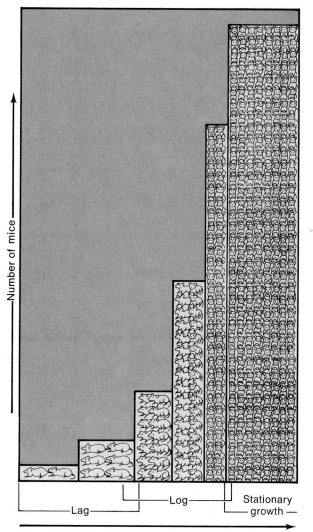

Fig. 17.6 *Typical Growth Curve.* In this mouse population, the period of time in which there is little growth is known as the *lag* phase. When there is a **rapid** increase as the offspring reach reproductive age, the curve is in the *log* phase Eventually the population reaches a stable growth phase, during which time the birthrate equals the death rate.

population. The first portion of the graph is called the **lag phase,** and indicates that growth occurs very slowly. The first two mice may have a litter of four who are not ready to reproduce themselves for several weeks. The first few weeks after the invasion of mice, the numbers do not increase very rapidly; however, about the time the first litter is of reproductive age, mom and pop are producing a second or third litter. Now, not just one pair is reproducing; there are several pairs. When these several pairs have produced several litters, the several mice have become several tens of mice. Now the population is growing at an ever-increasing rate. This is called the **log phase** of growth. The population is growing at a faster and faster rate. However, the number of mice does not continue to increase indefinitely. Eventually, the number of individuals entering the population (birth) will equal the number leaving (death). Reproduction is still occurring within the population, but the population has stopped growing in size; the birthrate equals the death rate. This portion of the graph is called the **stationary growth phase.**

Why does the number of individuals in a population level off? The reason for this relates to the concept of **carrying capacity.** The carrying capacity of an area is the optimum number of individuals of a species that can survive and "do their thing" in that area over an extended period of time. The carrying capacity of an area is determined by such things as space, materials, and available energy. The kinds of waste products produced and the mechanisms for their disposal are also important (fig. 17.7). Some examples

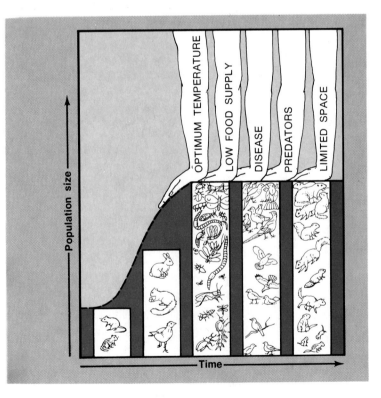

Fig. 17.7 _Carrying Capacity._ A number of factors in the environment—such as food, temperature, diseases, predators, and space—determine the number of organisms that can survive in a given area. This number is called the carrying capacity of that area.

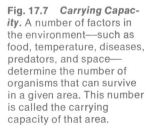

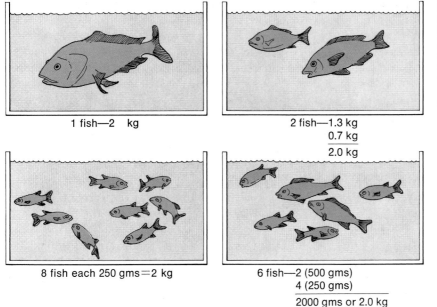

Fig. 17.8 *Biomass.* Each aquarium can support two kilograms of biomass. The number of fish in each aquarium determines the size of these fish. Why does the aquarium with the largest population have the smallest sized individuals?

1 fish—2 kg

2 fish—1.3 kg
0.7 kg
2.0 kg

8 fish each 250 gms=2 kg

6 fish—2 (500 gms)
4 (250 gms)
2000 gms or 2.0 kg

may give you a feeling for the concept of carrying capacity. There is only so much room (square meters) in your lawn. Each grass plant takes up a certain amount of space. This limits the number of grass plants. If the grass plants are too thick, some will not get enough minerals from the soil or will not get enough sunlight for photosynthesis. Thus, the number that can be supported well is related to space available and the amount of competition among the members of the grass population. An aquarium of a certain size can only support a certain number of fish. The size of each fish in the aquarium is important in determining carrying capacity. The aquarium illustration introduces a new problem. How do you measure a population that has individuals of different sizes? To solve this problem, we generally use the concept of **biomass.** Biomass is simply the weight of the organisms involved. Thus, the biomass of fish that can be supported might be two kilograms. These two kilograms might include only one fish weighing two kilograms; two fish, each weighing one kilogram; four fish, each weighing five-hundred grams; or various other combinations (fig. 17.8). The carrying capacity of the aquarium is related to the available space and competition for food, oxygen, and other essentials.

The Big Four

In most populations, four factors interact to define the carrying capacity of a given area for that population. These four factors are (1) availability of raw materials; (2) available energy; (3) accumulation of waste products, and the means by which they are disposed; and (4) interactions between organisms.

These four factors are all tied very closely to each other. In the example of the grass plants, nitrogen and other trace minerals in the soil are used in the manufacture of chlorophyll. This is precisely the reason why lawn and garden centers do big business in fertilizer sales. The plant requires light as well as chlorophyll for the process of photosynthesis; therefore, raw materials such as nitrogen and energy in the form of sunlight are closely tied to each other. Since there are few waste products from the grass, they do not generally influence the carrying capacity to a great degree; but the number and kinds of animals using the grass for food and the number and kinds of other plants are involved in determining the carrying capacity of the lawn.

In the aquarium, it is a little more difficult to see the difference between the energy and the raw material that the food provides. On the other hand, oxygen is easily identified as a raw material used in the release of energy from food.

A third process that helps determine optimum population size is waste disposal. One of the best examples of this occurs in a bacterial culture. This is a very simple situation, since the organisms have a very limited environment. When one puts a small number of one species of bacteria in a petri plate with **nutrient agar,** the population growth follows the curve shown in figure 17.9.

Fig. 17.9 Bacterial Growth Curve. The rate of increase in the population of these bacteria follows the typical curve in a favorable environment. As the environmental conditions change, with the increasing numbers and the pileup of waste products, the carrying capacity is lowered. This decreasing population size is known as the death phase.

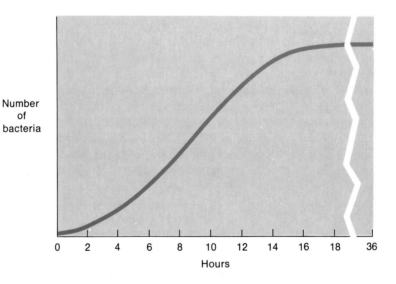

Number of bacteria

0   2   4   6   8   10   12   14   16   18   36

Hours

As expected, the number of bacteria increase through a lag and log phase of growth, and eventually reach stability during the stationary growth phase. But as the waste products pile up, the organisms literally drown in their own wastes. In this case, there are no other ways to handle the metabolic wastes, since space for disposal is limited and other kinds of organisms are not present to take care of these wastes. The wastes poison the environment such that the organism can no longer live; therefore, the population decreases in size. This portion of the population curve is called the **death phase.**

Brewers and wine makers also realize the truth of this situation when they use a small population of yeast cells. Yeast cells ferment sugar to alcohol. When the alcohol concentration reaches a certain limit, the yeast cells die. Therefore, wine can naturally reach an alcohol level from only 12 to 15 percent; but to make any drink stronger than that (higher alcohol content), water must be removed (to distill) or alcohol added (to fortify). The yeast population has a natural limit, since there are no interactions with other organisms to take care of the accumulated waste product, alcohol.

The interaction between species of organisms is very important in controlling population size. This happens indirectly when decomposer organisms help with the disposal of metabolic waste products, and directly when other species of organisms act as predators to kill some of the individuals of the prey species. A good example of this is the interaction between the wolf (the predator) and the moose (the prey) populations on Isle Royale in Lake Superior (fig. 17.10).

The moose have a high reproductive capacity that the wolves help to control by using the moose for food. The wolf can capture and kill the weak, the old, the stupid, or the diseased moose. Thus, the stronger, smarter, and

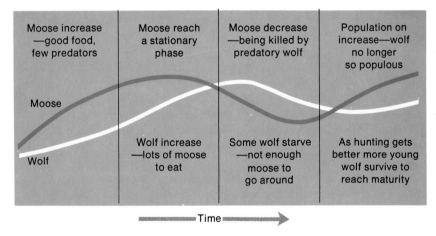

Fig. 17.10 *Population Interaction.* Notice that the populations of the wolf and the moose are interdependent.

healthier moose live to reproduce. This arrangement keeps the population at its most favorable level and also keeps the gene pool in good condition. This is another case of natural selection.

The example of the moose population shows several things. One is that populations interact with each other (these interactions are discussed in a later chapter). A second is that there are **control mechanisms** that determine the carrying capacity. These control mechanisms might include a lack of food, predatory organisms, or hunting pressures from man.

Some studies have shown that certain populations are controlled not by external factors, such as available food, energy, predators, or disease;

but by internal factors in the makeup of the organisms themselves. A study of rats and crowding shows that a breakdown in normal social behavior may be a factor in controlling laboratory rat populations and adjusting the rat population to match the available resources. The kinds of breakdowns include abnormal mating behavior, decreased litter size, fewer litters per year, lack of infant care, as well as increased aggression in some rats, or withdrawal in others.

So far we have considered populations that reached a stationary growth phase while maintaining a constant population size. The bacteria and yeast cultures illustrate how a change in their surroundings (waste products) could result in a decrease in their populations. This is also true of all other populations. A decrease in the food supply, an increase in disease organisms, or abnormal weather patterns may cause a decrease in population size. On the other hand, some organisms such as man have been able to eliminate competing organisms, increase food production, and control disease organisms. This has led to an increase in the human population.

Man, the Prolific

Probably one of the most interesting questions of recent years concerns the population of man. Man's population growth curve has a long lag phase followed by a very sharp and rapid log growth phase with no sign of leveling off (fig. 17.11). What does this very rapid rate of growth mean in terms of man as a biological species? First, we as a species must follow the same rules that determine carrying capacity, just as do all the other species. We cannot increase beyond our ability to acquire food, raw materials and energy; nor beyond our ability to safely dispose of our waste materials.

Let's look at the four factors that determine the carrying capacity of other organisms and see how they apply to man. Raw materials to many of us simply means the amount of food available, but we should not forget that man is a species that has become increasingly dependent on technology and that the life-style and quality of life of modern man is tied directly to our use of many of the world's resources. Food production in the mid-70s is not yet a limiting factor. More important than just agricultural productivity is the aspect of dispersal of food to those areas of the world where hunger is evident. Not only should we consider the problems of production of calories and protein, but also we need to consider its acceptability to people of different cultures. For example, native Africans find certain insect larvae to be treats, but have you tried any lately?

It is biologically accurate to say that the developed world of today can produce adequate food supplies for the undeveloped world, but there are many reasons why these countries can't get it or won't eat it. There are political, economic, and social issues involved in the production, transportation, and utilization of the food produced. In addition, the statement only applies

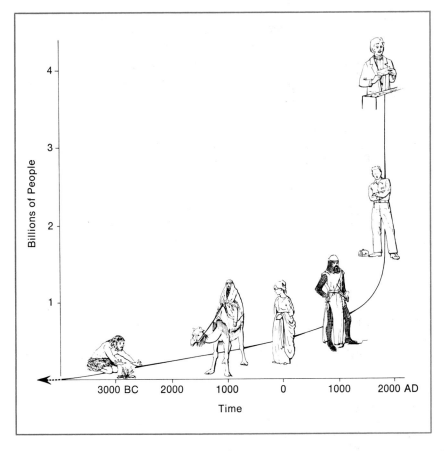

Fig. 17.11 *Human Population Growth.* The number of humans doubled from 1850 AD to 1930 (from one billion to two billion) and then doubled again by 1975 (four billion) and could double again (8 billion) by the year 2010. How long can man continue to double in even shorter periods of time?

for the moment. The world population is growing at the rate of 2.0 percent per year. This amounts to one new person born into the world each second. With such a rate-increase in mouths to feed, it is unlikely that food production will keep pace with population growth. The severity of this problem has finally become recognized on a worldwide basis. In 1974, the first World Food Conference was held to discuss possible approaches to solving the problem. If man, as an intelligent animal, does not solve the problem, nature will; and her solution will be an increased death rate. She is not very humane.

The second factor, that of available energy, has problems similar to those of available raw materials. One important fact we should not ignore, is that all species on earth are ultimately dependent on sunlight for their energy. Whether one produces electrical power from a hydroelectric facility, burns petroleum products, or uses a solar cell, the energy can be related to present or past radiation from the sun. Man should realize that there is an ultimate limit to the amount of energy that arrives on earth from our star. New and less disruptive methods of harnessing this energy should be developed.

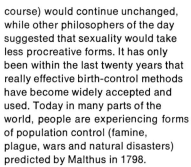

Comparable progression

■ Rate of food production (arithmetic)

▨ Rate of population increase (geometric)

Box VII
Thomas Malthus and
His Essay on Population

In 1798 an Englishman, Thomas Robert Malthus, published an essay on human population. It presented an idea that was contrary to popular opinion. His basic theme was that man reproduces at a geometric rate (2, 4, 8, 16, 32, ...) while food increases at an arithmetic rate (1, 2, 3, 4, 5, . . .). The ultimate outcome would be the lack of enough food to support the human population. Furthermore, wars, famines, plagues and natural disasters would be the ultimate control on the size of the human population.

At the time he wrote his essay, there was a popular opinion that man's knowledge and "moral con-straint" would be able to create a world that would supply all of mans' needs in abundance. One of Malthus' basic postulates was that "commerce between the sexes" (sexual inter-course) would continue unchanged, while other philosophers of the day suggested that sexuality would take less procreative forms. It has only been within the last twenty years that really effective birth-control methods have become widely accepted and used. Today in many parts of the world, people are experiencing forms of population control (famine, plague, wars and natural disasters) predicted by Malthus in 1798.

One of the unforeseen influences of Malthus' essay was the effect it had on the young Charles Darwin. When Darwin read it, he saw in it the seeds of an idea that could be applied to the whole of the plant and animal kingdoms; namely, that overreproduction of organisms and the death of the excess would lead to natural seelection. (Photo courtesy of The Bettmann Archive.)

One of the most talked about aspects of technological man is how he disposes of his wastes. Much of what we have come to call pollution is in reality our own waste products. Earlier, the example of bacteria in a petri dish was used to show the importance of metabolic waste disposal. In this simple situation, the organisms so "befouled their nest" that their wastes poisoned them. Isn't man in exactly the same boat, but on a much larger scale? Aren't we dumping so much poison in our air, water, and onto our land that it cannot be disposed of? Some biologists are convinced that this disregard for the quality of our environment will be the major factor in decreasing our population growth rate. In any case, it just makes good sense to do everything possible to stop our pollution, and in fact, work toward cleaning our nest.

The fourth factor that determines carrying capacity of a species is that of interaction with other organisms. We also interact with other kinds of organisms. Man needs to become more aware of the fact that he is not the only species of importance. As man converts the land to meet his needs, he must displace other species from their homes. Many of these displaced organisms are not able to compete successfully with man and must leave the area or become extinct. Unfortunately, as man expands his domain, the areas available to these displaced animals become more rare. Our parks and natural areas have become tiny refuges for plants and animals that at one time occupied vast expanses of our land. If these refuges fall to the developer's ax, many organisms will become extinct. What today seems like an unimportant kind of organism, one which man could easily do without, may tomorrow be seen as an important link to man's very survival.

Summary

A population is a group of organisms having such characteristics as age distribution, sex ratios, and gene frequencies that make it unique. All organisms have the inherent capacity to overreproduce. This results in a population growth curve with the following characteristics: an initial slow growth (lag phase) that soon becomes very rapid (log phase) and eventually levels off (stationary growth phase) as the population reaches the carrying capacity of its environment.

The carrying capacity is determined by such factors as availability of raw materials, energy, disposal of wastes, and the way a population interacts with other populations. Man, as a species, has the same limits placed on his population growth as do other species. Our current problems of food production, energy shortage, pollution, and disruption of other populations of organisms are ample evidence of this.

Consider This

If you return to figure 17.11, you will note that it has very little in common with the growth curve seen in figure 17.6. What factors have allowed for the human population to grow in such a rapid manner? What natural factors will eventually bring this population under control? What alternatives to the natural population control methods would also bring the human population in balance with the available resources?

Consider in your answer reproduction, death, diseases, food supplies, energy, farming practices, food distribution, cultural biases, and the kitchen sink.

1. Draw the population growth curve of a yeast culture for making wine; and label the portions as lag, log, and stationary growth phases.
2. List three characteristics that a population might have.
3. Why do populations grow?
4. What changes might result in a death phase?
5. List four characteristics that could determine the carrying capacity of an animal species.
6. How do the concepts of population size and biomass differ?
7. How does the population growth curve of humans compare with that of the yeast in a wine culture?
8. What is meant by the term gene flow?
9. As man's population continues to increase, what might happen to other species?
10. All organisms overreproduce. What advantage does this provide for the species? What disadvantages may occur?

Chapter Glossary

age distribution   The ratio of juvenile, sexually active, and postreproductive individuals within a population.

biomass   The total weight of a particular kind of organism in a given situation. It is used for comparison purposes when numbers of organisms or size of organisms would lead to confusion.

carrying capacity   The optimum number of individuals of a species that can survive in an area over an extended period of time.

control mechanism   The limiting factor or combination of factors that determines the population size in an area.

death phase   That portion of the growth curve indicating that there is a decrease in numbers of individuals in the population.

gene flow   The movement of genes within a population from place to place as a result of migration; and from generation to generation as a result of sexual reproduction.

growth curve   The graphic expression of increasing or decreasing numbers of individuals in a population through time.

lag phase   That portion of the growth curve indicating that the increase in numbers is slow. It is usually the first phase of a growth curve.

log phase   That portion of the growth curve indicating that the increase in numbers is very rapid.

nutrient agar   A nutrient medium used as a source of food for bacteria.

population   A group of individuals of the same species within a specified area who are able to reproduce with each other.

reproductive capacity   The potential number of offspring that a population can produce.

sex ratio   The relative number of male and female members in a population.

stationary growth phase   That portion of the growth curve indicating that the number of births is equal to the number of deaths; therefore, the number of individuals in the population is static.

Purpose All living things require a continuous source of energy. This energy is used in growth, movement, reproduction, and many other activities. However, there are certain physical laws that describe how energy changes occur. Probably the most important rule is that during the process of converting energy from one form to another useful energy is lost as useless heat energy. This is known as the Second Law of Thermodynamics. Many of the world's problems result from the fact that man has failed to recognize the limits imposed by the laws of thermodynamics. The purpose of this chapter is to show how energy is used and converted within groups of interacting organisms, and how the laws of thermodynamics apply to living systems.

Energy and Life

18

Ecology, Environment—Big Deal

Today many people use the "in-words" **ecology** and **environment.** Students, housewives, politicians, various types of planners, and union leaders speak of "environmental issues." Although the words are commonly used, they are often used incorrectly or in ways slanted toward the speaker's particular point of view.

Ecology is nothing more than the study of organisms in relationship to their environment. This is a simple statement for a very complex study. Both living and nonliving factors play a part in the environment of any organism. When a fisherman decides upon which bait to use, he is dealing with a living part of his environment. A nonliving factor in the life of a fish is the temperature of the water. In any ecological study, a vast number of living and nonliving factors must be taken into account (fig. 18.1).

What is an ecologist? Is a college degree needed in order to become an ecologist? The simple fact is that we are all ecologists in one form or another. If you are a fisherman, your goal is to catch fish. The more you know about fish and their relationship to their environment, the more successful you'll be at catching them. Yes, all of us are ecologists to some extent; we are inter-

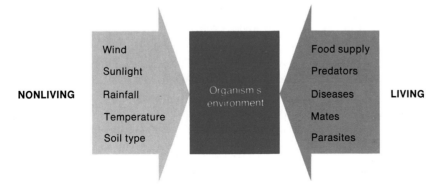

NONLIVING

Wind
Sunlight
Rainfall
Temperature
Soil type

Organism's environment

LIVING

Food supply
Predators
Diseases
Mates
Parasites

Fig. 18.1 *Environmental Influences.* Many factors, both living and nonliving, are part of any organism's environment.

ested in the relationship of organisms to their environment, even if the only organism we are concerned about is ourselves.

The environment is very complex. Therefore, the study of any organism's environment is very complex. A plant is influenced by many different factors during its lifetime. The type and amount of minerals in the soil, the amount of sunlight hitting the plant, the animals that eat plants, and the wind, water, and temperature are all important factors. Each item in this list may be further subdivided into many other areas of study. For instance, water is important in the life of plants, and so rainfall is studied in plant ecology. Not just how much rain, but the time of year the rain falls—is it a hard, driving or a soft, gentle rain? Does the water soak into the ground for later use, or does it quickly run off into the rivers? Is it a warm or cold rain? Even though rainfall seems to be an easily understood portion of an ecological study, it is really a very complex subject when examined closely.

Temperature is also a very complex subject and is important in the life of a plant. For example, two areas of the world may have the same average daily temperature of $10°C$,* but not have the same plants because of different temperature extremes. In one area the temperature may be $13°C$ in the day and $7°C$ at night, for a $10°C$ average. In another area, the temperature may be $20°C$ in the day, and $0°C$ at night, for a $10°C$ average. Plants react to extremes in temperature as well as to the average. Temperature effects may be specific and only influence certain parts of a plant. In tomatoes, the plant will grow at a temperature below $13°C$, but will not set fruit.

The animals in an area are influenced as much by nonliving factors as are the plants. If the nonliving factors do not favor the growth of plants, there will be little food and few hiding places to support animal life. Two types of areas that support a small animal biomass are polar regions and desert areas. Near the polar regions of the earth, the temperature inhibits plant growth. As a result, these areas have relatively few species of animals, and these animals have small populations. Deserts receive little rainfall, which results in poor plant growth and low animal biomass. In contrast to these two situations, tropical rain forests have excellent plant growth and a high animal biomass.

Living organisms themselves are a vital part of any environment. If there are too many animals in an area, they could demand such large amounts of food that all plant life would be destroyed and the animals themselves would die. In the human population, living parts of the environment include the family, co-workers, fellow students, the neighborhood mugger, and "the other guy." They all have an influence on your life. Please don't forget the fly on the table, the bacteria in your food, the rat in the sewer, the shade tree in the yard, and the barking dog next door. This may seem like a long list, but these are only a few examples of the many living things that are a part of your environment.

---

* See Box I, p. 17 for conversion to Fahrenheit.

Because of transportation, and social and political ties, man has the whole world as his environment. Today your cotton may come from Texas, your oranges from Florida, your lettuce from California, your camera from Japan, your copper from Chile, and your oil from Saudi Arabia. If hundreds of acres of orange groves in Florida are destroyed to make way for an amusement area, there may be certain local economic rewards. But that area is no longer able to produce oranges, which changes the price of oranges for Midwest housewives. As a more distant example, the government of Chile decided to process copper within its own country to raise the standard of living of the native people. This was good for their environment, but now the price of copper has increased. What about the cost of building a home in the United States? The cost of electric wiring and copper plumbing in a house has risen, and therefore, it costs more to build a house.

Surely your environment and that of all other people in the world is a very complex one. Before you decide that something is good or bad for the environment, take a good, long, hard look. Step back and view the whole picture: look at all aspects of everyone's environment, since changes will influence some part of the environment, either now or in the future. Such long-term changes have occurred along the banks of good trout streams as a result of lumbering. The trees next to the stream had provided shade and kept the water cool enough for the maintenance of a healthy trout population. Once the trees were removed, the water temperature rose to a point at which trout were no longer able to survive.

One of the most important items influencing any population is the amount of available energy. Since energy for living organisms is captured by green plants, they are the key organisms for determining the kinds and numbers of different populations in an area.

Have You Thanked a Green Plant Today?

Green plants play the role of an energy trapper and food manufacturer. They are referred to as **producers** in ecological terms. The energy that plants trap may be transferred through a number of other organisms before it is completely lost to the environment as useless heat energy. Each time the energy enters a different organism it is said to enter a different **trophic level** (fig. 18.2). The plants are the first to receive the energy directly from the sun, and they represent organisms that occupy the first trophic level. All animals are called **consumers,** but may occupy different trophic levels depending on whether they receive their energy directly or indirectly from plants. Those animals that feed directly on plants are called **herbivores** and occupy the second trophic level. Those that feed on herbivores are called **carnivores** and occupy the third trophic level. There are even higher trophic levels that are occupied by organisms that receive their energy from eating carnivores. For example, a man may eat a fish that ate a frog, that ate a spider, that ate an insect that relied on plants for food (fig. 18.3). In this example, there are six

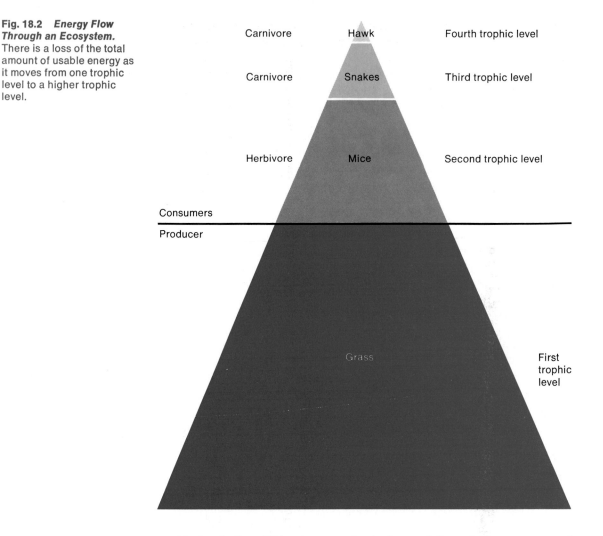

Fig. 18.2   *Energy Flow Through an Ecosystem.* There is a loss of the total amount of usable energy as it moves from one trophic level to a higher trophic level.

Carnivore   Hawk   Fourth trophic level

Carnivore   Snakes   Third trophic level

Herbivore   Mice   Second trophic level

Consumers

Producer

Grass   First trophic level

trophic levels. In addition, some animals do not fall neatly into any one of these categories, but may function as both carnivores and herbivores. These are called **omnivores.** Their trophic level is not easy to identify.

If a plant or animal dies, the energy contained within its body is finally released to the environment as heat by organisms that decompose the body into its most basic molecules, such as carbon dioxide and water. These organisms of decay are called **decomposers.** Organisms such as bacteria and fungi occupy this last of the trophic levels. This is the oldest and most effective form of **recycling.** As long as the sun provides the necessary energy, elements are recycled over and over again. This process is almost as old as life on the earth and is essential if life is to continue.

The total amount of energy trapped by the producers of a given area will determine the number of carnivores, omnivores, herbivores, and decomposers that can exist at the various trophic levels. The energy also determines the carrying capacity of a particular population. Figure 18.4 illustrates an area that can support one hundred deer from January through March, when plant food for deer is at its lowest point. As spring arrives, plant growth increases, and the carrying capacity for deer increases. It is no accident that deer breed in the fall and fawns are born in the spring. For it is during the spring of the year that the producers are increasing and the area has more food. It is also no accident that wolves and other carnivores that feed on the deer bear their young in the spring. The increased available energy of the producers means more food for herbivores (deer). In turn, this means more energy for carnivores (wolves) at the next trophic level.

The carrying capacity of an area is not static. A decrease in producers during the fall and winter reduces the available food for consumers and the population of all carnivores drops.

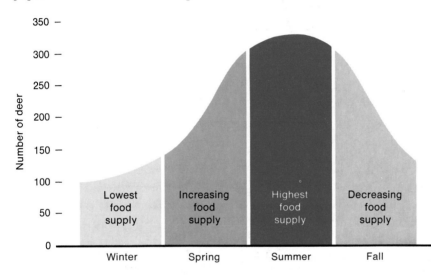

Fig. 18.3 *Food Chain.* As one organism feeds upon another organism, there is a flow of energy through the series. This is called a food chain. (Adapted from Ralph D. Bird, "Biotic Communities of the Aspen Packland of Central Canada." *Ecology* II (April, 1930): 410.)

Fig. 18.4 *Carrying Capacity.* The carrying capacity of an area will vary during the year. The availability of food is the primary factor in determining the carrying capacity.

Survival—The Name of the Game

This sequence of organisms (plants, deer, and wolves) is an example of a **food chain.** Basic food chains involve a producer and various levels of consumers and decomposers. Figure 18.5 illustrates several food chains. Many factors are important in determining an animal's place in a food chain. One such factor is the ability of animals to digest specific kinds of food. Cellulose, a carbohydrate, is a major part of wood. Man does not have the enzymes to obtain energy from this particular carbohydrate. Yet many other forms of animals do digest wood, since they have the proper enzymes.

Every animal, including man, must compete with other organisms that are part of his **food web** (fig. 18.6). If the codling moth destroys twenty percent of the apples in an orchard, there is less food for human consumption. If

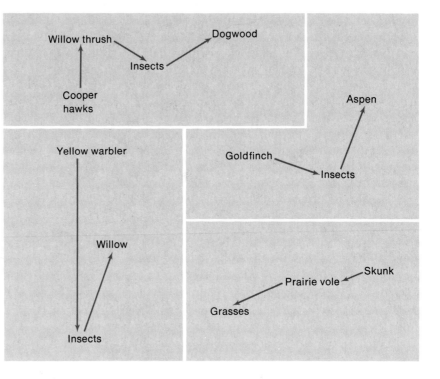

southern cornleaf blight destroys 17 percent of the corn crop in a given state, less food is available for man's domestic livestock, and therefore, less meat for human consumption. In addition to the food loss, this 17 percent reduction in crop yield would mean a financial loss to those farmers for that year. In order to survive, man has for centuries waged war on the many creatures that can diminish the supply of energy in the food chains he manages.

In recent years, the growing world population has forced man to increase his efforts in this never-ending fight. As in most human endeavors, mistakes have been made. Various pesticides and other controls have been criticized, but the fact remains that these tools are used to help man survive. Man must use controls, but he should use controls that will result in the least amount of disruption within the environment. In an era of food shortage and growing world population, this need for control of the organisms that compete for man's food supply becomes all the more critical.

Like any organism, man is bound by the laws of nature, and no matter how badly he needs the food, there is only a limited amount of sunlight energy available to the world. Currently, man is attempting to maintain his present trophic level through successful competition, using control mechanisms such as pesticides. However, as the population increases, the competition will become even more intense, and man will have to find other ways of assuring an energy supply for food production. He will have to be aware of the laws of thermodynamics in order to make intelligent decisions.

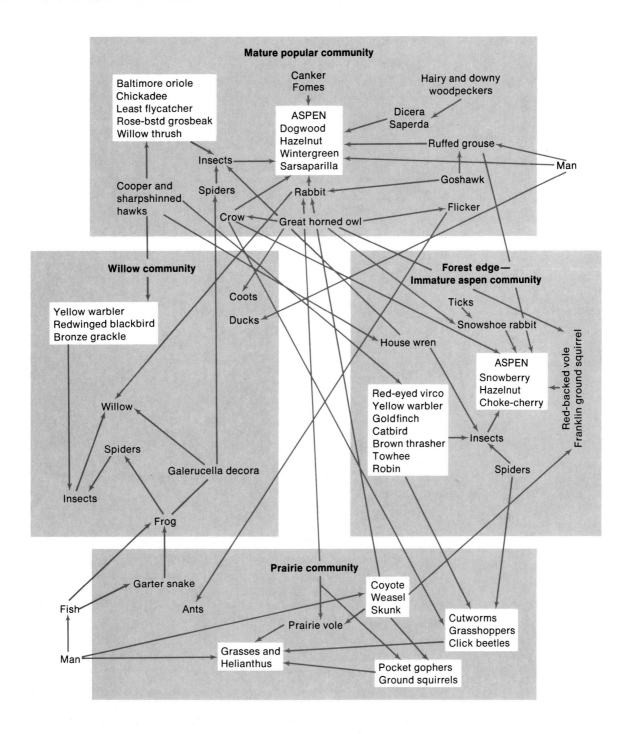

Fig. 18.6

The Mighty Pyramid

The pharaohs of Egypt constructed one of the wonders of the world when they ordered the building of their elaborate tombs, known as pyramids. The Second Law of Thermodynamics has built a far more important pyramid, the pyramid of energy. In every pyramid, the greatest amount of material is at the base, and as the pyramid gets higher, the amount of material at any level becomes less and less.

At the base of the pyramid of energy is the producer. The producer trophic level contains the greatest amount of energy. The energy takes the form of food. Figure 18.7 illustrates a pyramid of energy having a producer base of 10,000 kilograms of corn. The next level is that of the consumer

Fig. 18.7 *Pyramid of Energy.* Due to the loss of energy in feeding the corn to cattle, it requires 10,000 kilograms of corn to produce approximately 100 kilograms of humans.

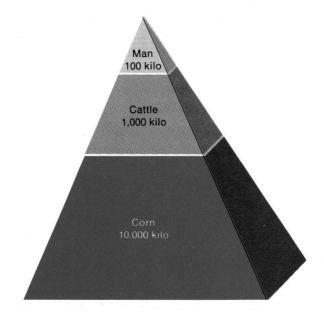

at the second trophic level. In order to grow and survive, these consumers must change the energy of the plants into their own energy. There is roughly a 90 percent loss of usable energy during this conversion. In figure 18.7, the 10,000 kilograms of corn can support 1,000 kilograms of beef cattle. The consumers at the third trophic level again demand energy, and there is another 90 percent loss. The 1,000 kilograms of cattle support 100 kilograms of humans. With man as a consumer at the third trophic level in the food chain, there has been a 99 percent loss of energy from corn to man. Ten thousand kilograms of corn are required to sustain 100 kilograms of human life in this food chain.

Man does not have to be a carnivore at the third trophic level. If man were to assume the role of consumer at the second trophic level and eat the corn directly, there would only be a 90 percent loss of energy from corn to man. In this case, the 10,000 kilograms of corn would support 1,000 kilograms of human life, ten times more than before (fig. 18.8). By eliminating the cattle in man's food chain, ten times as much human life can be supported from the same amount of plant life. In parts of the world where food is scarce, man cannot afford the energy loss involved in passing food through animals. As a result, people become consumers at the second trophic level and use plants as food. Much of the world's human population relies on corn, wheat, rice, and other first trophic level organisms as their main sources of food. Because much of the world's population is already at the second trophic level, we should not expect the world to be able to support ten times as many humans as presently exist by just a change in food habits.

Man's food requirements include a need for calories and proteins. Figure 18.9 shows the basic diet of different countries throughout the world. One of the best sources of protein is meat. Although protein is available from plants, the amount from animals is greater. Figure 18.10 shows the protein intake for people in various countries and also shows what part is plant protein and what part is animal protein. Figure 18.10 reveals that people in Mexico receive a large amount of protein in their diet from plants. In Pakistan, the protein intake is low and mainly from plants. These people have very little food, and what food they do have is mainly from plants. These examples illustrate that even if man does live as a consumer on the second trophic level, he may not get enough food, or if he does, it may lack the necessary protein.

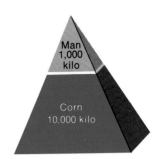

Fig. 18.8 *Pyramid of Energy.* When corn is fed directly to humans, 10,000 kilograms of corn will produce approximately 1,000 kilograms of humans.

Fig. 18.9 *Geography of Hunger.* This map illustrates the amounts of calories and proteins consumed by the various nations of the world. (From *Human Ecology: Problems and Solutions* by Paul R. Ehrlich, Anne H. Ehrlich and John P. Holdren. W. H. Freeman and Company. Copyright © 1973.)

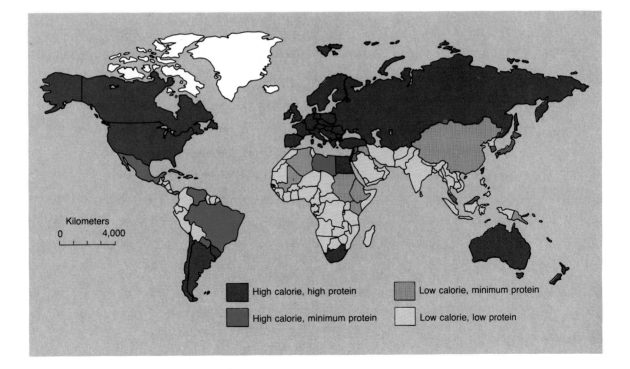

Kilometers
0   4,000

High calorie, high protein
High calorie, minimum protein
Low calorie, minimum protein
Low calorie, low protein

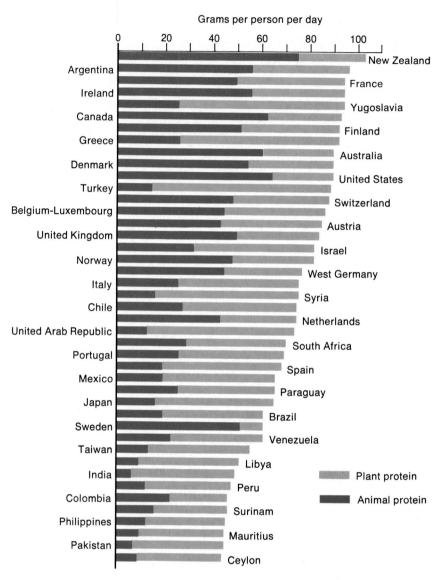

Fig. 18.10 *Protein Intake.* In the developed countries, animals are a major source of proteins. Undeveloped nations depend upon plants as their source of protein. (From *Introduction to Livestock Production,* 2d ed., by H. H. Cole. W. H. Freeman and Company. Copyright © 1966.)

Grams per person per day

Argentina, New Zealand, France, Ireland, Yugoslavia, Canada, Finland, Greece, Australia, Denmark, United States, Turkey, Switzerland, Belgium-Luxembourg, Austria, United Kingdom, Israel, Norway, West Germany, Italy, Syria, Chile, Netherlands, United Arab Republic, South Africa, Portugal, Spain, Mexico, Paraguay, Japan, Brazil, Sweden, Venezuela, Taiwan, Libya, India, Peru, Colombia, Surinam, Philippines, Mauritius, Pakistan, Ceylon

Plant protein

Animal protein

Ecosystem

In this chapter a number of concepts have been presented: (1) producers are at the base of every food chain, (2) a loss of energy occurs as it passes through the various trophic levels, and (3) the role of the decomposers is to recycle materials so that they can be used time and time again. When these and other concepts are viewed from an overall point of view, a more complete picture comes into view.

An **ecosystem** is the interaction between living organisms and the non-

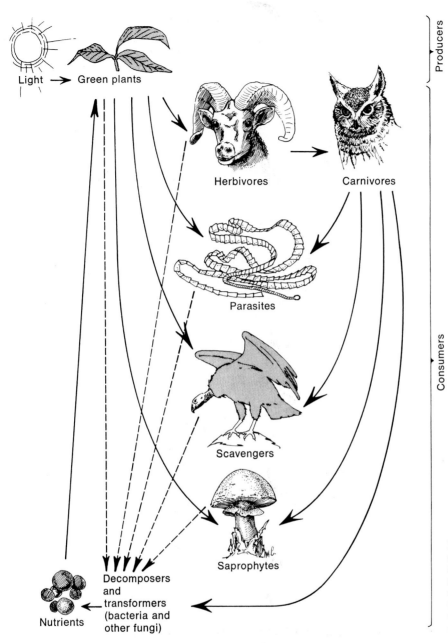

Light → Green plants

Producers

Herbivores

Carnivores

Parasites

Scavengers

Saprophytes

Consumers

Decomposers and transformers (bacteria and other fungi)

Nutrients

Fig. 18.11 *Ecosystem.* The energy to support an ecosystem originates from light energy. The producers convert this light energy into food energy. A number of various types of consumers utilize this food energy.

living environment in which they exist. The populations of an ecosystem that interact with one another constitute a **community.** Figure 18.11 illustrates how energy and materials flow through the basic parts of any ecosystem. Note that the sun furnishes the energy to convert the inorganic materials into the organic material of the producers. The producers become

Fig. 18.12 *Forest Eco-system.* This illustration represents a typical forest ecosystem. Determine the niche of the various organisms in this scene.

the food for the various consumers. The role of decomposers is to constantly recycle the materials within the ecosystem. There are many types of ecosystems. An ecosystem in the northern parts of North America would have lichens and other small plants as the producers. Various consumers such as rabbits, mice, and caribou would feed upon the producers. Wolves and foxes would serve as a consumer on the third trophic level. Man could feed upon any producer or consumer in the area.

In the days before the discovery of North America, the North American ecosystems furnished all the energy requirements for the native human population of this area. Figure 18.12 illustrates a typical forest ecosystem, and figure 18.13, an aquatic ecosystem. As you study these figures, try to identify the organisms that serve as producers, second trophic level consumers, third trophic level consumers, and decomposers.

Fig. 18.13 *Aquatic Ecosystem.* This illustration represents a typical aquatic ecosystem. Determine the niche of the various organisms in this scene.

Hero or Villain

Many types of ecosystems exist in assorted shapes and sizes, but all of these rolled together make up one single worldwide **biosphere.** A certain amount of sun energy strikes the earth and all living creatures must obtain their energy from the sun. Man can control ecosystems in such a way as to direct much energy into his own food chain. When this energy is used by man, it is not available for other animals and consequently their populations become threatened, even to the point of extinction.

The native American Indian living in the Great Plains area of this country used buffalo as a source of food. There was much grass, many buffalo, and few Indians. Therefore, in the American Indian's pyramid of energy, the base was more than ample. But, with the discovery of America and the coming of the settlers, the human population in North America increased at a rapid rate. The top of the pyramid became larger. The food chain (prairie grass → buffalo → human) could no longer supply man's energy requirements. As the top of the pyramid grew larger, it became necessary for the producer base to grow larger also. Since wheat and corn will yield more food than native prairie grass, the settler's domestic grain and cattle replaced the prairie grass and buffalo. That is fine if you are human, but lousy if you happen to be a buffalo.

Is Man Following the Rules for Survival?

In his haste to improve his lot, man has often failed to look at what he has been doing to the total ecosystem, and in the end, to himself. Many minerals are obtained from ore deposits that are the result of past ecosystems. When these ores are used up, none will be left. Coal, oil, and natural gas are also products of a past ecosystem. These natural resources are available to us today because they have been built up over millions of years. Man only began using these resources within the past two hundred years, but millions of years worth of the stored energy has already been used. Even though these kinds of resources are being produced today by green plants, the total process takes years, and man is using the reserves so fast that there will be no new stores of energy in the near future.

It has been pointed out that survival is the name of the game. Examples of what man has done in order to survive have been given. It is a fact of life that in order to live as we do, man must change the ecosystem. The question is: Does man have to change it as much, or as fast as he does?

The United States makes up 5 percent of the world population. Yet we consume 27 percent of the resources used in the world, annually (table 18.1). Much of these resources must be imported. As other countries improve their standard of living, they will demand more of the world's energy and raw

Table 18.1 Material Consumption
The United States contains 5 percent of the world's population and annually uses 27 percent of the world's materials.

	U.S. (percent)	Rest of world (percent)
Population	5	95
Material Consumption	27	73

materials. Such a demand will change our own standard of living. We will have to do with less and pay more for what we use. The shortage of many materials has come as a shock to many Americans. It shouldn't have. Remember, we are only part of a complex ecosystem, and all the people in the world are a part of it. Their actions must, of necessity, influence our way of life.

Man has complex needs and desires. Some of his needs are basic to all animals, but some are unique. "Man-made wants" determine our standard of living. And this standard of living is a part of the human ecosystem. Like all ecosystems, it requires energy to convert raw materials into finished products, to move our cars, planes, trains, and to cool and heat our homes.

For all practical purposes, man's present forms of energy and his raw materials are nonrenewable resources. He has often lost sight of this fact and lived as if there were an endless supply of energy and natural resources. In any ecosystem, the decomposers are essential. If man is to maintain his present standard of living, he must take a lesson from the decomposers and recycle his raw materials.

Summary

An ecosystem requires the sun as the source of energy. The producers use this light energy to convert nonliving materials into organic substances that serve as food for the consumers.

The flow of this food energy can cross over into many food chains. Complex food webs are formed with many organisms competing for the available food. The decay organisms will eventually convert all organic material into inorganic matter. It will again be recycled starting with the producers. The energy relationship of an ecosystem can be described as an energy pyramid.

An ecosystem is a vast, complex set of living and nonliving factors. Any change in one aspect of an ecosystem will have some bearing on the rest of the system. Sometimes the changes brought about may be very small, other times they may be great. Often man looks only at a small portion of the system and only becomes concerned about his actions after he has "screwed up" things.

Describe a world in which there are no decomposers. List ten ways in which it would be different from the present world. *Consider This*

1. Why are rainfall and temperature important to any ecosystem?
2. Describe the flow of energy through an ecosystem.
3. What is the difference between *ecosystem* and *environment?*
4. What role does each of the following play in an ecosystem: plants, consumers, omnivores, carnivores, producers, decomposers, herbivores?
5. Give an example of a food chain.
6. What is meant by the term *trophic level?*
7. Why is there always a larger herbivore biomass than carnivore biomass?
8. Describe two different kinds of ecosystems; and list the ultimate source of energy, and a member of each trophic level in that ecosystem.
9. Can energy be recycled through an ecosystem?
10. In a balanced ecosystem, what will happen to species *B* if species *A* increases in number?

Chapter Glossary

biosphere   That area in, on, and around the earth that supports life.

carnivore   Meat-eating animal.

community   The interrelationships among various populations that share a similar habitat.

consumer   Various plant-eating or meat-eating animals.

decomposer   Bacteria or fungi that convert organic material into inorganic material.

ecology   The study of an organism in relation to its environment.

ecosystem   A system of interacting organisms; influenced by abiotic factors and requiring light as the initial source of energy.

environment   The total of all living or nonliving factors that influence an organism.

food chain   The direct flow of food and energy from the producer through a given series of consumers.

food web   The flow of food and energy between food chains.

herbivore   A plant-eating animal.

omnivore   An animal whose diet includes both plants and other animals.

producer   An organism that can convert completely inorganic material into organic material. Green plants are usually considered to be the producers.

recycling   The reprocessing of a material so it can be reused many times.

trophic level   Stages of energy flow through an ecosystem.

Purpose Within populations of organisms, there are many ways in which plants and animals influence one another. Even organisms of the same species will influence one another as they go about their normal daily activities. It will be the purpose of this chapter to consider some of these interactions. We will try to get a feeling for the tremendous variety of interactions and complexity of links that exist within a *community*, such as a forest, grassland, or desert.

Communities

Home Is Where the Niche Is

You would not expect to find a whale in the desert nor an elephant in the ocean. Each organism has particular requirements for life and lives wherever the surroundings will meet its needs. This place, locality, or portion of an ecosystem is defined by biologists as the **habitat** of an organism. Habitats are usually described in terms of their more stable and widespread parts. The idea of space is the key to understanding the concept of habitat. For example, the habitat of a prairie dog is usually described as grassland, while the habitat of a tuna fish is described as marine (salt water). In the habitat, each organism interacts with other organisms simply because they share the same living space. Each organism will have its own **niche** or functional role to perform in its habitat. Just as the word *space* is the key to understanding habitat, the word *function* is the key to understanding the concept of niche. Some of the things included in an organism's niche might be the kind of food that it eats, the kind of organisms that feed upon it, the temperature range and the pH range that it can tolerate, the kinds and amounts of growth factors needed in the diet, and the amount of water that the organism needs to stay alive. Some organisms have very broad niches while others have narrow niches that have very particular requirements. An opossum has a very broad niche since it feeds on a variety of foods, both plant and animal; it can tolerate a wide range of temperatures; and it can reproduce many young even though the environment may not be the best. The koala "bear" has a very narrow niche, since it only feeds on the leaves of certain eucalyptus trees in Australia; it cannot tolerate low temperatures; and is defenseless against most fast-moving hunting animals (fig. 19.1). The niche includes the requirements for life as well as the methods for meeting these requirements. For example, we might consider the role of consumers in a wooded area. There are many animals in this group, such as owls, robins, woodpeckers,

Fig. 19.1 *Opossum and Koala.* The opossum has a very broad niche, and the koala has a narrow, restricted niche. (Opossum photo courtesy of Michigan Department of Natural Resources; koala photo courtesy of Australian News and Information Bureau— Photo by J. Fitzpatrick.)

weasels, snakes, and frogs. All these animals may be consumers. However, they have great differences in food habits, water requirements, and abilities to move through their environment.

Therefore, we need more information to define each animal's niche; just being a consumer is not definite enough. The complete definition of a niche for an organism involves many details that are often difficult to identify. It would include the interactions of the organism with other living things (biotic) as well as with the nonliving parts (abiotic) of the habitat.

Let us consider the earthworm as an example (fig. 19.2). If you have ever dug worms to use as bait to go fishing, you learned something about their niche. Generally, you can identify their habitat as the soil. But, you may have been disappointed to find that you just can't dig into any soil to find worms. The soil in a pine woods is not likely to contain earthworms since worms feed on decaying leaves from broad-leaved trees, such as maples and oaks. In addition to moisture content of the soil; pH, concentration of dissolved salts, texture, and temperature of the soil are all nonliving factors that are a part of the earthworm's niche. This list is far from complete. We should also recognize that robins, garter snakes, and the fishermen who capture worms are a part of the worm's niche.

Good Guys, Bad Guys, and the Other Guys

When we watch a snake slithering up to strike at a mouse, we may feel sorry for the mouse. The mouse is so soft and furry and seems so helpless. The snake appears to be the "bad guy," and the mouse plays the role of the "good guy." But, this isn't the whole picture! Mice have the ability, just like all organisms, to overpopulate an area to such an extent that huge numbers will

The primary source of energy is the sun.

Producer

Consumer

Consumer

Salts   Moist topsoil   pH   Decaying leaves   Warmth

Fig. 19.2 *The Earthworm Niche.* The niche of the earthworm is more than a place. The niche includes what the worm does, as well as the living and nonliving things with which it interacts.

die from starvation or epidemic diseases. Let us multiply the mouse population by bringing in his sisters, his cousins, his aunts—his whole family. How would we feel if the mice were so abundant that they came into our houses, food stores, and restaurants? If they scampered across our tables and counters, leaving their droppings on our food and dishes, would we still think of them as soft, furry and helpless? If they chewed their way into our stored grain, cereal boxes, and loaves of bread, wouldn't we get just a little disturbed? Now, who's the bad guy and good guy?

The snake may not appeal to us, but it is one of the animals that kills and eats mice. Various hawks, owls, foxes, and coyotes are also **predators** that help to keep the mouse population in check. Predators are animals that kill and eat other animals, called **prey organisms** (fig. 19.3). Predators are useful to man, since they control the populations of man's competitors. Even though the predators harm the individuals of the species they prey upon, they have a beneficial role to play for the entire population. For example, the predators prevent overpopulation of mice, and help to prevent epidemic diseases in the mouse population by killing and eating the sick individuals.

All food-getting does not necessarily involve predator and prey organisms. For instance, the fleas that live in the fur of rats feed on the rats' blood, but could not strictly be called predators, since they do not kill and eat the rats. This association of flea and rat is an example of **parasitism.** In para-

Fig. 19.3 *Predator-Prey Relationship.* Predation is one type of interaction within a community. (Mark Boulton from National Audubon Society.)

sitism, the parasite (flea) lives in or on the **host** (rat) and benefits by obtaining nutrients and shelter from the arrangement while the host is harmed. The rat also serves as a host for other parasites, such as tapeworms, viruses, and bacteria (fig. 19.4). One bacteria, *Yersinia pestis,* does little harm to the rats, but if carried to humans, this bacteria causes the disease known as "black death," or "plague." In the flea–rat example, the flea can take in these disease organisms from one rat's blood and spread them to other rats as it hops from host to host. The rat's fleas may also hop onto humans and use them as hosts. Thus, the disease can be spread to man. It was in just this way that the "black death" was spread in the mid-14th century, killing thousands of people. In some countries of Western Europe, 50 percent of the population was killed by this disease (fig. 19.5). Man has hated and attempted to destroy rats as a result of understanding this relationship.

Predation and parasitism are both interactions in which one individual benefits and the other is harmed. However, there are other interactions in which one individual benefits, but the other is not harmed. This type is called **commensalism.** You can see an example of this in some aquarium displays. Sharks may have a smaller fish called a remora with them. The remora hitchhikes a ride with a shark by attaching itself to the ventral surface (belly) of the shark (fig. 19.6). The remora has a sucking disc on its dorsal surface (back) to permit this. While the remora benefits by eating the leftovers from the shark's meal, the shark does not appear to be troubled by this uninvited guest. Another example of commensalism is the relationship between trees and some orchid plants. The orchids live high in the branches of the trees where they receive more sunlight and rain. The trees receive no benefit from this relationship; they simply serve as a support for the orchids.

So far in our examples, only one individual has benefited from the association. However, there are situations in which individuals of two species

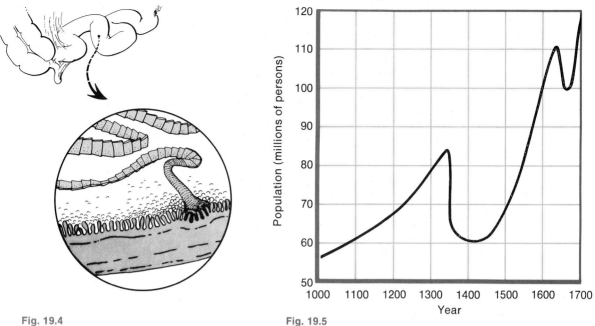

Fig. 19.4

Fig. 19.5

Fig. 19.6

Fig. 19.4 *Parasite-Host Relationship.* Parasitism is one type of interaction within a community.

Fig. 19.5 *Impact of Black Death on World Population.* The sharp reduction in the population as a result of the plague are difficult for us to appreciate today. (From "The Black Death" by William L. Langer. Copyright © 1964 by Scientific American, Inc. All rights reserved.)

Fig. 19.6 *Commensalism.* Commensalism is one type of interaction within a community. (New York Zoological Society Photo.)

live in close association and both benefit by the arrangement. This type of association is called **mutualism.** One of the interesting examples of mutualism is shown by digestion in rabbits. Rabbits eat plant material that is high in cellulose even though they do not produce the digestive enzymes capable of breaking down cellulose molecules into simple carbohydrates. While they cannot digest cellulose by themselves, they manage to get energy out of these molecules with the help of special bacteria living in their digestive tract. These bacteria produce cellulose-digesting enzymes that break the cellulose molecules into smaller carbohydrate molecules which the rabbit's enzymes can break down further. The bacteria benefit because the gut of the rabbit provides them with a moist, warm, nourishing habitat. In return for these living quarters, the bacteria provide the rabbit with food molecules that the rabbit would otherwise be unable to digest.

Another mutualistic relationship exists between certain flowering plants and bees. Undoubtedly you have all seen bees visiting flowers to drink the sugar water (nectar) from the blossoms. They sometimes accidentally pick up pollen (sperm-containing packages) during their visit and aid in the transfer of pollen to the female part of another flower (fig. 19.7). Plants pollinated in this manner produce less pollen than plants that are pollinated by relying on the wind to transfer the sperm containing packages. This saves the plant energy, since it doesn't have to manufacture as many pollen particles.

Fig. 19.7 *Mutualism.* Mutualism is one type of interaction within a community. (Courtesy of A. I. Root Co., Medina, Ohio.)

One additional term that should be mentioned here, because it is so commonly used in magazine and newspaper articles, is **symbiosis.** Unfortunately, this word is used in several ways, none of which are very clear. However, it is usually used as a synonym for mutualism or to describe all the interactions except for predation. If we use the latter meaning, then we can say that each of the following is an example of symbiosis, or has a symbiotic relationship: flea and rat (parasitism), shark and remora (commensalism), and rabbit and bacteria (mutualism).

Is Winning Really Everything?

In our discussion of interactions between organisms, we have so far left out the most common kind of interaction, **competition.** Competition is a kind of interaction between organisms in which both organisms are harmed to some extent. It may be a snarling tug-of-war between two dogs over the same scrap of food, or it may be a silent struggle between plants for light. If you have ever started tomato seeds in a garden and not weeded the garden, you have had experience with competition. The tomato plants don't stand a chance in the competition. If you don't remove the competing weeds, the tomatoes will not get the sun and water they need. This example illustrates the principle that if two species have the same requirements for life and the same methods of meeting these requirements, they cannot live in the same area for any extended period of time. One of the species will have some advantage that will help it to be naturally selected as the winner. In this case, death may come to the loser after a period of greatly stunted growth. It is possible for a population of a losing species to evolve into a different niche if competition continues over many generations. In the case of animals, a losing species may die, evolve, or may migrate out of the area. In natural habitats, room is available for many different life-styles. In other words, there are many different niches. Each species will have a relationship with other species in its habitat. All species will have some influence on others and on the habitat. There is a cycling of organic and inorganic materials through the ecosystem.

Ashes to Ashes, and Dust to Dust

The earth is a closed biosphere, since no significant amount of new matter comes to the earth from space. Only light energy comes to the earth in a continuous stream, and ultimately, this energy is released back into space. The energy is used on earth to drive all biological processes. Living systems have evolved ways for using this energy to continue life through growth and reproduction. Since no new atoms are being added to the earth, living systems must use the available atoms over and over again. In this recycling, inorganic molecules are combined to form the organic compounds of living things. If there were no way of recycling this organic matter back into its inorganic form, the organic material would build up as dead organisms. The decomposers play a vital role in this process if they are given the chance. But if they are kept from doing their job, the organic material may build up. This has happened on earth in the past, and we identify this absence of recycling as deposits of oil, natural gas, and coal.

Living systems contain many different kinds of atoms, but some are more common and important than others. Carbon, nitrogen, oxygen, hydrogen, and phosphorus are found in all living things and must be recycled when an organism dies. Let's look at some examples. Carbon and oxygen are combined to form the molecule carbon dioxide, which is found as a gas in the atmosphere. During photosynthesis, the carbon dioxide is combined with water to form complex organic molecules. At the same time, oxygen molecules are released into the atmosphere. This additional organic matter present in the bodies of plants may be used by herbivores as food. When an herbivore eats a plant, it breaks down the complex organic molecules into more simple molecules that are used for building its own body. These carbon and oxygen molecules may be transferred to a carnivore for its use if the herbivore is preyed upon. Finally, decomposers may completely break down waste products and the organic molecules of dead organisms into carbon dioxide and water. The carbon atoms that started as carbon dioxide in the atmosphere passed through a series of organisms as organic carbon, and were finally returned to the atmosphere as carbon dioxide (fig. 19.8).

Another very important atom is nitrogen. This atom is essential in the formation of proteins and nucleic acids. Nitrogen is found as a gas in the atmosphere. However, only a few kinds of bacteria are able to change the gas into a form that other organisms can use. The amount of nitrogen available to plants is an important factor that limits their growth. There are two ways in which plants and animals can get usable nitrogen compounds. First, symbiotic bacteria in the roots of some plants can convert nitrogen gas into a form that the host plant can use to make amino acids and nucleic acids. These bacteria are called **symbiotic nitrogen-fixing bacteria.** This is another example of a narrow niche, since only certain plants, particularly those known as **legumes** (beans, peas, and clover), can form this kind of relationship.

The second way in which plants and animals can get usable nitrogen compounds involves a series of different bacteria that can convert ammonia (NH_3) into nitrite (NO_2^-) and then into nitrate (NO_3^-) containing compounds. Plants can use the nitrates in the soil to make amino acids. These bacteria are not symbionts, but are found living free in the soil. All the organic nitrogen found in plants, herbivores, and carnivores is returned to inorganic nitrogen (ammonia) through a different series of bacteria. These bacteria are capable of converting either the nitrate, nitrite, or ammonia into nitrogen gas (fig. 19.9).

The amount of nitrogen in the soil is one of the major determining factors in the growth rate of plants. Farmers can make usable nitrogen

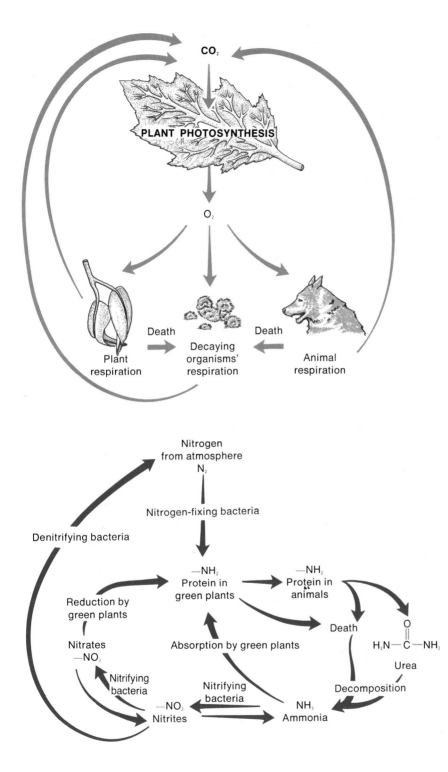

Fig. 19.8 *The Carbon and Oxygen Cycle.* The use and reuse of carbon and oxygen are closely tied together for the benefit of life on earth.

CO₂

PLANT PHOTOSYNTHESIS

O₂

Death

Death

Plant respiration

Decaying organisms' respiration

Animal respiration

Nitrogen from atmosphere
N₂

Nitrogen-fixing bacteria

Denitrifying bacteria

—NH₂
Protein in green plants

—NH₂
Protein in animals

Reduction by green plants

Death

O
‖
H₂N—C—NH₂

Absorption by green plants

Urea

Nitrates
—NO₃

Nitrifying bacteria

Nitrifying bacteria

Decomposition

—NO₂
Nitrites

NH₃
Ammonia

Fig. 19.9 *The Nitrogen Cycle.* Nitrogen is circulated through a community through the action of bacteria, plants, and animals.

available to their crops in a number of different ways. One year, they may plant crops that have symbiotic nitrogen-fixing bacteria; and the next year in the same field, they may plant a nitrogen-demanding crop. Rotating the crops in this way helps to maintain nitrogen in the soil. The farmer can also add nitrogen directly to the soil in a variety of ways. He may spread manure on the field and rely upon the soil bacteria to convert the nitrogen in the manure to a usable form, or he may add industrially produced fertilizers. These are usually nitrate compounds or ammonia. But even if the farmer adds industrially produced fertilizers to the field, he is still relying on the soil bacteria to make the fertilizer nitrogen available to the plants.

Fertilizers usually contain more than just nitrogen compounds. The numbers on the fertilizer bag tell you the percentage of nitrogen, potassium, and phosphorus in the fertilizer. These other elements also cycle through ecosystems, and as crops are removed from the land, so are these elements. And so the farmer must replace them by adding more fertilizer. In a more natural ecosystem, the bacteria would decompose the dead plants and animals in the field and recycle the elements.

If Ever You Should Leave Me

Since all organisms in a community interact, the loss of a single species will have an influence on other species. This may occur as a chain of events through the food web. In South Dakota, for example, the decision was made to reduce the fox and coyote populations because it was thought that they preyed on pheasants. Although the fox and coyote populations were not completely killed off, their numbers were drastically reduced. Even when the supposed predators were reduced in number, the pheasant populations did not increase. However, the populations of rabbits and mice increased rapidly and became serious pests. This helps us to understand that a community of organisms is a very complex set of interactions, and we should carefully consider any actions that may upset this balance. What seemed to be a simple relationship of foxes and coyotes preying on pheasants turned out to be more complex. Rabbits and mice were actually the prey of the foxes and coyotes, not the pheasants. The controversy about the value of eliminating such predatory organisms from a community is still a topic of great debate and continues to break into the news.

The situation could be compared to the act of dropping a rock from a bridge into a pond. Large disturbances will form where the rock hits the water. As the waves move out, they get smaller and smaller, and only small ripples reach the shore. This disturbance will be felt throughout the pond just as the death of a population will be felt by all the other populations in a community. Suppose we were to drop the same rock into a shallow pan of water. We would splash most of the water out of the pan. The same event in the large pond had a relatively minor effect. Similarly, a change in a community may have a great or small effect depending on the degree of its complexity. If there are a great number of different species in a given area, the death of one species will cause only a small disturbance in the lives of most of the other species. If there are a small number of species, the elimination of one may result in drastic alterations in the community. For example, if deer mice are completely eliminated from a community, those predators that eat them will not starve or migrate as long as there are other types of mice available. However, if the deer mice are the only source of food for the predators in this community, then the disappearance of these mice would be serious. Therefore, we should not take the possibility of extinction of a species lightly. Consider the various organisms that are placed on the list of endangered species (fig. 19.10). You will note that some of these are commercially valuable, while others may appear to have only aesthetic value. In either case, the loss of these species may have far-reaching effects within each of their communities. All the organisms on this list are not found in the same place, but occur in a variety of different kinds of communities. We will look at a few of the major types of communities in more detail.

Fig. 19.10 *Endangered Species.* A major problem in preserving endangered species, such as these, is awakening the people to the fact that there is a problem. (Courtesy of Michigan Department of Natural Resources.)

Types of Communities

Since communities are so complex, man artificially sets boundaries to allow himself to better study and understand the interactions of organisms. If you wished to define such an area, one that has natural rather than man-made boundaries, you might select a small lake. The water's edge naturally defines the limits of this community. You would expect to find certain animals and plants living in the lake, such as fish, frogs, snails, insects, algae, pondweeds, bacteria, and fungi. The lake would be the habitat that determines the limits of the community. You might be ready at this point to ask, what about the plants and animals that live right at the water's edge? And that question will lead us to mention other animals that spend only part of their life in the water. That awkward looking, long-legged bird, wading in the shallows and darting its long beak down to spear a fish, actually has its nest atop some tall trees away from the water. Should it be considered as a part of the pond community? Should we also include the deer that comes down at dusk for a drink and then wanders away? What seems at first to be a very well-defined community has been stretched so that we are now wondering about casual visitors. There could be very small parasites in the water that could enter the deer as it drinks the water. These parasites may have spent part of their life in the snails that inhabit the pond. They will mature within the deer and feed at its expense. This establishes a relationship that would functionally include the deer in this community. We can see that although the general outlines of a community can be established, it is very difficult to decide just exactly who the members of a community are (fig. 19.11).

Fig. 19.11 *Community Inhabitants.* Deer and trout may both be considered as part of the lake community, even though the deer is only a transient member of this community. (Courtesy of Michigan Department of Natural Resources.)

The lake is only one of many naturally defined areas that form small communities. These smaller communities are a part of large, regional communities called **biomes.** One of the large land-based biomes in the eastern part of the United States is the temperate deciduous forest. This is a forested region made up largely of deciduous trees. Deciduous trees are those that lose their leaves more or less completely during a particular season each year.

Aspen, birch, cottonwood, oak, hickory, beech, and maple are all examples of deciduous trees. This biome, like other land-based regional biomes, is named after the major plant type. This naming system works fairly well, since the major type of plant is a general guide to what other plants and animals would be found in this region. Of course, since the region is so large and has different climatic conditions, we would expect to find some differences in particular species. For instance, in Maryland the tulip tree is one of the common large trees, while in Michigan it is so unusual that people plant it in lawns and parks as a decorative tree. Animals typical of this biome are skunks, porcupines, opossums, hawks, and owls.

Refer to the map of the various regional communities (fig. 19.12). The

Fig. 19.12 _Biomes of the World._ Although most of the biomes are named for a type of vegetation, they would each include a specialized group of animals.

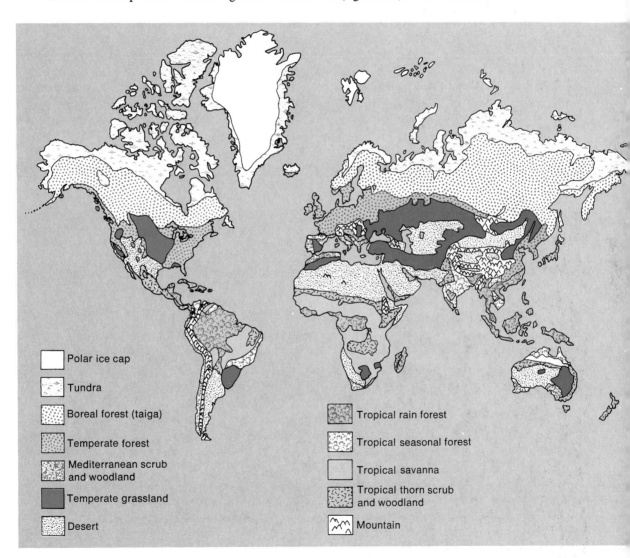

Polar ice cap

Tundra

Boreal forest (taiga)

Temperate forest

Mediterranean scrub and woodland

Temperate grassland

Desert

Tropical rain forest

Tropical seasonal forest

Tropical savanna

Tropical thorn scrub and woodland

Mountain

temperate deciduous forest covers a great deal of territory, from the Mississippi River to the Atlantic Ocean, and from Florida to Vermont and New Hampshire. However, many areas within this general region are quite different from one another, and some of them have no trees of any kind. For example, the tops of some of the mountains along the Appalachian Trail, the sand dunes of Lake Michigan, and the scattered grassy areas in Illinois are natural areas lacking deciduous trees. Many areas have no trees because they have been removed to provide agricultural land.

Another community located to the west of the temperate deciduous forest is the prairie biome. The rainfall in this grassland is not enough to support the growth of trees (fig. 19.13). The only places that trees are common in this biome are along streams. The plants that can survive in this biome are

Fig. 19.13 *Prairie Community.* This typical short-grass prairie of our western states is associated with an annual rainfall of 15–20 inches. This community contains a unique grouping of plant and animal species.

those that can grow in drier conditions. Animals found in this biome include the prairie dog, pronghorn antelope, and the prairie chicken. However, most of the original grasslands have been converted to agricultural uses. This required the breaking of a thick layer of sod formed by the original species of grasses that grew on the plains of the United States. Sod is a thick spongy layer of roots that helps to retain water and to hold the nutrient laden soil in place. The breaking of the sod and growth of wheat, corn, and other grains exposes the soil directly to the wind. This change may result in excess drying and loss of soil in the wind.

Moving North

Through parts of southern Canada and along the mountains of the western United States, we find communities that are dominated by evergreen trees. These areas are known as the coniferous forest (fig. 19.14). In some areas it consists of spruce trees in very wet soil, which can support animal life such as moose and wolves. In other coniferous forest areas, the most prominent trees are the different kinds of pines. A good example of this would be the ponderosa pines on the east side of the Rocky Mountains. These trees are very tall and straight with their branches high off the ground. They are widely scattered, giving a parklike appearance, since there is very little plant growth on the forest floor.

Fig. 19.14 *Coniferous Forest Community.* Conifers are the dominant vegetation in the higher altitudes of sections of western North America. This type of forest also contains a unique variety of other plants and animals.

Fig. 19.15 *Tundra.* The tundra biome is located in the parts of the world where permafrost is characteristic. These harsh environmental conditions dictate the types of plants and animals that can survive in these regions. (Courtesy of Chugach Nat. Forest.)

Further north, the trees are entirely absent. We refer to this area as the tundra (fig. 19.15). Severe long winters prevent many types of plants and animals from living in this area. Only those plants and animals that can withstand these winter conditions can grow and reproduce in the very short summer of the tundra. Typical plants and animals of the tundra include reindeer moss, snowy owl, caribou, musk ox, flies, mosquitos, flowering plants, and shrubs. Because the weather conditions are so severe, only a few species of plants and animals survive. This community is relatively simple, and therefore any changes in this community may have drastic and long-lasting effects. The tundra is easy to injure and is slow to heal; therefore, we must treat it very gently.

Fig. 19.16 *Tropical Rain Forest.* A tropical rain forest is noted for the tremendous variety of plant and animal life. (Courtesy of Department of Natural Resources, Puerto Rico—Douglas J. Pool.)

Tarzan's Jungle

The climate opposite that of the tundra is the tropical rain forest. They are located primarily around the equator in South America, Africa, and some of the islands of the Pacific (fig. 19.16). The temperature is high, the rain falls nearly every day, and there are hundreds of different species of plants and animals. Balsa wood, used in many model airplanes, is found in the rain forest, as is teakwood, used in fine furniture. Other plants of the rain forest include orchids, many kinds of vines, fern trees, and mosses. Termites, tree frogs, bats, lizards, monkeys, and an almost infinite variety of unique insects are typical of the rain forest. These forests are very dense and prevent sunlight from penetrating to the floor. When the forest is disturbed by any event that opens it up (such as a hurricane), the light is able to reach the forest floor, and this allows very rapid overgrowth of the disturbed area. Since plants grow so rapidly in these forests, many attempts have been made to bring this land into cultivation. North American agricultural methods and crops require clearing of large areas and the planting of a single species such as corn. The rain falling on these fields quickly removes the soil's nutrients so that the corn is incapable of growing and requires heavy applications of fertilizer. However, because of the high cost of fertilizer and other associated problems, the use of these lands for agricultural purposes is impractical.

Community Evolution

All of the biomes we have just described are relatively long-lasting, stable mixtures of plants and animals. Many stable communities have been destroyed so that man could grow food crops. In some cases, he was unsuccessful and left the land to return to its natural state. This return to the original community does not happen instantaneously, but occurs through a series of recognizable stages. In the region of the temperate deciduous forest, abandoned agricultural land will first fill with weeds. Grasses will quickly follow and then, in turn, low shrubs, bushes, and finally, short-lived trees will begin to grow in the area. These trees will eventually be replaced by longer living and slower growing trees (fig. 19.17). As the plants change, so do the animals that live in the community. This series of changes of recognizable communities is called **succession,** and ultimately leads to a relatively stable,

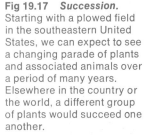

Fig 19.17 *Succession.* Starting with a plowed field in the southeastern United States, we can expect to see a changing parade of plants and associated animals over a period of many years. Elsewhere in the country or the world, a different group of plants would succeed one another.

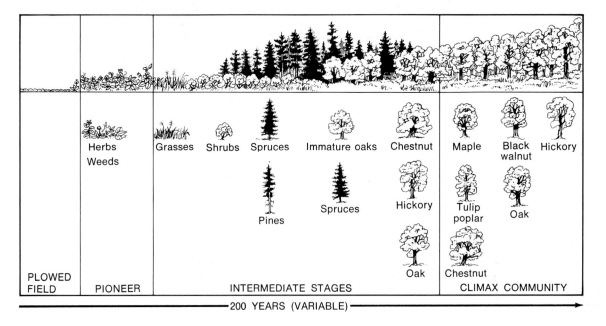

PLOWED FIELD	PIONEER	INTERMEDIATE STAGES	CLIMAX COMMUNITY
	Herbs Weeds	Grasses Shrubs Spruces Immature oaks Chestnut Pines Spruces Hickory Oak	Maple Black walnut Hickory Tulip poplar Oak Chestnut

← 200 YEARS (VARIABLE) →

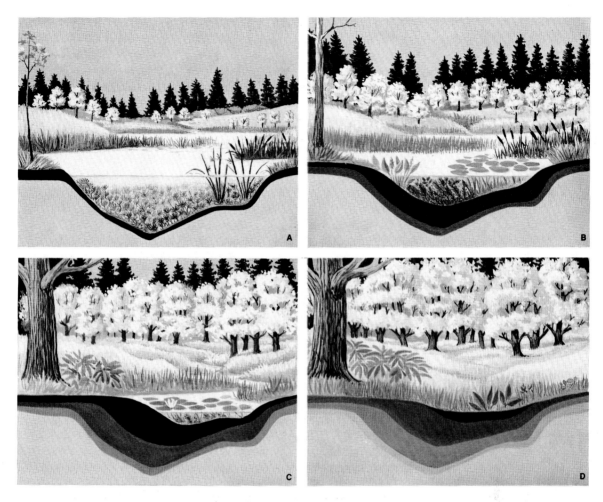

long-lasting mixture of plants and animals called the **climax community.** We have already pointed out examples of climax communities in our discussions of the temperate deciduous forest, the grasslands, the tundra, the coniferous forest, and the tropical rain forest.

Sometimes it is difficult to recognize that communities change because the changes are usually slow. However, when the shallow portions of ponds get clogged with algae, it is easy to recognize that a change has occurred. It might not be obvious that this is a natural process of change that has been speeded up by the fertilization of the ponds with our wastes. The succession can be observed by noticing the changes in the kinds of plants growing along the shore. Away from the shore, we only find floating plants, such as the water lilies that send their roots down to the mucky pond bottom. Still shallower water has rushes and cattails, and on the marshy shore are alder and willow trees (fig. 19.18). The higher ground beyond the shore supports large trees. This series of plants illustrates the sequence of changes that

Fig. 19.18 *Succession from Pond to Wet Meadow.* The pond is slowly filling up with layers of soil; the newest layers of soil are darker. Notice the tree at the left as it ages. This will give you some idea of the time required for succession from pond to wet meadow.

results in the conversion of the shallow pool into solid ground. As the living things die, the bottom muck slowly builds up and the pond fills. The whole series of plants creep farther and farther into the filling pool. Given enough time, this pond will become a wet meadow. This gradual change of plants will produce a corresponding change in the populations of animals in the community.

Summary   Some of the kinds of interactions that occur between the members of a community are predation, parasitism, commensalism, mutualism, and competition. In predation and parasitism, the interaction favors one of the individuals at the expense of the other. Commensalism benefits one, but has no effect on the other; while mutualism provides benefits for both interacting individuals. Competition results in harm to both of the organisms. There is a distinction between habitat and niche. Habitat is a place, while the niche involves the functional role of an organism. The concept of niche is important in understanding interactions of a community, since two species cannot occupy the same niche in the same place for any length of time. Competition between them will result in one being killed off or being forced to migrate. The members of a community depend on one another. Chemical elements are recycled through the ecosystem as some organisms change inorganic molecules to organic compounds, and other organisms change organic compounds to inorganic molecules. The death of a population may drastically alter the whole community. Communities are a natural grouping of populations and range from the small ones, based on a geographic feature such as a lake, to large regional biomes. The land-based biomes are named after the principal type of plants growing in the region, such as the temperate deciduous forest, coniferous forest, grassland, tundra, and tropical rain forest. All of these communities are constantly changing. This process of succession leads to a climax community. However, even this is subject to change by fire, flood, or other events.

Consider This   This is a thought puzzle: put it together! Here are the pieces:

—People are starving.
—Commercial fertilizer production requires a temperature of 900°C.
—Geneticists have developed plants that grow very rapidly and require high amounts of nitrogen to germinate during the normal growing season.
—Fossil fuels are stored organic matter.
—The rate of the nitrogen cycle is dependent on the activity of the bacteria.
—The sun is expected to last for another million years.
—Crop rotation is becoming a thing of the past.
—Clearing of forests for agriculture changes weather in the area.

1. Describe your niche.
2. What is the difference between habitat and niche?
3. What do parasites, commensal organisms, and mutualistic organisms have in common? How are they different?
4. Describe two situations in which competition may involve combat, and two in which combat is not involved.
5. What may happen to an atom of carbon in a community that contains plants, herbivores, decomposers, and parasites?
6. What organisms are involved in the maintenance of the nitrogen cycle?
7. What is the value of a complex ecosystem as opposed to a simple ecosystem?
8. What are the major biomes of the world, and how do they differ?
9. How does a climax community differ from any of the stages that precede it?
10. What is the difference between a climax community and a biome?

biome   Large geographic areas that are composed of particular kinds of communities.

climax community   A stable stage in succession, in which the numbers and kinds of organisms remain relatively unchanged.

commensalism   The relationship between two kinds of organisms in which one benefits and the other is not affected.

community   The interrelationships among various populations that share a similar habitat.

competition   The relationship between two species in which each population is adversely affected by the other.

habitat   The natural place where an organism lives.

host   An organism that provides the necessities for a parasite—generally food, a place to live, etc.

legumes   Types of plants, members of the bean family, that can have a mutualistic association with nitrogen-fixing bacteria in their roots.

mutualism   The relationship between two kinds of organisms in which both benefit from the association.

niche   The functional role that an organism plays in its habitat. The life-style of an organism.

parasitism   The relationship between two kinds of organisms in which one (the parasite) feeds on the other (the host) while living in or on the host.

predation   The relationship between two kinds of organisms in which one (the predator) directly attacks and eats the other (the prey).

predator   The organism that attacks and eats its prey.

prey organisms   The organism that is attacked and eaten by its predator.

succession   The orderly process of change in the populations of a community over a period of time.

symbiosis   Any of a number of close relationships between two species of organisms, which may or may not be beneficial to the various kinds of organisms.

symbiotic nitrogen-fixing bacteria   Organisms mutualistically associated with the roots of legumes, which change atmospheric nitrogen into a form of nitrogen that the plant can use.

Purpose   One of the important ideas held by most scientists is that plant and animal species have changed from their first appearance on earth and continue to change today. Some primary questions can be raised. (1) How do species change? (2) What causes new species to be formed? (3) What evidence exists that new species are being produced? This chapter introduces you to the process of speciation and presents evidence that supports this theory.

Speciation

Population Genetics Revisited

The past few chapters have pointed out that a variety of life-styles exist on earth today. Each organism is specialized to live in a specific ecosystem. The organisms that fill each of the various niches do so because they have the genes necessary to survive there. Their genes have been selected by the actions of the environment. The process of natural selection operates on all organisms over many generations of time. Chapter sixteen dealt with the Hardy-Weinberg Law, which pointed out how natural selection could alter the frequency of genes in a particular population of organisms. This change in the gene pool is brought about by the environment and adapts the species to those particular conditions. However, the fact still remains that these organisms share the same gene pool. It is this sharing that allows biologists to classify organisms as belonging to the same species. Over generations of time, the genes of a species are passed from one generation to another, and a gene that originates in one geographic location may flow to another geographic location (fig. 20.1). This is possible because organisms migrate or

Fig. 20.1 *Gene Flow in Rabbits.* Gene flow occurs when organisms migrate or are carried from one place to another and produce offspring in this new territory. If the rabbits with white coat color genes were to migrate toward the east, there would be a flow of white coat color genes to the east.

are carried from one place to another. This movement of genes is referred to as **gene flow.** A species tends to disperse into new geographic areas by migrating or being carried by such outside forces as storms and wind, or by being attached to other organisms. If the new home is suitable, a new colony is started and the species has a wider geographic distribution. As a species expands its **range,** the members become more separated from one another.

This separation means that certain members of the gene pool may have less frequent gene exchange (mating) with their more geographically distant relatives. It is also likely that this geographic separation may become so complete that there is no gene flow between the original pool and the "suburban" relatives (fig. 20.2). If we define a species as being a group of individuals that share the same gene pool, are these separated groups really of

Fig. 20.2 *Original and "Suburban" Populations.* The original population may give rise to a number of satellite populations. As long as gene flow occurs between these populations, they are usually considered to be of the same species.

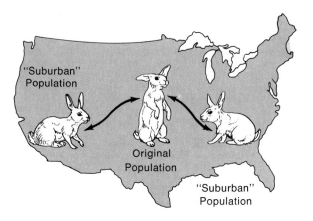

the same species? This question has long been considered by biologists and is at the heart of understanding the evolutionary process. Put in other words, is it possible that one species may give rise to another? And, what factors may contribute to the production of a new species?

The Species Problem

Before considering the question of the production of new species, let us consider how a single species may be distinguished from other species. A **species** is commonly defined as a population of organisms that can interbreed naturally to produce fertile offspring. Let us look at some examples to see how this definition may be applied. Coyotes have been known to mate with dogs to produce pups. However, this mating does not commonly happen in nature, and so coyotes and dogs are considered to be separate species, despite these occasional successful matings. A second example involves matings between a male donkey and a female horse. The young produced will grow to be adult mules, incapable of reproduction (fig. 20.3). This inability of the mules to produce young means that their parents (horses and donkeys) do

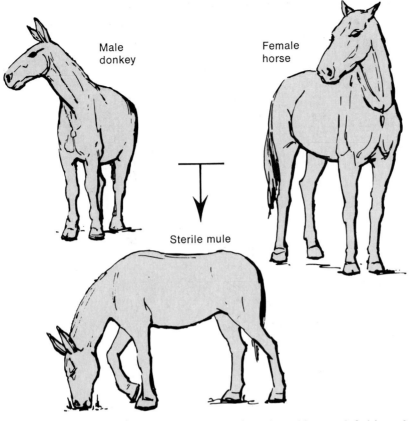

Male donkey

Female horse

Sterile mule

not belong to the same species. The word interbreed used in our definition of species means that the offspring will be able to produce young when they are adults.

How Species Originate: Geographic Isolation

The most common way to isolate a portion of a gene pool from its original population is by the formation of **geographic barriers.** The history of the earth tells us that changes have occurred on its surface that could have physically divided a species into two or more **geographically isolated** populations. The uplifting of mountains, the rerouting of rivers, and the formation of deserts all may separate one portion of a gene pool from another. These are large scale changes, but even small changes may cause isolation. A fallen tree, a plowed field, or even a new freeway may serve as a very effective isolating mechanism for those organisms that have very little ability to be transported from one place to another. Snails in two valleys separated by a high ridge have been found to be closely related, but are different species. The snails cannot get from one valley to the other because of the barrier of height and climate that the ridge presents (fig. 20.4).

Fig. 20.4 *Effect of Geographic Isolation on a Snail Population.* If a single population of snails was divided into two populations by the upheaval of a mountain, then the two populations might evolve enough differences to become separate species.

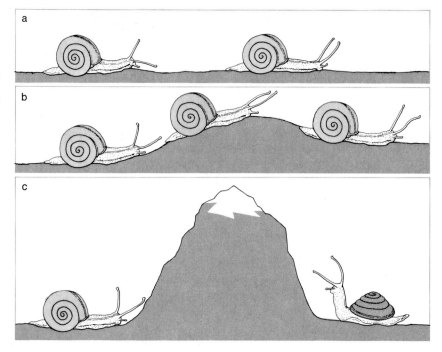

Separation of a gene pool into several parts is not enough to generate new species. It is possible that even after many generations of isolation, these groups may still be able to exchange genes if they overcome the geographic barrier. If gene flow is possible, then **speciation** has not occurred. The separation of the gene pool into smaller gene puddles is not the only requirement for the generation of new species.

Natural selection and differences in environments play a very important role in the process of speciation. It is very likely that following separation from the main gene pool the individuals within the small local population will experience different environmental conditions from the main population. If, for example, a mountain has separated a single population into two, one side may receive more rain or more sunlight than the other (fig. 20.5). These environmental differences act as natural selective agents on the gene pools and differentially select different gene combinations from the two gene pools. As a result, the two populations may show differences in color, height, enzyme production, time of seed germination, or many other characteristics. If these differences are great enough, these separated populations are called **subspecies.**

On Not Getting It All Together

The most important genetic changes leading to the production of new species are those that control reproduction. If differences in reproduction

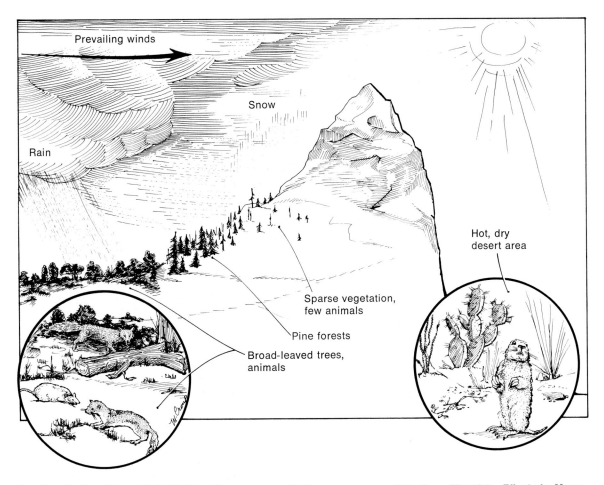

Prevailing winds

Rain

Snow

Hot, dry
desert area

Sparse vegetation,
few animals

Pine forests

Broad-leaved trees,
animals

develop during the period of time that two populations are geographically isolated, a reuniting of the two populations may not result in successful interbreeding. The two populations would then be considered separate species, since they no longer share the same gene pool. It is during the geographic isolation of two segments of a gene pool that genetic isolating mechanisms come about. The longer two groups are separated, the more likely it is that environmental changes, mutations, and natural selection will result in the development of **genetic isolating mechanisms.** These are any genetically determined characteristics that prevent reproduction between species. A great many types of these mechanisms are in operation today.

In central Mexico, two species of robin-sized birds, called *towhees,* live in different environmental settings. The collared towhee lives on the mountainside in the pine forests while the spotted towhee is found at lower elevations in oak forests. Geography presents no barrier to these birds. They are perfectly capable of flying to each other's habitat. Nevertheless, they are isolated from each other by their **habitat preference.** There are also differ-

Fig. 20.5 *Effect of a Mountain Range on Plant and Animal Communities.* More rain falls on the western side of the Rocky Mountains than on the eastern side. Consequently there is abundant vegetation on the western slopes and only scattered, desert-type plant communities on the east. This has a similar effect on the type and variety of animals living in these two situations.

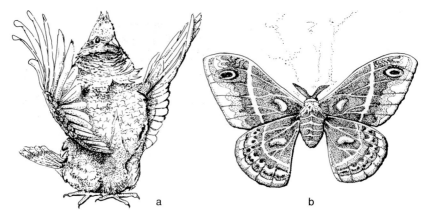

Fig. 20.6 *Courtship Behavior.* Dancing by the male prairie chicken only attracts females of the same species. This behavior tends to keep the prairie chicken reproductively isolated from other species of grouse. The male moth at the right is attracted to the female of the same species by a distinctive scent.

a   b

ences in the reproductive process that can act as genetic isolating mechanisms to prevent two species from interbreeding. Some plants flower only in the spring while other closely related species flower only later in the summer. These two groups of plants cannot pollinate each other because of this **seasonal isolation.**

Inborn behavior patterns are still another mechanism that prevents breeding between species. The courtship activities of birds and the mating calls of frogs are highly specific. For example, prairie chicken males will gather on meadows shortly before dawn in the early summer. By the time there is enough light for anyone to see these birds, they have started their solo dances (fig. 20.6). Air sacs on either side of their neck will be inflated so that the bright red skin can be clearly seen by the females. Their feet move up-and-down very fast while their wings are outspread and quiver slightly. This goes on for some time until a female prairie chicken appears. The males then compete for her attention by dancing. Eventually, she will mate with one of the males courting her. How does she know which one to select? They all look alike to us! Within an hour after sunrise, the party starts to break up. A few at a time, the birds leave in different directions until the dancing ground is empty except for droppings and stray feathers here and there on the grass. This has been a closed dance; not everyone was invited. Only one species of bird was out there beating its feet and mating. Furthermore, there had to be the proper exchange of signals between the male and female before mating could take place.

Other species of birds have similar, but not identical, dances. The dance differences are great enough that the females of one species can recognize a dance of a male of her own species. **Behavioral isolating mechanisms** such as this also occur among other types of animals. The strutting of peacocks, the fin display of Siamese fighting fish, and the light-flashing patterns of different species of fireflies are all examples of behavior that help to prevent different species from interbreeding and producing hybrids (fig. 20.7).

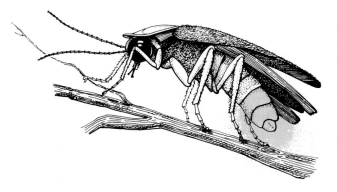

Fig. 20.7 *Behavioral Isolating Mechanisms.* Each species of firefly has its own pattern of light flashes. This pattern is a behavioral cue to members of the same species that mating is appropriate. Other flashing patterns would not signal members of this species in the same way. This behavior mechanism isolates one species from another.

Instant Speciation

So far we have only considered those hereditary changes that take a long time to add up to enough differences to make a new species. This is believed to be the manner in which all of the higher animals and most of the plants have developed new species. In plants we have a number of examples of speciation that are the result of a different kind of change called **polyploidy.** Polyploids are organisms that have increased their chromosome number because of improper cell divisions. If the original population had a diploid chromosome number of six, the polyploid population might have twelve, eighteen, or twenty-four chromosomes. If an organism has increased its chromosome number, it may be impossible for that organism to form normal gametes that could be exchanged with the parental gene pool. However, many of these polyploids can reproduce asexually. This results in a population of polyploids that can now reproduce sexually because each member of the population has the same number of chromosomes. In other words, a new gene pool has been formed, which is automatically isolated from the parental species. A few of the common polyploids are cotton, potatoes, sugarcane, wheat, and many types of garden flowers.

Biological History

The family tree of an organism is very difficult to trace because many of its ancestors are no longer in existence. Biologists must use a great deal of indirect evidence to piece together the series of evolutionary changes that have led to present-day organisms. Figure 20.8 is an example of a family tree illustrating a series of separate speciations leading to the formation of two present-day species. In reality, the construction of such a tree is very difficult, since most of the species involved are extinct. This pattern of spreading, or **divergent evolution,** can be seen in figure 20.9. The evolutionary tree is incomplete, since some of the evolutionary history is not yet known. As with speciation, divergent evolution is usually a slow process, but exceptions to this pattern have been seen.

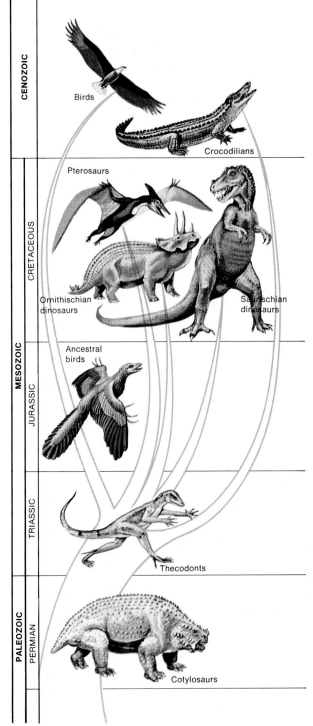

CENOZOIC

Birds

Crocodilians

Pterosaurs

CRETACEOUS

MESOZOIC

Ornithischian
dinosaurs

Saurischian
dinosaurs

Ancestral
birds

JURASSIC

TRIASSIC

Thecodonts

PALEOZOIC

PERMIAN

Cotylosaurs

Fig. 20.8 *Evolution of Present Species.* If you only had the two present-day species to look at, it would be difficult to tell exactly how they are related to one another.

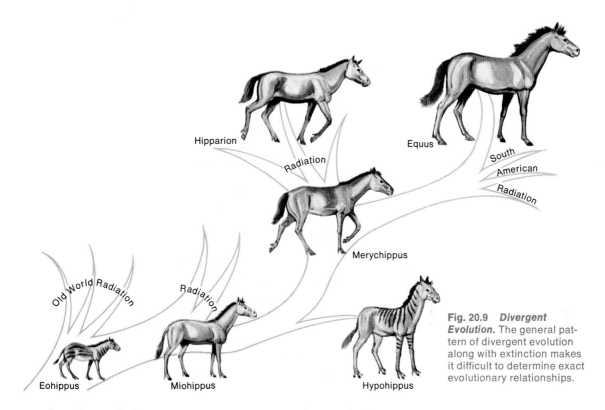

Fig. 20.9 *Divergent Evolution.* The general pattern of divergent evolution along with extinction makes it difficult to determine exact evolutionary relationships.

Labels on figure: Hipparion, Equus, South American Radiation, Radiation, Merychippus, Old World Radiation, Radiation, Eohippus, Miohippus, Hypohippus

Adaptive radiation is an evolutionary pattern that results in an explosion in the number of species of a particular group, such as amphibians, insects, birds, or reptiles. This usually involves the invasion of an unoccupied habitat, or the formation of a new set of characteristics that will cause the organism to force existing species out of their niches (fig. 20.10). For example, at one time there were no animals on the landmasses of the earth. The amphibians were the first animals able to invade the land. There was a rapid evolution of a variety of different kinds of amphibians as unoccupied niches were filled. Fossil evidence shows that there were many kinds of amphibians that are not found today. They were replaced by the reptiles that were derived from the amphibians. The reptiles were much better adapted to dry land. The resulting adaptive radiation of reptiles eliminated most of the amphibians as reptiles of every size, shape, habit, reproductive ability, and food preference took over the niches that the amphibians had formerly held. The adaptive radiation of mammals and birds eventually drove most of the reptiles from their niches. The result of this radiation is that today we find only a few of the many kinds of amphibians and reptiles that existed in the past (fig. 20.11).

Another evolutionary pattern that may lead to the misinterpretation of evolutionary trees is called **convergent evolution.** This occurs when a number of very different organisms evolve into the same type of niche. Since the

Fig. 20.10 *Adaptive Radiation.* The increase in differences between members of an invading group of organisms can be brought about by the opportunities for many different life-styles in this new habitat.

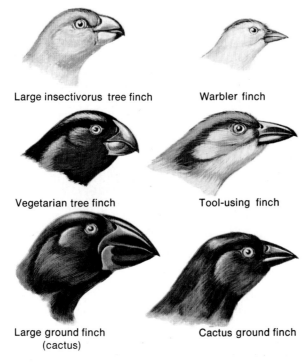

Large insectivorus tree finch

Warbler finch

Vegetarian tree finch

Tool-using finch

Large ground finch (cactus)

Cactus ground finch

Fig. 20.11 *Evolution of Higher Vertebrates.* The reptiles, birds, and mammals are all believed to have arisen from the amphibian class.

HISTORICAL RECORD OF THE VERTEBRATES

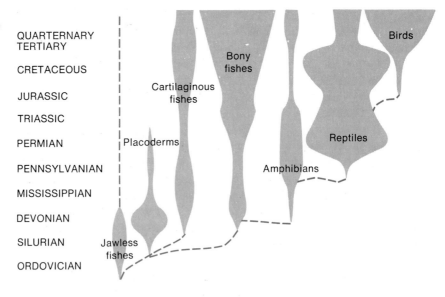

QUARTERNARY
TERTIARY

CRETACEOUS

JURASSIC

TRIASSIC

PERMIAN

PENNSYLVANIAN

MISSISSIPPIAN

DEVONIAN

SILURIAN

ORDOVICIAN

Cartilaginous fishes

Bony fishes

Birds

Placoderms

Reptiles

Amphibians

Jawless fishes

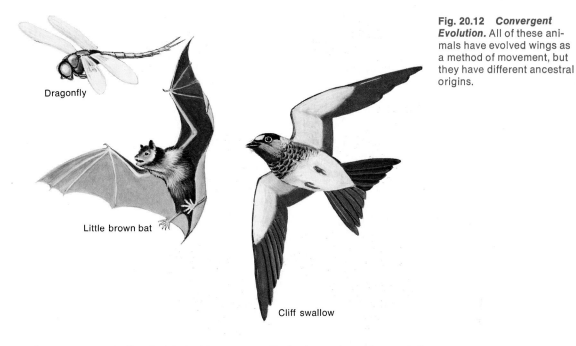

Fig. 20.12 *Convergent Evolution.* All of these animals have evolved wings as a method of movement, but they have different ancestral origins.

Dragonfly

Little brown bat

Cliff swallow

organisms occupy similar habitats, there are a limited number of ways of solving the same problems. For example, bats, swallows, and dragonflies all make their living in basically the same way (occupy similar niches). They fly about and catch insects, which they use for food (fig. 20.12). All three have wings that allow them to catch their prey, but their wings are all structurally different. These three animals have converged in structure, food organisms, and method of obtaining food. A casual study of these three may lead a person to think that they are all very closely related, but a more detailed examination of their structure reveals that this is not true. This is generally the case when convergent evolution is discussed. The organisms are thought to have converged upon the same point, from different origins.

Summary

In this chapter we have explored the ways in which species originate. Speciation involves many small changes in the offspring of many generations. The small changes must be adaptations, and there must be an isolation of two or more parts of a population so that interbreeding is prevented. Geographic isolation allows these species differences to develop, and a variety of other isolating mechanisms to keep the new species from successfully interbreeding once the geographic barrier is gone. Some isolating mechanisms that prevent interbreeding are: behavioral isolation, habitat preference, and seasonal isolation. Rapid evolution in plants may also occur because of polyploidy that results from abnormal cell division. In addition to the general pattern of divergence and extinction, more specific evolutionary patterns of adaptive radiation and convergence exist.

Questions

1. Why is geographic isolation necessary in order for speciation to occur?
2. How does speciation differ from the formation of subspecies or races?
3. Why aren't mules considered to be a species?
4. Describe three different kinds of genetic isolating mechanisms that prevent interbreeding between different species.
5. How does a polyploid organism differ from a haploid or diploid organism?
6. Can you always tell by looking at two organisms whether or not they belong to the same species?
7. What is the difference between divergent evolution and adaptive radiation?
8. How does convergent evolution differ from divergent evolution?
9. Give an example of seasonal isolation.
10. List the series of events necessary for speciation to occur.

Chapter Glossary

adaptive radiation   A rapid form of divergent evolution resulting in a great variety of related species.

behavioral isolating mechanisms   Genetically determined behavior that prevents interbreeding between species. Examples: courtship behavior and nesting behavior.

convergent evolution   A pattern of evolution leading to similarities among different lines of evolution. Example: fish and dolphins both have similar body shapes though they are unrelated.

divergent evolution   A pattern of evolution that slowly generates a greater variety of species from a common ancestor.

gene flow   The movement of genes from one geographical area to another over generations of time.

genetic isolating mechanisms   Characteristics determined by genes that prevent interbreeding between species.

geographic barrier   Any physical factor that prevents the movement of a population.

geographic isolation   A separation by barriers of members of the same gene pool into two or more groups.

habitat preference   A genetic isolating mechanism that controls the behavior of separate species and prevents these species from living in the same location.

polyploidy   The possession of three or more complete sets of chromosomes (3*N*, 4*N*, etc.) by a cell.

range Geographic distribution of a species.

seasonal isolation A genetic isolating mechanism that prevents interbreeding of species because the gametes are produced at different times of the year.

speciation Those processes that result in the production of a new species.

species A population of organisms that can naturally interbreed to produce fertile offspring.

subspecies A separate population that exhibits genetic traits different from the main population.

Purpose   Evolution is a series of changes that occur in a population over a number of generations. These changes are the result of natural selection. For natural selection to occur, three things are needed: (1) a reproducing population, (2) genetically inheritable differences among individuals, and (3) some factor within the environment to select certain individuals for survival, because they possess favorable genes.

Although millions of different forms of life exist on earth today, this was not always so. At one time there was that first living organism from which evolved millions of species. Some of these species are present today, but most are extinct.

In this chapter we will trace the evolutionary changes that are thought to have occurred from the first living thing through the following three billion years. The results of this evolutionary process can be seen in the various kinds of plants, animals, and microbes living today.

The Kingdoms of Life

21

Four Kingdoms of Earth

If we were to assemble before us one individual from every species on earth, there would appear such diversity that it would seem impossible for all of these individuals to have evolved from one common organism. But we should keep in mind that according to the theory of organic evolution, the organisms we are seeing today were not always present on the earth. Present-day organisms are the end product of about three billion years of evolution. The kinds of changes that have occurred in the evolution of living things can be compared to the changes that have occurred in the auto industry from the first vehicle to the present varieties. If we were to assemble one representative of all the present-day cars, trucks, tractors, and buses made throughout the world, there would be great variety. Yet, we know that at one time there appeared on the earth that first contraption powered by an internal combustion engine, and from that grew all of the motor vehicles we see in the world today. That first internal combustion engine allowed for the development of a large number of vehicles that failed and are now **extinct,** such as the Kaiser, Edsel, and Henry J. (fig. 21.1). Some of these still are preserved as "fossils." We can further trace that first motor driven contraption as it took to the highway as a truck or to the lawn as a self-propelled lawn mower. If we go back to the beginning, there was a time when nature also produced a first model of living things (chap. 5). From this common ancestor, through countless model changes, there came into being today's complexity of living things.

First Things First

The first species of life is thought to have been a heterotroph and probably utilized the organic materials in its ocean home as a source of food. These organic materials had been synthesized for millions of years prior to the appearance of the first form of life. Within this first species, as in all present

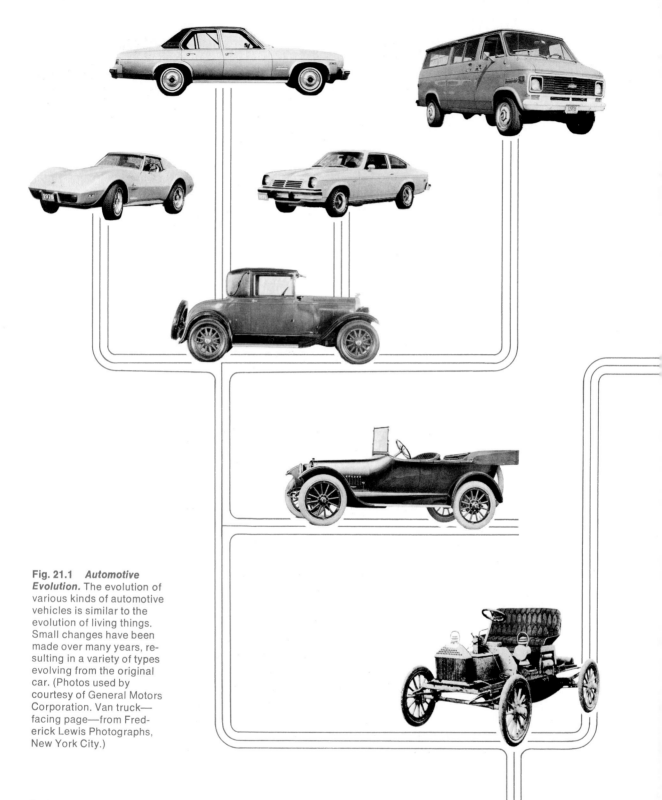

Fig. 21.1 *Automotive Evolution.* The evolution of various kinds of automotive vehicles is similar to the evolution of living things. Small changes have been made over many years, resulting in a variety of types evolving from the original car. (Photos used by courtesy of General Motors Corporation. Van truck—facing page—from Frederick Lewis Photographs, New York City.)

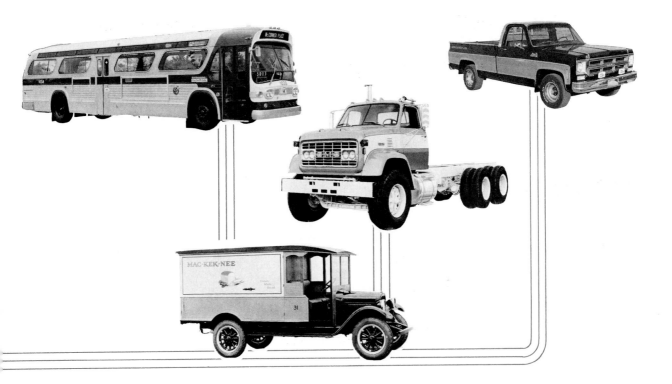

species, there was genetic variation within the population. Some individuals were better able to compete in that environment. As the number of individuals increased, the existing supply of food decreased. The organisms were living in a changing world; a world with less food available. The increasing competition would favor those organisms that required little organic food. As a result of various mutations, some forms of early life synthesized enzymes that allowed them to produce their own food. These organisms were the world's first autotrophs. Thus, we now have two models for life on the earth, the original heterotrophs and the new autotrophs. This was an extremely important change, since there was an efficient biological assembly line for the constant production of large amounts of organic molecules. Since the heterotrophs eat these organic molecules, they ultimately became dependent on the autotrophs.

Based on various lines of evidence, these first autotrophs and heterotrophs were probably small, uncomplicated single cells. They may have been something like the present-day **procaryotic** bacteria or blue-green algae (fig. 21.2). Procaryotic cells lack a distinct nucleus and many of the complex organelles described in chapter six. As competition continued and new genes (mutations) were introduced into the populations, some of the mutations may have resulted in a more complex cell structure. This allowed these new cell types to expand into new niches to avoid competition or out-compete

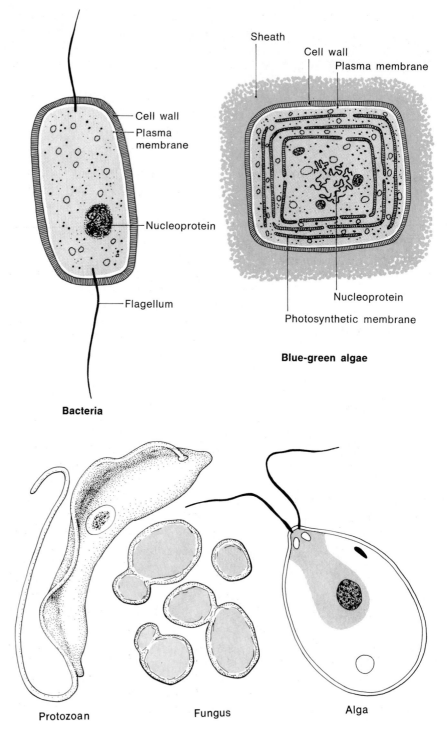

Fig. 21.2 *Procaryotic Cells.*
Some of the earliest organisms to evolve may have been similar to the present-day bacteria and blue-green algae. These are examples of procaryotic cells—cells without a definite nucleus.

Cell wall

Plasma membrane

Nucleoprotein

Flagellum

Bacteria

Sheath

Cell wall

Plasma membrane

Nucleoprotein

Photosynthetic membrane

Blue-green algae

Fig. 21.3 *Eucaryotic Cells.*
These single-celled organisms are examples of eucaryotic cells, cells with a definite nucleus.

Protozoan

Fungus

Alga

their ancestors. Such cell types may have resembled present-day single-celled **eucaryotic** organisms, such as the protozoans, algae (other than blue-green), and fungi (fig. 21.3). Eucaryotic cells contain a complex array of cell organelles such as nuclear membranes, mitochondria, and endoplasmic reticula.

Biologists have chosen to categorize these organisms into two major groups called **kingdoms.** The first kingdom contains the procaryotic cells (bacteria and blue-green algae) and is called the **Monera.** The second kingdom contains the eucaryotic protozoans, algae, and fungi, and is called the **Protista.** In the kingdom Protista, there are both autotrophic photosynthetic organisms and heterotrophic nonphotosynthetic organisms. These two kinds of protists may have been the ancestors of the more complicated plant and animal kingdoms, **Plantae** and **Animalia** (fig. 21.4). Two and a half billion years of evolution resulted in a great variety of species in the ocean. You can see some of that variety in present-day organisms and fossils such as corals, seaweeds, protozoa, starfish, bacteria, worms, and oysters.

Out of all the species that are known to have been alive during this long period of evolution, only a few are in existence today. The rest of the species have become extinct as the environment changed, and they were unable to adapt (fig. 21.5). Many other adaptations did allow for continued existence in the marine environment and may have also made these species less dependent on the marine environment.

All Ashore That's Going Ashore

A continuing parade of mutations resulted in the introduction of new traits into the gene pools of various species that existed within the seas. As a result of such changes, various forms of life developed characteristics that eventually allowed them to spend short periods of time on land. Life on land presented a much different type of environment. In the absence of being constantly surrounded by water, characteristics were needed to provide for: (1) a moist membrane that would allow for adequate gas exchange between the atmosphere and the organism, (2) a means of support and locomotion suitable for land travel, (3) a covering that would conserve internal water, (4) a means of reproduction and early embryonic development without the need for a large amount of water, and (5) methods to survive the rapid and extreme climatic changes that characterize much of the land environment.

Fossil evidence suggests that the first organisms to successfully adapt to a terrestrial environment were the plants. Today we recognize four major types of plants: mosses, ferns, cone-bearing trees, and the flowering plants (fig. 21.6). The mosses were the first to develop the adaptations necessary to live on land. However, these small plants lacked an efficient method for transporting water and other materials. They also produced sperm that required water in order to swim to the female part of the plant to fertilize the

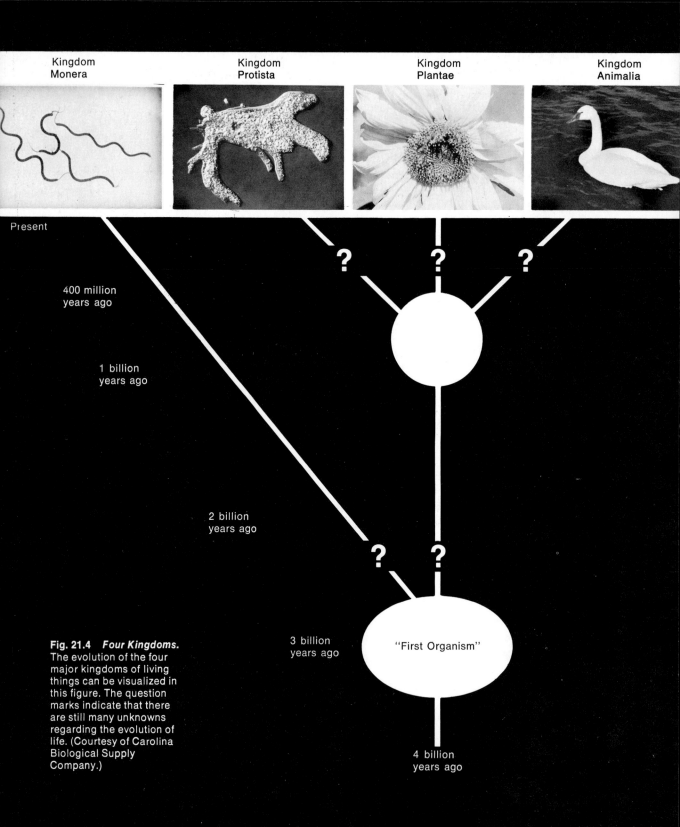

Kingdom
Monera

Kingdom
Protista

Kingdom
Plantae

Kingdom
Animalia

Present

400 million
years ago

1 billion
years ago

2 billion
years ago

3 billion
years ago

4 billion
years ago

"First Organism"

Fig. 21.4 Four Kingdoms.
The evolution of the four
major kingdoms of living
things can be visualized in
this figure. The question
marks indicate that there
are still many unknowns
regarding the evolution of
life. (Courtesy of Carolina
Biological Supply
Company.)

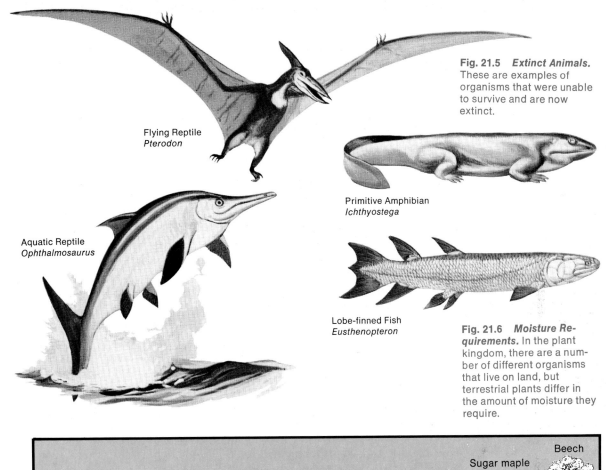

Flying Reptile
Pterodon

Fig. 21.5 *Extinct Animals.* These are examples of organisms that were unable to survive and are now extinct.

Primitive Amphibian
Ichthyostega

Aquatic Reptile
Ophthalmosaurus

Lobe-finned Fish
Eusthenopteron

Fig. 21.6 *Moisture Requirements.* In the plant kingdom, there are a number of different organisms that live on land, but terrestrial plants differ in the amount of moisture they require.

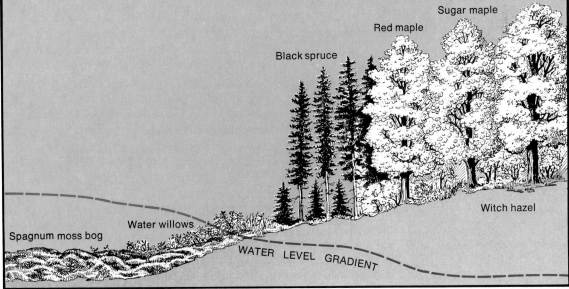

Beech

Sugar maple

Red maple

Black spruce

Witch hazel

Water willows

Spagnum moss bog

WATER LEVEL GRADIENT

egg. These two conditions have limited the distribution of the mosses to continuously moist areas such as riverbanks, damp forests, and swamps. Over millions of years, there were a number of additional mutations and a trend toward a drier environment. Plants that had developed tubes capable of transporting water through their bodies could increase in size and succeed in these drier places. Present-day plants that illustrate this higher level of development are the ferns. However, ferns still produce sperm that must swim to the egg, and therefore, at least part of their life must be spent in a wet area.

Ferns were very successful on land because the tubes allowed them to transport water from the soil throughout the plant body. Since all cells contain a high percentage of water, this was a very important advancement. Further success on land was achieved when some plants began to produce a male gamete that did not require water as a means of moving from one plant to another. Such a sperm-containing structure is known as **pollen.** Pollen can be carried for hundreds of miles through the air (ask anybody who suffers from hay fever!). It was the appearance of pollen that resulted in plants completely conquering the land.

Two different kinds of pollen-producing plants developed: (1) the cone-bearing plants rely primarily on the wind to transport the sperm-containing pollen—pine trees, spruce trees, and the giant redwoods of California all have cones. (2) Flower-bearing plants often rely on insects to carry the pollen—maple trees, corn, roses, crabgrass, and orchids are all examples of flower-bearing plants. To illustrate how effectively these two kinds of plants have adapted to drier conditions, you need only look at a desert. The cactus, tumbleweed, sagebrush, and the piñon pine are typical of our drier western states.

The animals had to solve these same problems if they were to find equal success on land. Maintaining body water, locomotion, and successful reproduction all required adaptive changes. Some of these adaptive changes can be seen in the fishes. Certain fishes possessed a combination of genes that produced strong fins, enabling them to crawl ashore for short periods of time. Some of these crawling fish also developed the ability to swallow air by forcing it into outgrowths of their digestive tract. These fish did not lose as much water from their bodies as did fish that could breathe only through their gills. Those animals that could leave the water and spend some time on land could escape the intense competition in the aquatic environment. Further adaptations along these lines eventually led to the evolution of the amphibians. Present-day examples are frogs, salamanders, toads, and newts.

With the appearance of the amphibians, vertebrate life moved to terrestrial portions of the earth, but it was still found only near a constant source of water. The business of reproduction kept the amphibians from going too far inland. When these animals mate, the male releases sperm into the water and the female releases eggs into the water. The sperm swim to fertilize the eggs. The egg of amphibians must remain in water to prevent dehydration, which results in the death of the young.

For some forty million years, the amphibians were the only vertebrate animals on land. During this time, mutations continued to take place. Some of these mutations resulted in the development of organs that would allow for **copulation** (internal fertilization), and the male could thus deposit sperm within the female. The sperm and egg could remain within the moist interior. With such a method of reproduction, it was not necessary to return to the water for mating.

Internal fertilization was not enough to completely free animals from water, since the developing young required a moist environment for their early growth. Many animals solved this problem by adding food to the fertilized egg and surrounding it with membranes or a shell that would protect the young from dehydration outside the mother's body. The first animals to use this mechanism for survival of the young were the reptiles. Snakes, dinosaurs, turtles, alligators, and lizards all produce these kinds of shelled eggs. With the arrival of internal fertilization and the egg shell, the vertebrates had truly conquered land. The reptiles had evolved.

These developments allowed the reptiles to invade new land areas. As a result, the reptiles spread over much of the earth to occupy a large number of previously unfilled niches. For millions of years they were the only large animals on land. The evolution of reptiles increased competition for space and food. The amphibians generally lost in this competition and consequently most of the amphibians became extinct. However, some were able to avoid competition because they had adaptations that allowed them to hide, live away from reptiles, and survive on a different diet. Those that were successful led to the present-day frogs, toads, and salamanders.

Even though the reptile had mastered the problem of coming ashore, mutations and natural selection continued and so did evolution. As good as the egg in a shell was, it did have drawbacks. These drawbacks were the lack of protection from sudden environment changes, and the lack of protection from predators that used eggs as food.

A constant series of mutations resulted in an animal that overcame the disadvantages of the egg by providing for internal development of the young. Such development allowed for a higher survival rate. This internal development of the young, along with milk gland development, a constant body temperature, and care of young by parents marked the entrance of mammals on the scene.

At about the same time the mammals were evolving from the reptiles, the evolution of a second major group was occurring. In this group, the shelled egg remained the method of protecting the young. However, a series of mutations in some of the reptiles produced an animal with a more rapid metabolism, feathers, and adaptations for flight. These early birds also possessed behavioral instincts such as nest building, defense of their young, and feeding of the young. Because of these adaptations and the invasion of the air, an unoccupied niche, they became one of the very successful groups of animals.

Another extremely successful group of animals began to evolve at about the time the first amphibians began to move onto land. The insects, spiders, and their relatives solved the same problems of terrestrial existence with somewhat different adaptations. These animals have remained small in size and have tremendous reproductive capacity. They are very adaptable and have been able to compete successfully with the other larger land animals. As a matter of fact, three quarters of all the species on the earth belong to this group of animals, and are man's chief competitors for food.

For over a period of some three billion years, life that began in the water underwent mutations and natural selection to evolve into the complex array of plant and animal forms we see today.

As these new forms of life emerged, they caused changes on the earth just by their presence. As a result of these changes, some species could not survive. They did not have the necessary genes to compete in the new environment and became extinct. There is nothing new about extinction, it is as old as life itself. Species have become extinct in the past, they are becoming extinct today, and they will become extinct in the future.

Summary   Early in this text the interrelationship of plants and animals was stressed. This interaction has occurred ever since the appearance of the first heterotrophs and autotrophs. The first organisms to evolve were single-celled organisms of the kingdoms Monera and Protista. From these simple beginnings, more complex, many-celled organisms evolved creating the kingdoms Plantae and Animalia. For millions of years, these plants and animals were confined to watery habitats. Through the processes of mutation, natural selection, and environmental change, these groups evolved into a variety of organisms capable of living in the more severe and changeable land environment. The features that allowed for success on land included a moist membrane for gas exchange, fertilization away from standing water, water-conserving methods, methods for protecting developing young, means of support and locomotion, and methods of surviving rapidly changing environmental conditions. The foldout (inside the back cover) represents a summary of the three billion years of evolution of these four major kingdoms of life.

Consider This   There are more species of insects alive today than any other group of organisms. These various insects fill a great variety of niches. There are about 750,000 species of insects in the world, but there is only one species of man, *Homo sapiens*. If the insects are truly our greatest competitors, what are our chances of winning the battle, and what resources are available to both insects and man in this fight?

1. What are the four kingdoms of living things?
2. What is the difference between the kingdom Monera and the other three kingdoms?
3. List the series of changes that resulted in the evolution of living things as we know them today.
4. What major adjustments do land organisms need to make in order to live on land?
5. How did reptiles and flowering plants solve their problems of reproduction?
6. What is the difference between a heterotroph and an autotroph?

Animalia   Classified into this kingdom are multicellular heterotrophic organisms that require a source of organic material as food.

copulation   The act of transferring sperm from the male into the female reproductive tract.

eucaryotic   Cell with a true nucleus separated from the rest of the protoplasm by a nuclear membrane.

extinct   Types of organisms that once existed but are no longer in evidence today.

Homo sapiens   The scientific name of man.

kingdom   The largest grouping used in the classification of organisms.

Monera   Classified into this kingdom are one-celled organisms that do not possess a definite nucleus.

Plantae   Classified into this kingdom are multicellular autotrophic organisms.

pollen   The male portion of a plant capable of forming sperm.

procaryotic   Cell having nuclear materials that are not separated from the rest of the protoplasm; they do not have a nuclear membrane.

Protista   Classified into this kingdom are one-celled organisms that possess a definite nucleus.

Purpose   In our everyday lives we usually categorize organisms as either plant or animal. There is a basic difficulty with this casual way of classifying all living things. They just won't fit neatly into these two groups. Of course we have no problem with dogs, fish, snakes, and birds; they are animals. Similarly, the trees, grass, and raspberry bushes are plants. But there is a huge assortment of organisms that are not so easily classified. This general group, the microbes, is the subject of this chapter. We will first consider ways in which the *microbes* differ from plants and animals. Next, we will become acquainted with each of the broad groups of microbes— the Monera and Protista.

Microbes

22

What's the Difference?

A basic difference in living things became apparent when biologists first began to be interested in the details of the structure of cells. Some cells were found that lacked a clearly defined nucleus. Although a cell membrane was present, other membranous structures that might have been within the cell, such as mitochondria, were missing. Such cells are said to be **procaryotic,** while those with membranous structures are **eucaryotic.** The procaryotes are classified here as the kingdom **Monera.** The eucaryotes are divided into three **kingdoms:** Protista, Plants, and Animals. The **Protista** includes those organisms that are one-celled or are made of many similar cells. The Plants and Animals have cells that are modified for a variety of purposes, such as conduction of materials, strength, and protection (fig. 22.1).

It is convenient to be able to subdivide each kingdom into smaller groups and to have definite names for each of these instead of calling them *groups* or some other indefinite name. In order to see the relationship between these names easily, they are listed in figure 22.2 with examples from each of the four kingdoms.

You may wonder about the blanks in figure 22.2. Let us consider the reason for filling some blanks and not others in the group called **subphylum.** Within this phylum of the Animals, you can see the subphylum space filled in with the name Vertebrata. It just happens that animals included in the phylum Chordata can be divided into several groups, one of which has vertebrae, or backbones. This is an important difference from other organisms within the phylum Chordata. Its placement here is a statement that this difference was a major development in the evolution of chordates. There is no comparable difference in the phylum Pterophyta of the Plant kingdom. It is not worthwhile to make up a subphylum name if there is no special need for that classification.

Fig. 22.1 *Two Basic Types of Cells.* Note the absence of the nucleus and other double-membrane structures in the procaryotic cell, and their presence in the eucaryotic cell.

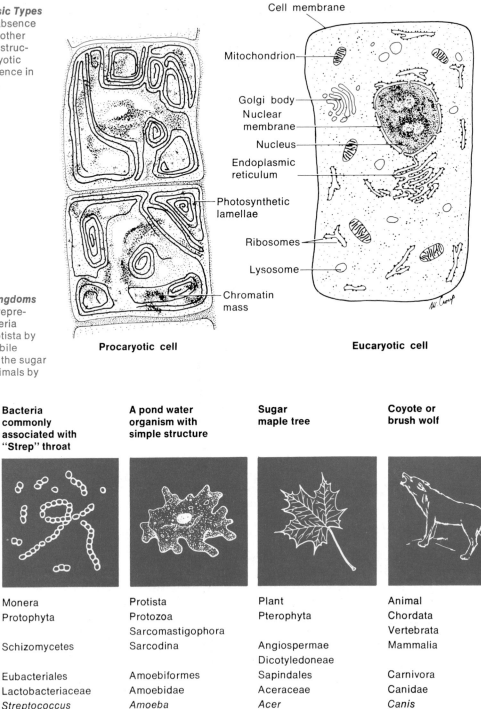

Cell membrane

Mitochondrion

Golgi body
Nuclear membrane

Nucleus

Endoplasmic reticulum

Photosynthetic lamellae

Ribosomes

Lysosome

Chromatin mass

Procaryotic cell

Eucaryotic cell

Fig. 22.2 *Four Kingdoms of Life.* Monera is represented by the bacteria streptococcus; protista by the one-celled, mobile *amoeba;* plants by the sugar maple leaf; and animals by the coyote.

	Bacteria commonly associated with "Strep" throat	**A pond water organism with simple structure**	**Sugar maple tree**	**Coyote or brush wolf**
Kingdom	Monera	Protista	Plant	Animal
Phylum	Protophyta	Protozoa	Pterophyta	Chordata
Subphylum		Sarcomastigophora		Vertebrata
Class	Schizomycetes	Sarcodina	Angiospermae	Mammalia
Subclass			Dicotyledoneae	
Order	Eubacteriales	Amoebiformes	Sapindales	Carnivora
Family	Lactobacteriaceae	Amoebidae	Aceraceae	Canidae
Genus	*Streptococcus*	*Amoeba*	*Acer*	*Canis*
Species	*pyogenes*	*proteus*	*saccharum*	*latrans*

The last two names, **genus** and **species,** together make up the scientific name of an organism. The name *Canis latrans* is the **scientific name** of the animal commonly called a coyote by some people, and a brush wolf by others. The scientific name has the advantage of being recognized all over the world, regardless of the native language.

Now that we have our classification system organized, let's face it: the organisms haven't been listening to us. They still don't quite fit *our* system. By saying that it is "our" system, we have pointed out the difficulty with various classification systems. It is ours in the sense that it is artificial, or man-made. It doesn't completely show how the various organisms are related. What is even worse is that many systems of classification, including the one we are using, actually hide some relationships. This point will be made more clear as we become acquainted with the various groups of organisms. So, let's start getting acquainted.

Viruses

The viruses are peculiar. In the past, they were not considered to be organisms at all. They are not cells, but they consist of a nucleic acid enclosed by a covering of protein. One could say that they have no life until their nucleic acid enters a host cell. Then the relationship between the virus and the cell is comparable to a pirate and a merchant ship. The "pirate" virus enters the host cell, which is loaded with all the materials needed by the virus. The virus takes command and puts the "captured cell" to work (fig. 22.3). Once inside

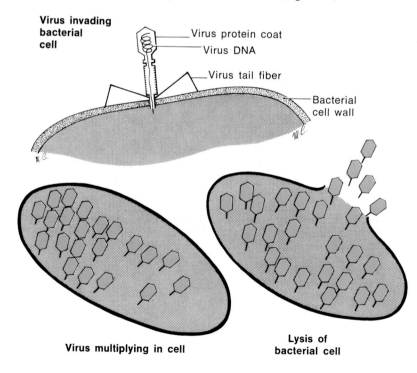

Virus invading bacterial cell

Virus protein coat
Virus DNA
Virus tail fiber
Bacterial cell wall

Virus multiplying in cell

Lysis of bacterial cell

Fig. 22.3 *Viral Invasion of a Cell.* The viral nucleic acid takes control of the energy resources of the living cell that it invades.

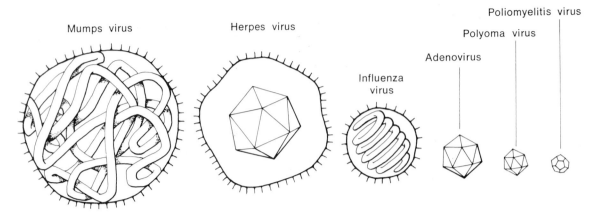

Mumps virus

Herpes virus

Influenza virus

Adenovirus

Polyoma virus

Poliomyelitis virus

Fig. 22.4 *Viral Types.* Even as large as these viral particles are, they are still smaller than the cells that they invade. These are very tiny particles. Mumps is a common childhood disease and influenza is that disagreeable wintertime visitor called flu. Cold sores are caused by the Herpes virus, while the Adenovirus is associated with respiratory disease. Poliomyelitis was a dreaded paralyzer, but with the development of vaccines, protection is now available. The threat of poliomyelitis has been so successfully met that some people have become careless about getting the vaccine for their children. Tumors have been induced in mice by the Polyoma virus.

the cell, the viral nucleic acid makes use of the available enzymes and ATP to start producing copies of itself. With enough protein present to coat the nucleic acid, many complete virus particles are assembled. The virus is a parasite that can only operate when inside a living cell. After the assembly of all the duplicates of the original virus, the host cell bursts open and the virus offspring are released to infect other cells. We call this process a disease when the virus is infecting our cells, or those of plants and animals. A few of the difficulties caused by different viruses are cold sores, warts, polio, mumps, measles, the flu, tobacco plant disease, and foot-and-mouth disease in cattle (fig. 22.4).

Monera—The Have Nots

The kingdom Monera includes the **bacteria** and the blue-green algae. We are most familiar with bacteria that cause disease, but it would be a great mistake to think only of bacteria in this way. It is certainly true that many serious diseases are caused by bacteria. However, a type of bacteria in our large intestine, *Escherichia coli,* is usually helpful to the person carrying it around. It provides certain vitamins (such as vitamin K) to man. There are others used for making food, such as those used in the process of making yogurt. Many thousands of gallons of vinegar are produced each year by bacterial fermentation.

The process of bacterial decay is both a nuisance and a great help to us. We lose much valuable food each year by bacterial spoilage, but we also have countless quantities of organic material recycled to a useful condition in ecosystems. Sewage treatment plants rely on the action of bacteria to break down wastes for recycling (fig. 22.5). The bacteria mentioned thus far obtain their energy from food already made by some other organism. There are a few types of bacteria that can make their own food by using light to carry on photosynthesis. Other bacteria can make use of inorganic materials by oxidizing them, such as some of the bacteria involved in the nitrogen cycle (fig. 22.6). It should not be surprising to learn that bacteria occupy a wide

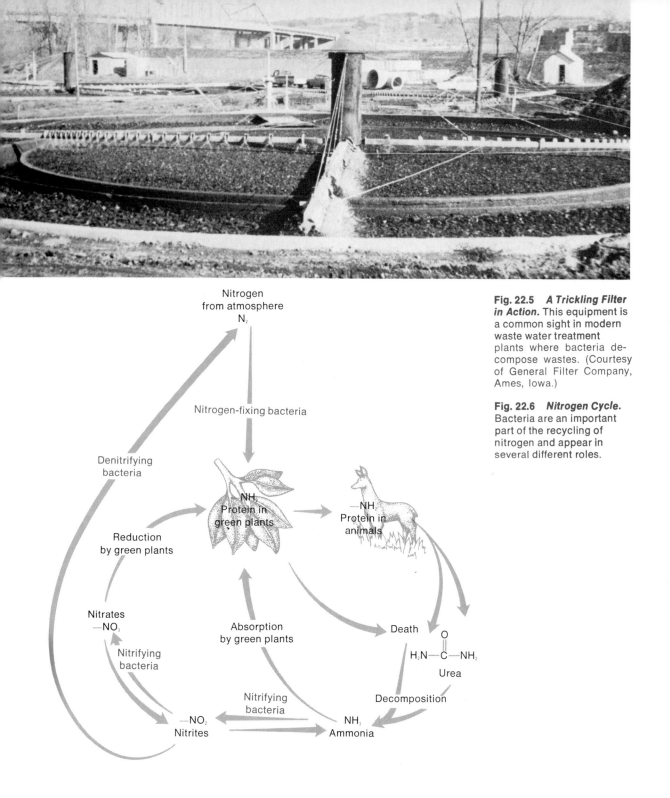

Fig. 22.5 *A Trickling Filter in Action.* This equipment is a common sight in modern waste water treatment plants where bacteria decompose wastes. (Courtesy of General Filter Company, Ames, Iowa.)

Fig. 22.6 *Nitrogen Cycle.* Bacteria are an important part of the recycling of nitrogen and appear in several different roles.

Nitrogen from atmosphere N_2

Nitrogen-fixing bacteria

Denitrifying bacteria

Reduction by green plants

NH_2 Protein in green plants

$—NH_2$ Protein in animals

Nitrates $—NO_3$

Nitrifying bacteria

Absorption by green plants

Death

$H_2N—\overset{\overset{\displaystyle O}{\|}}{C}—NH_2$ Urea

$—NO_2$ Nitrites

Nitrifying bacteria

Decomposition

NH_3 Ammonia

Fig. 22.7 *Bacterial Types.* Bacteria are classified by shape into one of three major groups. The rod-shaped are *Bacilli*, sphere-shaped are *Cocci,* and the bent or corkscrew-shaped are the *Spirilla.*

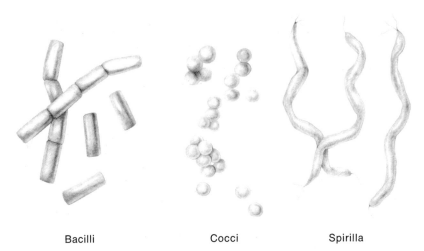

Bacilli   Cocci   Spirilla

variety of habitats, since we have seen that there are many ways in which bacteria get food. The ways in which different bacteria break down foods and other biochemical differences are used to classify the bacteria.

You can identify your friends at a great distance merely by looking at them. This method does not work for the identification of bacteria, even the friendly ones. When you look at one of the thousands of different kinds of bacteria, you can only place it in one of three groups: coccus is spherical, bacillus is rod-shaped, and spirillum is spiral- or corkscrew-shaped (fig. 22.7). From here on you must depend largely on biochemical tests to identify the bacteria.

Blue-Green Algae

These cells occur singly, as various clusters of cells, or as a series of cells organized into filaments. Like all the algae, they have chlorophyll. But the chlorophyll makeup of the blue-green algae is not the same as that of all other algae. In addition to the green chlorophyll, most of them have a unique bluish pigment in their cells. Unfortunately for easy sight identification, the blue-green color is not a reliable characteristic. There are other algae that imitate this color, and there are some blue-green algae that show other colors: red, yellow, purple, brown, and black. The term algae is only a term of convenience, not a scientific term for the simpler types of organisms with chlorophyll. All algae were once considered to be closely related. But whether or not a close relationship exists, they have received increased attention as the interest in environmental quality has risen. Some indicate organic pollution, while others are pollutants themselves. Some cause foul odors or tastes in drinking water and may produce poisons that kill animals. Occasionally a sudden increase in the population (a **bloom**) of a species of blue-green algae will occur and cause trouble for water-living plants and animals. This bloom can shut off the light to submerged plants, causing their death and decay. The decay may then remove enough oxygen from the water so as to suffocate the fish and other animals (fig. 22.8). It should be noted that the blue-green algae are found in a variety of habitats, not just in fresh water. A small quantity are found in salt water; they are common in soil, on damp rocks, on tree bark; and they even grow in the hot springs of Yellowstone National Park (fig. 22.9).

Fig. 22.8 *An Algae Bloom.* The warm summer sun shining on a pond rich in nutrients causes this rapid multiplication of algae cells. (Courtesy of A. H. Gibson.)

Fig. 22.9 *Hot Springs of Yellowstone National Park.* Some types of algae are able to grow in even this superheated environment. (Courtesy of the United States Department of the Interior—National Park Service Photo.)

Protista—The Original Motley Crowd

We mentioned artificial classification groups earlier. The kingdom Protista must surely take the prize for artificiality. Even from the brief description we give in this chapter, you will see that there are great differences among the organisms of this kingdom. According to evolutionary theory, great differences in structure should mean great differences in relationships. However, the Protists have only two things in common: (1) they are all eucaryotic cells, and (2) they lack complex structures with differentiated cells. The common name for the green Protista is algae, and the nongreen are called fungi and protozoa. The algae, with their chlorophyll, can carry on photosynthesis, while the fungi and protozoa must obtain their food from organic materials, such as living or dead organisms.

Algae

The algae are separated into phyla on the basis of the different (1) kinds of coloring materials, (2) compounds used for storage, and (3) details of their reproductive cycles. Rather than consider these technical details, let's consider some facts relating more to our experience. The algae are "pond scum" or seaweed, and are generally considered to be a great nuisance by many people. It is true that they can create a nuisance by fouling beaches and drinking water, as well as by producing poisonous substances. It is also true that they have tremendous importance for all water-living animals. The algae occupy a key position. They are the first link in the food chain within all bodies of water. They are the producer organisms and as such they deserve our attention, since we depend on them in many hidden ways.

The green algae grow mostly in fresh water, but there are some in damp soil, salt water, and even in snowfields high in the mountains. In addition to being single cells, some occur as long filaments of single cells, as spherical clusters, or as lettucelike sheets (fig. 22.10). Most of them live up to their common name, green algae, since they are grass green.

The **euglenoids** are an interesting group of single-celled algae that have the plant characteristic of chlorophyll in addition to some animal characteristics. They pull themselves through the water by lashing **flagella** back and forth. The flagellum is a long, flexible whiplike filament. Euglenoids ingest food particles in addition to carrying on photosynthesis. They are equipped with a light sensitive spot that enables them to move toward or away from light, and they lack a cell wall. Most of this small group live in fresh water, but a few live in damp soil, and some in the food tubes of some animals (fig. 22.11).

The diatoms are the most important producer in saltwater ecosystems. They are also common in fresh water. The statement that diatoms are producers tells you that the survival of animals of the sea depends on these organisms, which are so small that we need a microscope to see them. They occur mostly as individual cells, but some remain attached to each other

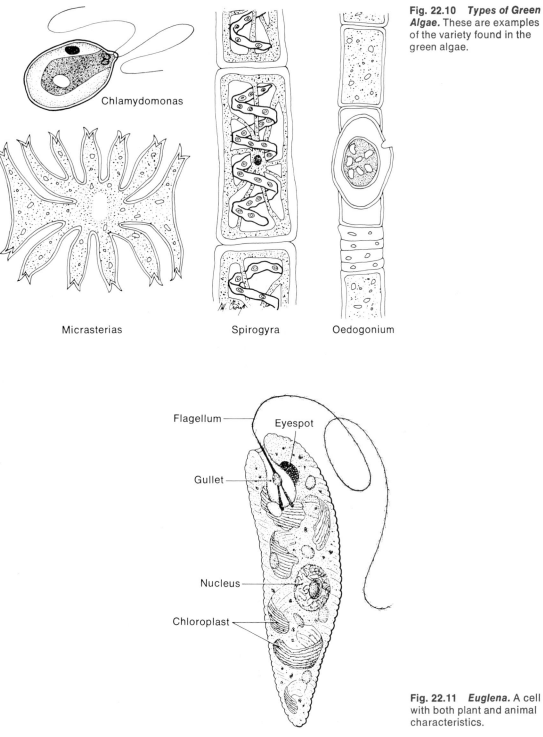

Fig. 22.10 *Types of Green Algae.* These are examples of the variety found in the green algae.

Chlamydomonas

Micrasterias

Spirogyra

Oedogonium

Flagellum

Eyespot

Gullet

Nucleus

Chloroplast

Fig. 22.11 *Euglena.* A cell with both plant and animal characteristics.

after division and form a cluster called a **colony.** The diatoms are unique in that they deposit silicon dioxide in their cell walls. When the organisms die, everything breaks down and disappears except the silicon dioxide. These cell walls are arranged in pairs like a little dish with its cover (fig. 22.12). The glassy walls of diatoms are decorated with grooves and holes that are so small they are used to check the quality of microscopes (fig. 22.13). Some of the markings are too small to be seen except under an electron microscope. The glassy remains of these algae have been deposited on the floor of ancient seas in such quantity that it is commercially profitable to remove these with power shovels and trucks. Since diatoms are so small, the mass has the texture of talcum powder, and is therefore used as a very fine abrasive in metal polishes. The cell walls of diatoms are able to pick up small particles of impurities in a liquid, and can be used as filters. The brewing industry has made use of diatoms to clarify beer. They can also serve as an excellent insulator and are not destroyed by extremely high temperatures.

The dinoflagellates are next in importance to the diatoms as a producer in the oceans. You may have read of another way in which they are important. Newspapers call blooms of these organisms *red tides,* since the cells are present in such quantities that they color the water. If it were only for the pinkish color added to ocean waves, there would be little fuss—it might even be an attraction. Unfortunately, this particular species of dinoflagellate produces a poison deadly to fish, many smaller organisms, and man. These blooms kill fish, which litter the beach and drive the tourists away. It could even be worse if people ate the oysters or clams growing in such waters, since these animals concentrate the poison in their bodies as they filter food out of the water. This concentration can be enough to cause illness to persons eating these seafoods. There is an old saying that states that oysters and clams are in season only during the months containing the letter *R*—"Oysters *R* in season." The statement was true only if refrigeration was unreliable and to some extent because the red tide occurred more frequently during the warmer months (none of the summer months contain the letter *R*). The red tides are confined to relatively small areas. Either the blooms are better reported in recent years or else there has been an increase in these red tides.

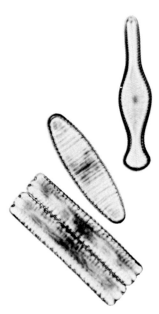

Fig. 22.13 *Types of Diatoms.* A few of the seemingly endless variety of diatoms. (Courtesy Carolina Biological Supply Company.)

Fig. 22.14 *Brown Algae.* This kelp is a common sight along our western sea-coasts. (Courtesy of Fred Ross.)

The brown algae are mostly saltwater organisms. The seaweed, called kelp, that covers the rocks along the ocean coasts, are mostly in this group. Some grow to quite a large size, up to one-hundred meters in length (fig. 22.14). Kelp is harvested mechanically and refined to a commercially valuable product depending on the particular species harvested. You may notice on the labels of many foods that they contain algin or alginates. This substance from brown algae is found in ice cream, cake frosting, pudding, cream-centered candies, and many cosmetics (fig. 22.15).

The red algae are also saltwater organisms. They grow on rocks along the seacoast. Red algae have attracted scientific attention not only because they are unlike other algae but also because they differ from the higher plants. They have been referred to as an evolutionary dead end. The red algae are also used as an additive in foods for thickening and flavoring. The genus *Porphyra* is "farmed" along the coast of Japan on wooden racks (fig. 22.16). You might look for the name *carrageenan* on packaged foods (fig. 22.15). It is produced from red algae and used as a stabilizer to keep solids suspended in liquids, such as the particles of chocolate in chocolate milk. A high protein cattle food has been produced from the red algae grown along Scandinavian coasts. Agar, another product of red algae, has been used worldwide in hospital and bacteriological laboratories. It is commonly sold as a granular powder and is added to hot water in much the same way gelatin dessert is made. When the mixture cools, it becomes semisolid, like gelatin, and is used principally as a medium on which to grow bacteria. Although some people eat agar, it is generally not used as a food. It acts as a laxative.

Fig. 22.16 *Algae Farming.* Algae are grown in Japan much the same as an agricultural crop is grown in this country. (Courtesy of Japan National Tourist Organization.)

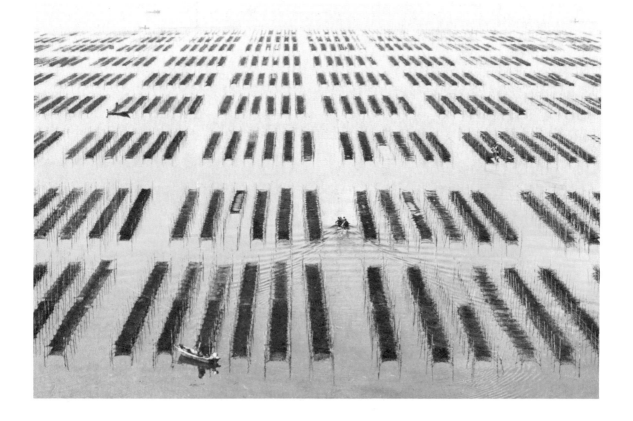

Fungi

This is another major group in the Protista, one that lacks chlorophyll. Many have cell walls with a very resistant material called **chitin** rather than the more common cell wall material, cellulose. The basic unit of structure is the **hypha,** a slender filament. Some fungi have so many filaments crowded into a firm mass that the individual filaments are difficult to recognize. This is the case with the mushrooms we slice for pizzas. In other fungi these filaments form a vast network extending down into the food material, and appear as a cottonlike mass. An example of this type of growth can be seen in bread mold or sometimes as a fuzzy growth on flies that have died on the windowsill. This mass of filaments, in either type of growth habit, is called the *mycelium* (fig. 22.17).

Fungi are important to us as destroyers, as well as creators. They cause losses of millions of dollars annually. They destroy food and manufactured materials; and expensive chemical dusts and sprays are needed to control them. Because they produce millions of spores that can be spread around easily, their control is difficult. On the other hand, antibiotics, such as penicillin and other mold by-products, are a great blessing. Mold on cheese may spoil it, but many cheeses such as blue and gorgonzola owe their distinct flavor to molds. They are also beneficial in a variety of industries, such as brewing, baking, and drugs.

Algae and fungi come together in a peculiar group called **lichens.** Alga is believed to furnish food for the fungus, and the fungus supplies moisture

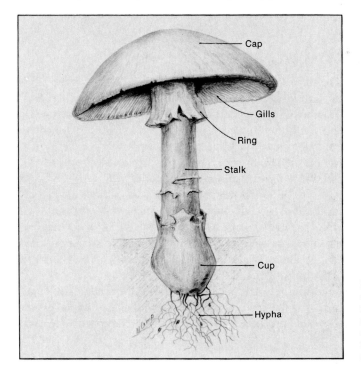

Cap

Gills

Ring

Stalk

Cup

Hypha

Fig. 22.17 A representative of the Fungi. Both the mushroom and the mold are characterized by widespread growth of tiny threadlike hyphae which absorb food materials.

Fig. 22.18 *Lichen.* A pioneer species which invades unoccupied territory and prepares the way for later plant settlers. (Photo by A. H. Gibson.)

and protection to the alga. Together, this association is important as a pioneer in ecological succession. Lichen is capable of growing on bare rock, and there it starts the soil-making process (fig. 22.18). The so-called reindeer moss is a lichen that provides caribou with a source of food in northern Canada and Alaska.

Protozoa

The third major group in the kingdom Protista is the phylum Protozoa. The phylum name is derived from Greek words meaning 'first animal.' It is still classified by many as an animal and is studied in zoology classes, just as algae and fungi are studied in botany classes. Most protozoans can move under their own power at some stage in their life cycle. This fact is used as a basis for classification. The phylum is subdivided according to the particular method of moving around (locomotion).

The *Amoeba* and its relatives flow without having any permanent body form. This type of flowing movement is so characteristic that it is called amoeboid movement. Most amoeba live in water, and some are parasitic. One such parasite in man causes amoebic dysentery, and causes death or serious illness in disaster stricken areas where drinking water has become contaminated (fig. 22.19).

Another class moves by means of flagella. The flagellates have one or more flagella, no cell wall, and a relatively simple structure. Figure 22.20 shows the protozoan *Hexamitus* as an example of this kind of flagellate. The

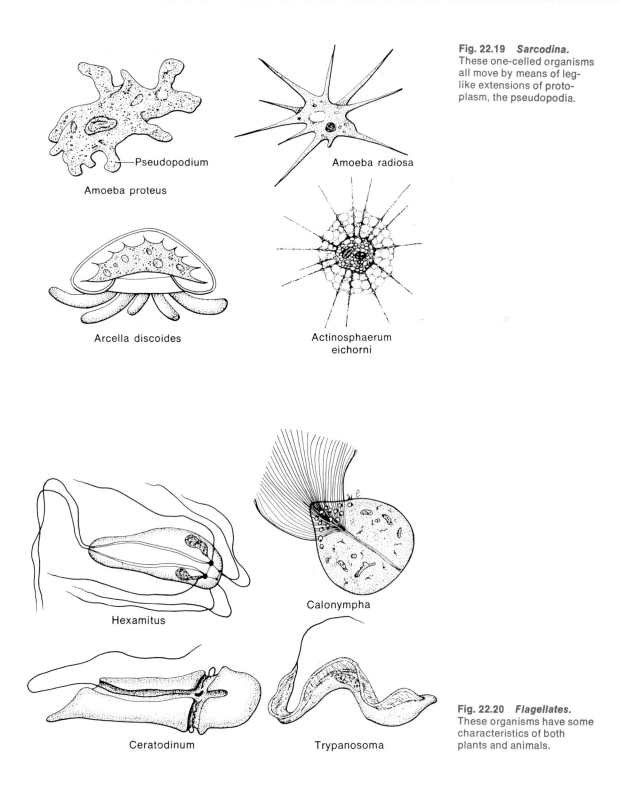

Fig. 22.19 *Sarcodina.* These one-celled organisms all move by means of leg-like extensions of protoplasm, the pseudopodia.

Pseudopodium

Amoeba proteus

Amoeba radiosa

Arcella discoides

Actinosphaerum eichorni

Hexamitus

Calonympha

Ceratodinum

Trypanosoma

Fig. 22.20 *Flagellates.* These organisms have some characteristics of both plants and animals.

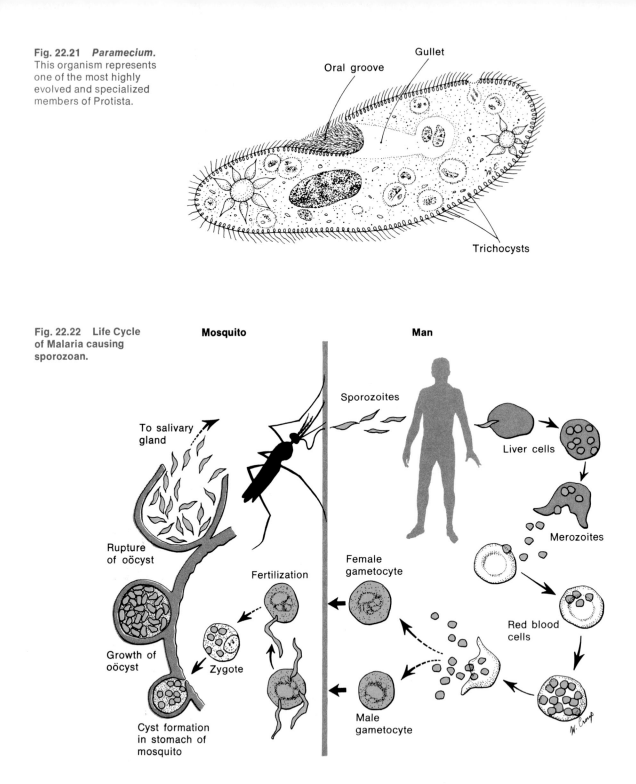

Fig. 22.21 *Paramecium.* This organism represents one of the most highly evolved and specialized members of Protista.

Oral groove

Gullet

Trichocysts

Fig. 22.22 Life Cycle of Malaria causing sporozoan.

Mosquito

Man

To salivary gland

Sporozoites

Liver cells

Rupture of oöcyst

Merozoites

Female gametocyte

Fertilization

Red blood cells

Growth of oöcyst

Zygote

Cyst formation in stomach of mosquito

Male gametocyte

organism causing the deadly African sleeping sickness is also one of these flagellated protozoans.

Still another class of Protozoa move by means of *cilia*. These are short, flexible filaments that frequently cover the cell completely. They beat in an organized, rhythmical manner and propel the cells so rapidly that it becomes a problem to keep them in focus under a microscope (fig. 22.21). These ciliates are commonly seen in cultures of pond water and hay. In a freshwater ecosystem, the ciliates are the primary consumers feeding on algae.

The organism causing malaria is representative of a fourth class of Protozoa. All members of this class, known as Sporozoa, are parasites. One of their major methods of reproducing is by producing resistant cells called spores. Many important disease organisms are in this group. They are often transmitted from person to person by animals such as mosquitos, ticks, and flies (fig. 22.22).

Summary

Classification names range from kingdom through species. The kingdom is the broadest group and the species is the smallest. Looking at the classification scheme another way, there are a few kingdoms and an increasing number of the lesser categories as one moves toward the species. The last two names of this scheme, genus and species, together form the scientific name of the organism being classified. The scientific name has several advantages, one of which is the fact that it is used internationally by all, regardless of native language.

Viruses are protein-nucleic acid particles that function only as intracellular parasites.

Monera include all organisms that are procaryotic, such as bacteria and blue-green algae. Members of the Monera are important as agents of disease, for carrying on fermentation, as decay organisms, and for their lowering of water quality.

The Protista include those eucaryotes that lack specialized cells. Eucaryotes are organisms whose cells possess a nucleus with a nuclear membrane as well as other membranous structures, such as mitochondria and chloroplasts. The protists include the fungi, the Protozoa, and all the algae except the blue-green variety. Algae and fungi are more plantlike, in general, while the protozoans are animallike. Algae produce their own food by photosynthesis with their chlorophyll while fungi and protozoa depend on organic materials produced by some other living thing. Algae are restricted in their living situation to a lighted area, but otherwise are wide ranging from water to moist land habitats. Fungi are not restricted by light or its absence and grow on almost any organic material, natural or man-made. Protozoa are largely aquatic, and some are parasites. The impact of protists on man includes disease production, industrial processes, food production, and recycling of organic materials.

Questions

1. What kinds of organisms are found in the group known as microbes?
2. Why are the two kingdoms Monera and Protista separated from one another?
3. Why is a classification system necessary, and what is meant by a scientific name?
4. The kingdom Protista is divided into three major groups. What are they?
5. What is meant by a bloom of algae?
6. How do the four classes of protozoans differ?
7. Why do many people consider the virus to be nonliving?
8. Name three products that can be extracted from algae and are used in the food industry.
9. What microbes are decomposers?
10. What is the difference between a procaryotic and a eucaryotic cell?

Chapter Glossary

algae   Plantlike protists that are green and can carry on photosynthesis.

bacteria   Procaryotic single-celled organisms of the kingdom Monera; generally do not contain photosynthetic pigments.

bloom   A rapid increase in the number of algae cells—a population explosion.

blue-green algae   Chlorophyll-containing monera that typically contain a blue-green pigment.

chitin   A substance resistant to many solvents and found in the cell walls of fungi. It differs slightly from material of the same name in insect body walls.

cilia   Short, flexible hairlike filaments that beat rhythmically and propel the cell through the water or bring food into the cell.

colony   A cluster of independent cells produced by cell division.

Escherichia coli   A type of bacteria found in the large intestines. It provides certain vitamins.

eucaryotic   A type of cell that has membranous organelles within its cell membrane, such as a nucleus and mitochondria.

flagella   Long, flexible hairlike filaments that lash back and forth, thus drawing the cell along behind them.

fungi   Protists that have cell walls and lack chlorophyll.

genus   A classification name given to groups of species that are very similar; together with the species name, it is the scientific name.

hypha   The basic unit of structure of a fungus consisting of a branching filament. Some have many nuclei not separated by cross walls, while others have walls.

kingdom   The largest division of the classification system.

lichen   An association of an alga with a fungus, in which each benefit. A pioneer in plant succession.

microbe   Any single-celled organism; a common name used to refer to members of the kingdoms Monera and Protista.

Monera   The kingdom of procaryotic organisms such as bacteria and blue-green algae.

mycelium   The body of a fungus composed of hyphae.

phylum   A classification name given to groups of organisms in the same kingdom.

procaryotic   A type of cell that lacks membranous organelles within its cell membrane, including the lack of a nucleus.

Protista   The kingdom of eucaryotic organisms such as algae, fungi, and protozoa.

protozoa   Animallike protists that lack cell walls.

scientific name   The one name of an organism that is internationally recognized. It consists of the genus written first and capitalized, followed by the species usually written in lowercase. It is printed in italics, or underlined.

species   The classification name given to members of a reproducing population; the smallest unit of the classification system.

subphylum   A classification name given to groups of organisms in the same phylum.

virus   A nucleic acid–protein particle that shows some characteristics of life only when found inside a living cell.

Purpose   You know a plant when you see it. It's the green colored organism that doesn't run away from you. There are interesting and important characteristics of plants, other than their green pigment and their nonmobile life-style. In this chapter, you will become familiar with some of these characteristics and begin to understand the basis for classifying and naming plants. Plant biologists, botanists, have a scheme that they think expresses the evolutionary advances that have occurred over millions of years. This chapter is organized around that scheme.

Plants

23

Birds Do It; Bees Do It; Even Mosses, Ferns, and Trees Do It

When the science of naming plants was in its infancy, the placing of plants into a particular group was based on the methods they used to reproduce. Carl von Linné formed categories of plants by determining the number and position of male parts in flowers. Although almost everyone has looked closely at a **flower,** few people realize that the flower is a structure associated with sexual reproduction in plants. To understand how and why the flower evolved, we need to go back in time and examine the primitive structures that were modified and changed over and over again until the flower came into existence.

One group of plants that shows many primitive characteristics are the **mosses.** Mosses grow as a carpet composed of many parts. Each individual moss plant is composed of a central stalk less than five centimeters tall with short leaflike structures that are the sites of photosynthesis (fig. 23.1). If you look at the individual cells in the leafy portion of a moss, you can distinguish the cytoplasm, cell wall, and chloroplasts (fig. 23.2); you can also distinguish the nucleus of the cell. This nucleus is haploid. If you recall, this means that it has only one set of chromosomes. Every cell in the moss plant is haploid. Even though all of the cells have the haploid number of chromosomes (the same as gametes), not all of them function as gametes. Because this plant produces cells that are capable of acting as gametes, it is called the **gametophyte generation,** or the gamete-producing plant. Special structures in the moss are responsible for producing mobile sperm cells capable of swimming to a female egg cell. These special structures are called **antheridia** (fig. 23.3). The sperm cells are enclosed within a jacket of cells until they mature. The jacket opens when the sperm are mature, and the cells swim by the undulating motion of flagella through a film of dew or rainwater. Sperm move toward the female structure, carrying their package of genetic information. Their destination is the egg cell of another moss plant having a different package

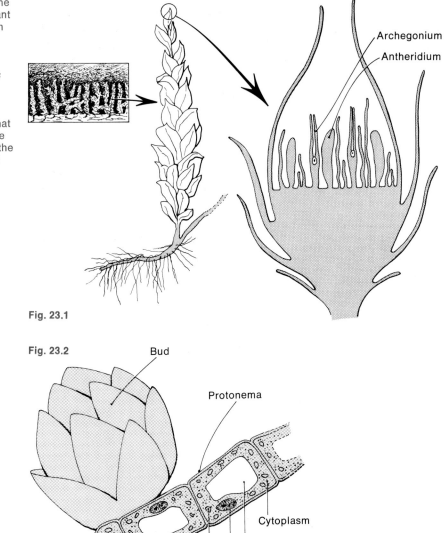

Fig. 23.1 *Moss Plants.* The insert shows one moss plant greatly enlarged, with both the male and female sex organs.

Fig. 23.2 *Cells of a Moss Plant.* These are typical plant cells; note the large central vacuole and cell wall. One characteristic that separates mosses from the photosynthetic protists is the presence of the individual chloroplasts.

Archegonium

Antheridium

Fig. 23.1

Fig. 23.2

Bud

Protonema

Cytoplasm

Vacuole

Nucleus

Chloroplast

Cell wall

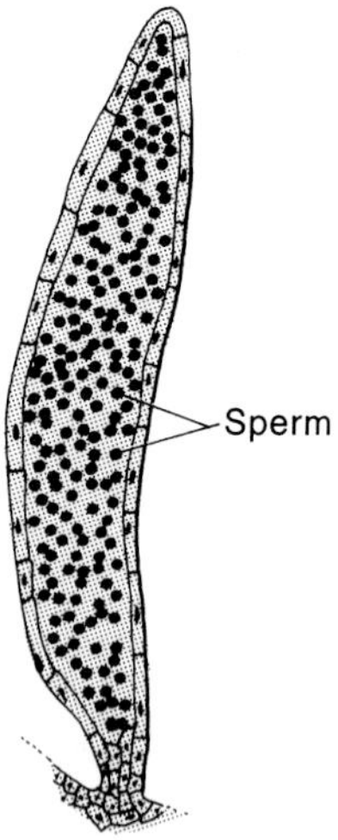

Sperm

Fig. 23.3 *Antheridium of a Moss Plant.* This male portion of the moss gametophyte plant is composed of a series of cells surrounding the immature sperm cells.

of genetic information. The egg is produced within a jacket, called the **archegonium** (fig. 23.4). There is usually only one egg cell in each archegonium. The sperm and egg nuclei fuse and a diploid cell results. The diploid zygote grows, divides, and differentiates into an embryo.

The embryo continues to grow into a structure called the **sporophyte** plant. It is called the sporophyte because it is the **spore** producing part of the **life cycle.** These spores are produced by the process of meiosis. This sporophyte plant grows a stalk with a swollen tip, the **capsule** (fig. 23.5). Inside the capsule, special cells undergo meiosis and form haploid spores. These spores are released and are carried around by air currents until they reach the ground. Some land in areas that are too wet, too dry, or too sunny; they will not **germinate** or survive. Others land in a suitable environment and grow into gametophyte plants. A quick review of the last few paragraphs will show that the haploid plant produces the diploid plant, which in turn produces the haploid plant. This aspect of the life cycle is called **alternation of generations** (fig. 23.6). The gametophyte generation is dominant over the sporophyte generation in mosses. This means that the gametophyte generation is independent of, and more likely to be seen than the sporophyte generation.

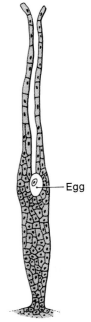

Fig. 23.4 *Archegonium of a Moss Plant.* This female portion of the moss gametophyte plant is composed of an egg cell located inside of a group of jacket cells.

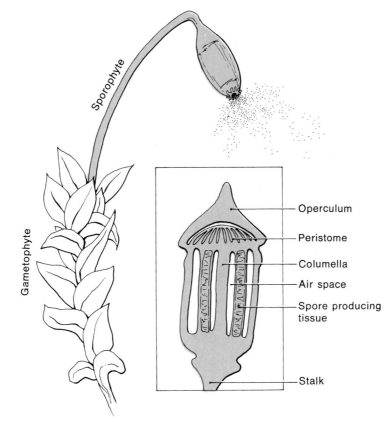

Operculum

Peristome

Columella

Air space

Spore producing tissue

Stalk

Fig. 23.5 *Sporophyte Generation of a Moss.* The fertilized egg cell matures into the sporophyte plant. The sporophyte is composed of a stalk and capsule. Certain cells inside of the capsule can undergo meiosis to become haploid spores.

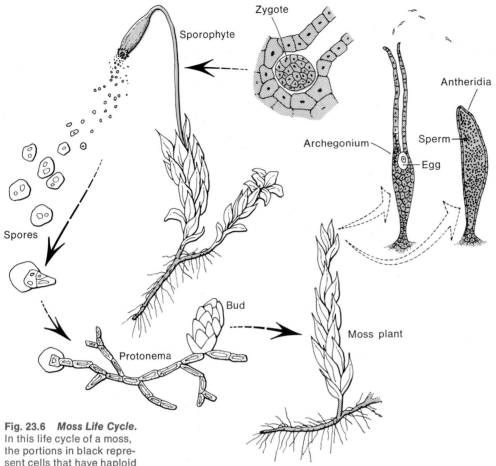

Fig. 23.6 _Moss Life Cycle._ In this life cycle of a moss, the portions in black represent cells that have haploid nuclei (gametophyte generation). Colored portions represent the diploid cells (sporophyte generation). Notice that the haploid and diploid portions of the life cycle alternate.

Labels in figure: Sporophyte, Zygote, Antheridia, Archegonium, Sperm, Egg, Spores, Bud, Moss plant, Protonema

Much Ado About Nothing

What characteristics of mosses allow botanists to consider them the lowest step of the evolutionary ladder in the plant kingdom? First of all, they are considered primitive, because they have not developed an efficient way of transporting water throughout their bodies. They must rely on the physical processes of diffusion and osmosis to move materials. You may ask, "what's so bad about that?" Although nothing is really bad about it, the fact that mosses do not have a complex method of moving water limits their size to a few centimeters and their location to moist environments. One other aspect of moss biology points out how closely related they are to their aquatic ancestors. Water is required for fertilization. The sperm cells "swim" from the antheridia to the archegonia. The small size, moist habitat, and swimming sperm are considered characteristics of a primitive organism. In a primitive way, mosses have adapted to a terrestrial niche.

Odds and Ends

There are a small number of organisms in existence today that show some of the unsuccessful directions of evolution. You might think of these evolutionary groups as experimental models that couldn't quite "cut it," but were important steps in the evolution of more successful plants. The advances are all concerned with greater specialization of some cells, which enables the plant to do a better job of acquiring, moving, and keeping water. Cells that are specialized to perform a particular function are called **tissues.** The tissue important in moving water is called **vascular tissue.** The vascular tissues in plants are of two types. One is **xylem** tissue; the other is **phloem** tissue. Xylem is a series of hollow cells arranged end to end so that they form a tube. These cells are responsible for carrying water absorbed from the soil to the upper parts of the plant. Associated with these tubelike cells are other cells that have thickened cell walls to provide strength and support for the plant.

The second type of vascular tissue, phloem, is responsible for carrying the organic molecules produced in one part of the plant to storage areas in others. With specialization of cells into vascular tissues, there has been the development of specialized parts of plants. **Roots, stems,** and **leaves** are examples of specialized parts, containing vascular tissue (fig. 23.7). The root is specialized for picking up water. It has special outgrowths called **root hairs** that increase the efficiency by which it absorbs water from the soil. The stem has well-developed vascular tissue and is responsible for transportation of

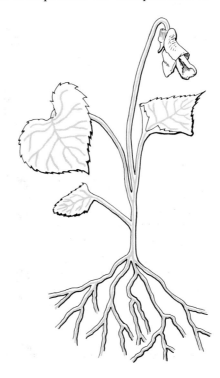

Fig. 23.7 *Vascular Tissue in Roots, Stems, and Leaves.* In this diagram, the colored portions represent the series of tubes in the roots, stems, and leaves which function to distribute fluids throughout the plant.

Fig. 23.8 *Liverworts.* These ribbon-shaped plants are related to the mosses. (Courtesy of Carolina Biological Supply Company.)

both water from roots to leaves and organic molecules from the leaves to storage areas in the roots. The leaf is the site of photosynthesis.

The experimental evolutionary groups have some vascular tissue and serve as links between the nonvascular mosses and the more successful land plants. They also show some specializations that are hints of true roots, stems, and leaves. But they tend to be small plants that still require moist environments because they still have swimming sperm. Some of the experimental groups are the liverworts, club mosses, and horsetails.

Liverworts are usually overlooked by the casual observer because they are low growing plants composed of a green ribbon of cells and are not very large (fig. 23.8). While they do not have well-developed roots or stems, the leaflike ribbon of tissue is well suited to absorb light for photosynthesis.

Club mosses are a group of low growing plants that are somewhat more successful than liverworts in adapting to life on land. They have a new development that allows them to be larger than mosses and not as closely tied to wet areas. This new development is a stemlike structure that holds the leafy parts above the low growing plants and allows them to better compete for the available sunlight. While not as efficient as the stems in higher plants, the club moss stem with its vascular tissue is a hint of what's to come (fig. 23.9).

One group of very common plants that are considered primitive, is called horsetails (fig. 23.10). Horsetails have scalelike leaves, a well-developed stem, and a primitive root. Horsetails are interesting plants because they have silicon dioxide as an additive in their cell walls. This glassy addition is in rows of cells, which makes the stem of the plant sharp and rough. Sometimes called *scouring rushes,* they can be used to scour a dirty pan when camping. (We have it on good authority, however, that a handful of sand does a better job of cleaning up the dirty pots and pans!)

Fig. 23.9 *Club Mosses.*
These plants are sometimes
called ground pines because
of their slight resemblance
to the evergreen trees.
(Courtesy of Carolina Biological Supply Company.)

Fig. 23.10 *Horsetails.*
These unusual plants have
silicon dioxide in their cell
walls. They are sometimes
called scouring rushes.
(Courtesy of Carolina Biological Supply Company.)

Onward and Upward

With vascular tissue, plants are no longer limited to wet areas. They could absorb water and distribute it to leaves many meters above the surface of the soil. The ferns are the most primitive vascular plants that are truly successful at terrestrial living. Not only is their range extended and their size larger than mosses and club mosses, but one additional change has been made. The sporophyte generation has assumed more importance, and the gametophyte generation has decreased in size and complexity. Figure 23.11 shows the life cycle of a fern. You might ask why we consider the dominance of the sporophyte as an advance. The diploid condition of the sporophyte is of advantage because a recessive gene can be masked until it is combined with another identical recessive gene. In other words, the plant does not suffer because the plant has one bad gene. The alternative is that the mutant is a good change, and again nothing but time is lost by having it hidden in the heterozygous condition. In a haploid plant, any change, whether recessive or not, shows up. Not only is a diploid condition beneficial to an individual, but the population is benefited when many alleles are available for selection.

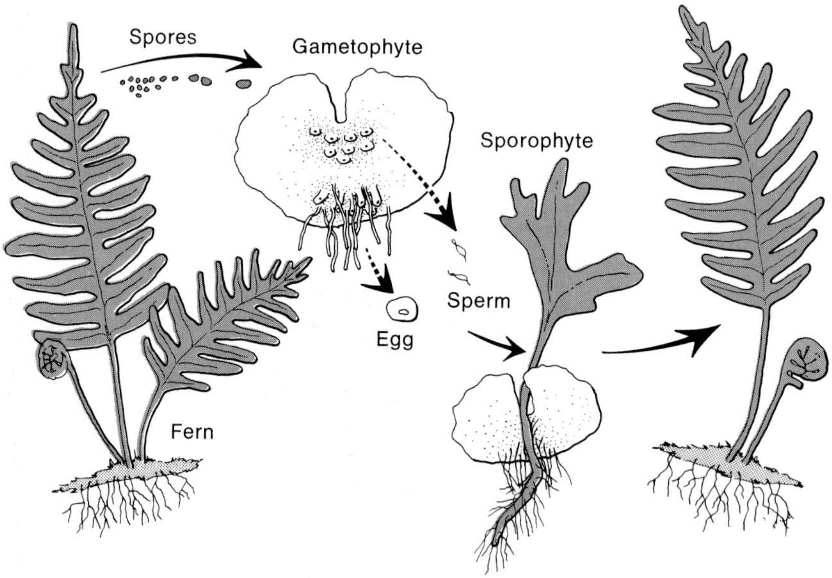

Fig. 23.11 *Life Cycle of a Fern.* In this life cycle of a fern, the portions in black represent cells that have haploid nuclei (gametophyte generation). Notice that the gametophyte and sporophyte generations alternate. Compare this life cycle with that of the moss (fig. 23.6). In the moss, the gametophyte generation is considered dominant, whereas in the fern the sporophyte is dominant.

There is a great deal of variety in the ferns. They take many forms, including the delicate cloverlike fern, the maidenhair fern of northern wooded areas, the bushy growth of the bracken fern (fig. 23.12), and the tree fern known primarily from the fossil record and seen today in tropical areas. With all of this variety, however, they still lack one tiny but very important structure—the **seed.** Without seeds, the ferns must still rely on spores to spread the species from place to place (fig. 23.13).

Fig. 23.12 *A Typical Fern.* (Courtesy of Carolina Biological Supply Company.)

Fig. 23.13 *Fern Sporangia.* On the back of some fern leaves, there are some small brown dots. These dots are the covering layer of tissue that protects the spore-producing structures called the sporangia

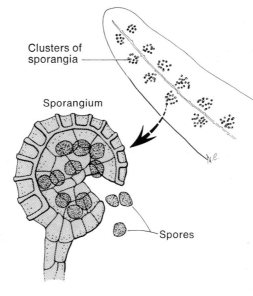

Clusters of sporangia

Sporangium

Spores

Oh! Naked Seeds

The next advance made in the plant kingdom was the evolution of the seed. A seed has an embryo that is enclosed in a protective covering called the **seed coat.** It also has some stored food available for the embryo. The first attempt at seed production is exhibited by the conifers, which are cone-bearing plants, such as pine trees. There are two types of *cones.* The male cone is a woody structure that produces **pollen.** Pollen is a miniaturized male

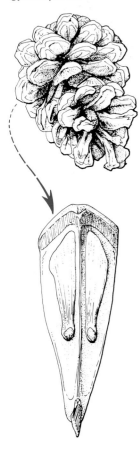

gametophyte plant. These pollen grains are very small dustlike particles. Each pollen grain contains a sperm nucleus. The female cone is larger than the male cone and produces structures that are the female gametophyte plants. The archegonia in the female gametophyte contain eggs. The pollen is carried by wind to the female cone. The female cone holds the archegonium in a position to gather the airborne pollen. The process of getting the pollen from the male cone to the female cone is called **pollination.** The production of seeds and pollination by wind are features of conifers that place them higher on the evolutionary ladder than ferns, since the sperm are transported to the archegonium by wind. They do not require water for the sperm to swim to the egg.

Because seeds with their embryo are produced on the surface of the woody leaflike structure (the female cone) they are said to be naked, or out in the open. The cone-producing plants are sometimes called **gymnosperms,** which means naked seed plants. Before you are convinced that botanists are dirty old men, let us assure you that this terminology points up a deficiency in the plant, not the botanist. Producing seeds out in the open allows this very important part of the life cycle to be vulnerable to adverse environmental influences, as well as to attack by insects, birds, or other organisms (fig. 23.14).

Oh Tannenbaum

One characteristic that the gymnosperms generally exhibit is the production of needle-shaped leaves. These leaves, or needles, do not all fall off at once. The tree is said to be **nondeciduous.** This term is misleading in that it suggests that the needles do not fall off at all. In reality, the needles are constantly being shed—a few fall off all the time. Perhaps you have seen the mat of needles under a conifer. The tree retains some leaves year-round, and therefore is called an evergreen (fig. 23.15). That portion of the evergreen with which you are familiar is the sporophyte generation. The gametophyte or haploid stages are reduced to only a few cells. Look closely at figure 23.16; it shows the life cycle of a pine with its alternation of haploid and diploid generations.

Fig. 23.15 *Needle-Shaped Leaves.* The leaves in the gymnosperms have been greatly modified and look like needles. Notice the scars where needles were attached. Evergreens do shed their leaves but they lose them a few at a time all year, rather than all at one time.

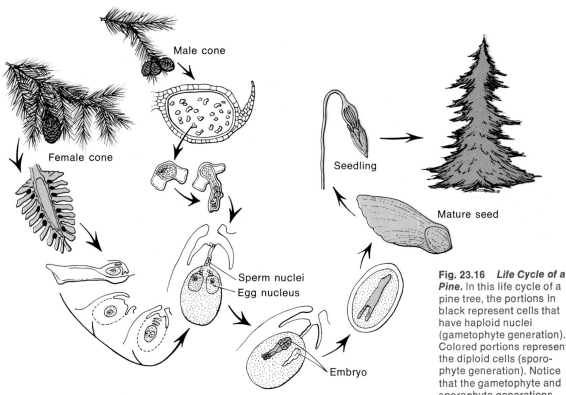

Male cone

Female cone

Seedling

Mature seed

Sperm nuclei
Egg nucleus

Embryo

Fig. 23.16 *Life Cycle of a Pine.* In this life cycle of a pine tree, the portions in black represent cells that have haploid nuclei (gametophyte generation). Colored portions represent the diploid cells (sporophyte generation). Notice that the gametophyte and sporophyte generations alternate. Compare the life cycle of the pine with the life cycles of the moss (fig. 23.6) and of the fern (fig. 23.11). Notice that a trend has developed with ever-increasing dominance in the sporophyte generation.

How Much Wood Would?

Gymnosperms are **perennials.** That is, they live year after year. Unlike **annuals,** which complete their life cycle in one year, gymnosperms take many years to grow from seeds to reproducing adults. The tree gets higher and bigger around each year, as it continually adds layers of strengthening cells and vascular tissue. As the tree becomes large, the strengthening tissue in the stem becomes more and more important. There is a layer of cells in the stem, called the **cambium,** that is responsible for this increase in size. Xylem tissue is the innermost part of the tree trunk. Phloem is outside of the xylem. The cambium layer of cells is positioned between the xylem and the phloem. These cambium cells go through a mitotic cell division, and two cells are formed. One cell remains cambium tissue and the other specializes to form vascular tissue. If the cell is inside the cambium ring, it becomes xylem; if it is outside the cambium ring, it becomes phloem. The one cambium cell then divides again, and again. One cell always remains cambium; the other becomes vascular tissue. Thus, the tree is constantly increasing in diameter (fig. 23.17).

The accumulation of the xylem in the trunk of gymnosperms is called **wood.** Wood is one of the most valuable biological resources of the world.

Fig. 23.17 *Cross Section of Woody Stem.* Notice that the xylem makes up most of what we call wood. Can you picture the relative position of the labeled structures twenty years from now?

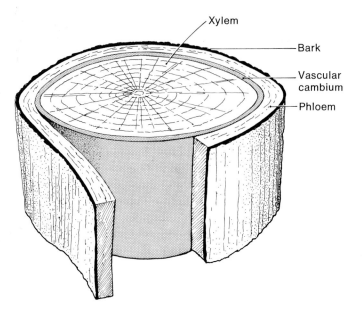

Xylem

Bark

Vascular cambium

Phloem

Fig. 23.18 *Several Gymnosperms.* How many of these do you recognize? They are: Torrey Pine, Piñon Pine, *Sequoia, Taxus Breuifobia* (Yew), *Juniperus Virginiana* (Cedar), *Cupressus Goveniana* (Cypress). (Courtesy of Field Museum of Natural History, Chicago.)

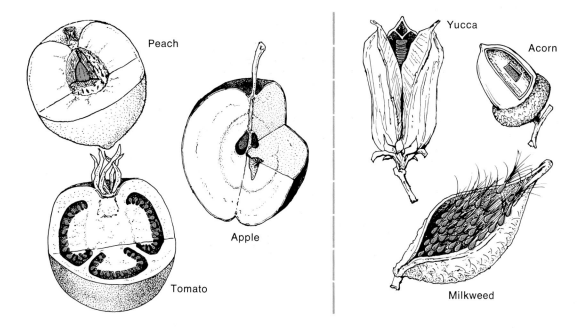

Peach

Apple

Tomato

Yucca

Acorn

Milkweed

We get lumber, paper products, turpentine, and many other valuable materials from gymnosperms. You are already familiar with many examples of gymnosperms, so rather than describe a number of these to you, refer to the picture shown in figure 23.18.

Fig. 23.19 *Types of Edible and Inedible Fruits.* Fruits are the structures that contain seeds. The seed containers on the left are used as food; those on the right are not.

Angiosperms—Plants with More Modesty

The group of plants that are considered most highly evolved are known as **angiosperms.** This name means that the seeds, rather than being produced naked, are contained within the surrounding tissues of the **ovary.** The ovary and other tissues mature into a protective structure known as the **fruit.** Many of the foods you eat are the seed-containing fruits of angiosperms. Green beans, melons, tomatoes, and apples are only a few of the many edible fruits (fig. 23.19).

Sex Is Perfect

A flower is the structure that produces the sex cells and enables the sperm cells to get to the egg cells. The important parts of the flower are the **pistil** (female part) and the **stamen** (male part) (fig. 23.20). Look at figure 23.20 and note that the egg cell is located inside the ovary. Any flower that has both male and female parts is called **perfect.** A flower containing just female or male parts is **imperfect.** Any additional parts of the flower are called accessory structures, since fertilization can be accomplished without them. Many flowers have **accessory structures,** such as **petals, sepals,** and glands that serve a protective function, or increase the probability of fertilization. Before

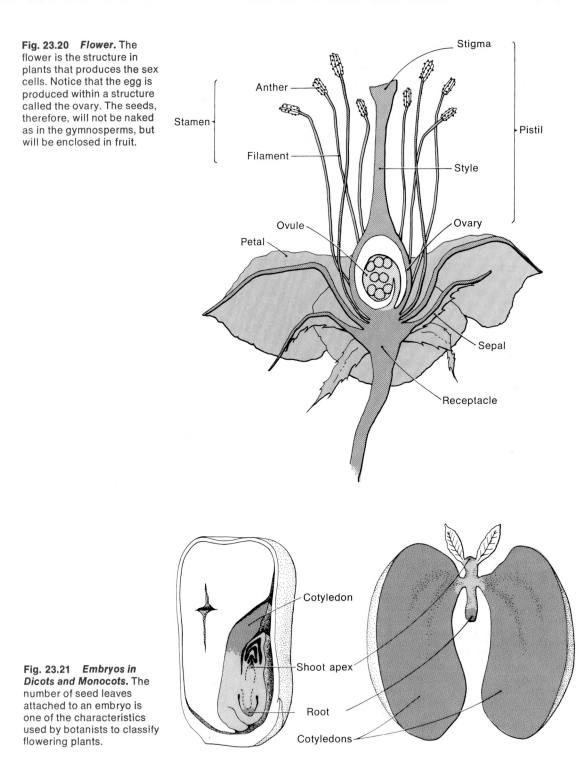

Fig. 23.20 *Flower.* The flower is the structure in plants that produces the sex cells. Notice that the egg is produced within a structure called the ovary. The seeds, therefore, will not be naked as in the gymnosperms, but will be enclosed in fruit.

Stigma

Anther

Stamen

Filament

Pistil

Style

Ovule

Ovary

Petal

Sepal

Receptacle

Fig. 23.21 *Embryos in Dicots and Monocots.* The number of seed leaves attached to an embryo is one of the characteristics used by botanists to classify flowering plants.

Cotyledon

Shoot apex

Root

Cotyledons

the sperm cell (contained in the pollen) can join with the egg cell, there must be some way of getting it to the egg. This is the process called pollination. Some flowers with showy petals are adapted to attracting insects, who will accidentally carry the pollen to the pistil. Others have become adapted for wind pollination. The important thing is to get the genetic information from the one parent to the other parent.

All of the flowering plants have retained the evolutionary advances that were made in the previous groups. That is, they have well-developed vascular tissue with true roots, stems, and leaves. They have pollen and the ability to produce seeds within the protective structure of the ovary.

A Rose Is a Rose Is a Skunk Cabbage

There are thousands of different kinds of plants that produce flowers, fruits, and seeds. Almost any plant you can think of is an angiosperm. If you made a list of these familiar plants, you would quickly see that there is a great deal of variability in structure and habitat. The mighty oak, the delicate rose, the pesky dandelion, and the expensive orchid are all flowering plants. How do we organize this diversity into some sensible and workable arrangement? Botanists classify all of these plants into one of two groups, either as **dicots** or **monocots.** The names dicot and monocot refer to a structure (called a cotyledon) in the seeds of these plants. If the embryo has two **seed leaves,** the plant is a dicot; those with only one seed leaf are the monocots (fig. 23.21). A peanut is a dicot as is a lima bean or an apple. Grass, lilies, and orchids are all monocots. Even with this separation into two groups the diversity is staggering. Characteristics used to classify and name plants are listed below. Figure 23.22 compares the extremes of these characteristics for you.

Summary

The plant kingdom is composed of organisms able to manufacture their own food by the process of photosynthesis. They have specialized structures for the production of the male sex cell (sperm) and the female sex cell (the egg). The relative importance of the haploid gametophyte and the diploid sporophyte that alternate in plant life cycles is a major characteristic used to determine an evolutionary sequence. The extent and complexity of the vascular tissue is also used to rank plants as primitive or complex. The degree to which plants rely on water for fertilization is also used to classify them. Within the gymnosperms and the angiosperms, the methods of production, protection, and dispersal of pollen is used in naming and classifying the organisms into an evolutionary sequence. Based on the information available, mosses are the most primitive. Liverworts, club mosses, and horsetails are experimental models. Ferns, seed-producing gymnosperms, and angiosperms are the most advanced and show development of roots, stems, and leaves.

Fig. 23.22 *Comparison of Structures in Dicots and Monocots.*

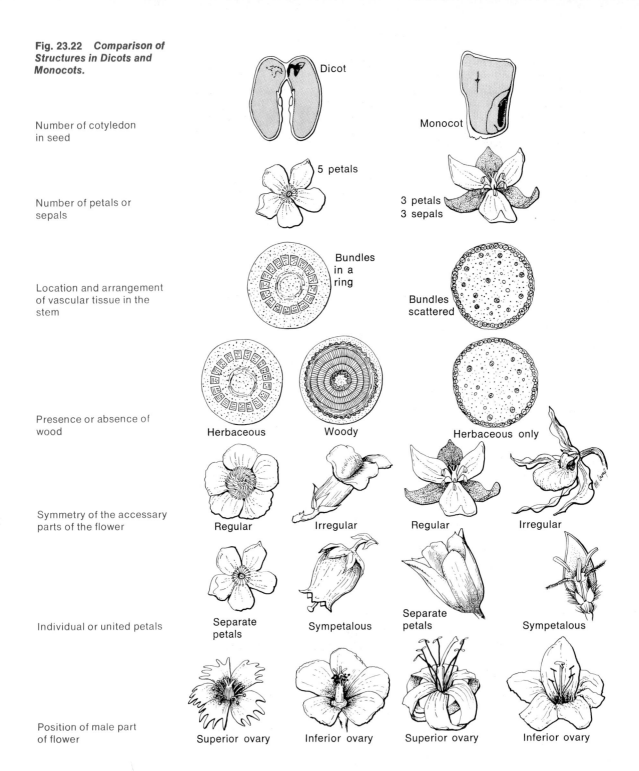

Number of cotyledon in seed

Dicot

Monocot

Number of petals or sepals

5 petals

3 petals
3 sepals

Location and arrangement of vascular tissue in the stem

Bundles in a ring

Bundles scattered

Presence or absence of wood

Herbaceous   Woody

Herbaceous only

Symmetry of the accessary parts of the flower

Regular   Irregular   Regular   Irregular

Individual or united petals

Separate petals   Sympetalous   Separate petals   Sympetalous

Position of male part of flower

Superior ovary   Inferior ovary   Superior ovary   Inferior ovary

Flash! "We interrupt this textbook *again* to bring you an important announcement! A chemical plant in California has accidentally released an experimental compound that selectively kills ferns, gymnosperms, and angiosperms. It is feared that the chemicals have reached the jet stream and will be widely dispersed. A committee of scientists has been called to Washington to advise the President on what action to take. We will give you more information from the scene of the accident as soon as it becomes available."

You are one of the scientists on the advisory committee to the President. Advise him concerning the possible effects this chemical may have on life on the earth. He will be interested to know what man will have to do in order to continue life.

1. What characteristics are used to distinguish between algae in the kingdom Protista and the organisms of the kingdom Plants?
2. List three similarities shared by mosses, ferns, and angiosperms.
3. What were the major advances that led to the development of angiosperms?
4. How is a seed different from pollen, and how do both of these differ from a spore?
5. How are cones and flowers different?
6. How are cones and flowers similar?
7. What is the dominant generation in mosses, ferns, gymnosperms, and angiosperms?
8. What is the difference between the xylem and the phloem?
9. Ferns have not been as successful as gymnosperms and angiosperms. Why?
10. What is the significance of the tissue cambium in perennials?

accessory structures   Structures that are parts of some flowers, but are not directly involved in gamete production.

alternation of generations   The cycling of a sporophyte generation and a gametophyte generation in plants.

angiosperms   Plants that produce flowers and fruits.

annual   A plant that completes its life cycle in one year.

antheridia (antheridium, sing.)   The structure in lower plants that produces sperm.

archegonium   The structure in lower plants that produces eggs.

cambium   A tissue in higher plants that produces new xylem and phloem.

capsule   Part of the sporophyte generation of mosses that contains spores.

cone   A reproductive structure of gymnosperms that produces pollen in males or eggs in females.

dicot   An angiosperm that contains two seed leaves in its embryo.

flower   A complex structure made from modified stems and leaves; it produces pollen in the males and eggs in the females.

fruit   The structure in angiosperms that contains seeds.

gametophyte generation   The haploid generation in plant life cycles. They produce gametes.

germinate   To begin to grow.

gymnosperms   Plants that produce their seeds in cones.

imperfect flowers   Flowers that contain either male or female reproductive structures, but not both.

leaves   A specialized portion of higher plants that function primarily in photosynthesis.

life cycle   The series of stages in the life of any organism.

monocot   An angiosperm that contains one seed leaf in its embryo.

mosses   Lower plants that have a dominant gametophyte generation, no vascular tissue, swimming sperm, and spores.

nondeciduous   Refers to trees that do not lose their leaves all at once.

ovary   The female structure that produces eggs.

perennials   A plant that requires many years to complete its life cycle.

perfect flowers   Flowers that contain both male and female reproductive structures.

petals   Modified leaves of angiosperms, a part of a flower.

phloem   One kind of vascular tissue found in higher plants; transports food materials from the leaves to other parts of the plant.

pistil   The female reproductive structure in flowers.

pollen   The male gametophyte in gymnosperms and angiosperms.

pollination   The transferring of pollen in gymnosperms and angiosperms.

roots   Specialized structures for the absorption of water in higher plants.

root hairs   Tiny outgrowths of roots that improve the ability of plants to absorb water.

seed   A specialized structure that is produced by gymnosperms and angiosperms and contains the embryo sporophyte.

seed coat   A protective layer around seeds.

seed leaves   Embryonic leaves in seeds.

sepals   Accessory structures of flowers.

spores   Haploid structures produced by sporophytes.

sporophyte   The diploid generation in the life cycle of plants that produces spores.

stamen   The male reproductive structure of a flower.

stem   The upright portion of a higher plant.

tissue   A group of specialized cells that work together to perform a particular function.

vascular tissue   Specialized tissue that transports fluids in higher plants.

wood The xylem of gymnosperms and angiosperms.

xylem A kind of vascular tissue that transports water from the roots to other parts of the plant.

Purpose   Processes such as respiration, cell division, reproduction, and heredity are common to all forms of life. This was true for the first living organisms, and is true for those many types of organisms that have evolved since. The evolution that resulted in a great variety of species was presented previously (chap. 21). At that point, only a passing reference was made to the various types of animals. This chapter will present the major groups of animals, giving some of the traits common to the members within each group.

Animals

24

Daddy, What's an Animal?

For this text, we will define animals as many-celled organisms that require food as an energy source. The life cycle of an animal has a number of different stages. Within the cycle, reproduction may be either sexual or **asexual.** It is the adult animal that is capable of producing gametes for sexual reproduction. Asexual reproduction may occur at different stages of the life cycle and differs from sexual reproduction in that there is no mixing of genetic material. Organisms that reproduce asexually produce carbon copies of themselves in a number of ways. **Budding** is one method of asexual reproduction and occurs when an animal grows an offspring off its main body. In a typical animal life cycle, the adult is capable of reproducing sexually to form a zygote (fig. 24.1). In some species these zygotes undergo development and emerge

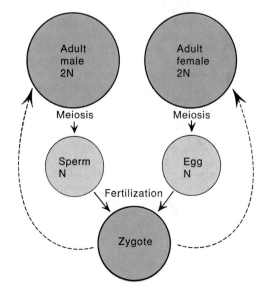

Fig. 24.1 *Animal Life Cycle.* The male and female produce the haploid number of chromosomes in sperm and eggs. These haploid cells combine to form a zygote, and another life begins.

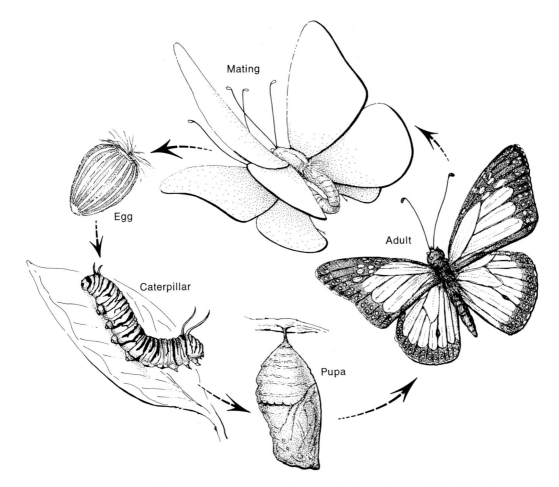

Mating

Egg

Caterpillar

Adult

Pupa

Fig. 24.2 *Life Cycle of a Butterfly.* The fertilized egg develops into a caterpillar —an undeveloped adult organism. The caterpillar enters into a pupa stage, undergoes metamorphosis, and emerges as a fully developed adult.

fully formed. For example, a newly born human baby has the same basic features as the adult. In other forms of animals, the young have little resemblance to the adult. Such young are known as **larvae.** Larva is an incompletely developed animal; it must undergo many changes to develop into an adult. For instance, a caterpillar is the larval stage in the life cycle of a butterfly (fig. 24.2).

The first forms of animal life were not much more advanced than the one-celled organisms. In these first many-celled animals, each cell lived an almost independent life. As the animals evolved, certain cells of their bodies began to specialize and perform a particular function. Such a change resulted in the development of **tissues.** A tissue is a group of cells that are similar in function and structure. The cells that specialize in body movement make up muscle tissue. The cells that line the intestine are specialized for digestion and absorption.

As the evolution of animals continued, **organs** developed. Organs are body units composed of many different tissues that operate together to perform a particular function. The stomach, brain, liver, and heart are examples of organs. Further evolution resulted in collections of organs known as **organ systems.** The circulatory system, the digestive system, the reproductive system, and the nervous system are examples. The present-day animal kingdom contains members displaying these various stages of evolution. One of the simplest kinds of animals present today are the **sponges.**

The Holey One—The Sponges or Porifera

Most people think of a sponge as a pastel-colored, rectangular-shaped object that comes wrapped in plastic. If you have seen natural sponges, you know they are brownish-colored, irregular-shaped objects; you probably didn't think of them as being members of the animal kingdom. Sponges represent one of the most primitive forms of animal life (fig. 24.3). Sponges are mainly

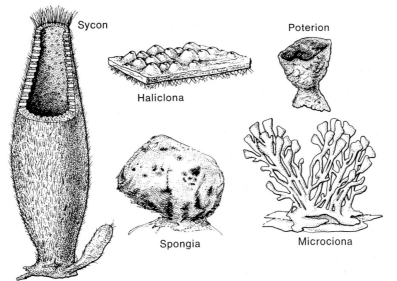

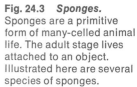

Fig. 24.3 *Sponges.* Sponges are a primitive form of many-celled animal life. The adult stage lives attached to an object. Illustrated here are several species of sponges.

found in saltwater environments, but a few species are found living in unpolluted fresh water. The adult sponge is attached to some object and does not have a great deal of cell specialization. The interior of a sponge is composed of numerous interconnecting tubes (fig. 24.4). Lining these tubes are a number of **flagellated cells.** The flagella of these cells cause a current of water to flow through the tubes. Each individual sponge cell gets the nutrients it needs from the water. The adult sponge can reproduce asexually by budding, or sexually by producing sperm and eggs. The fertilized egg will give rise to a free-swimming larva. This larva will develop into a mature adult. Figure 24.5 illustrates the life cycle of a sponge.

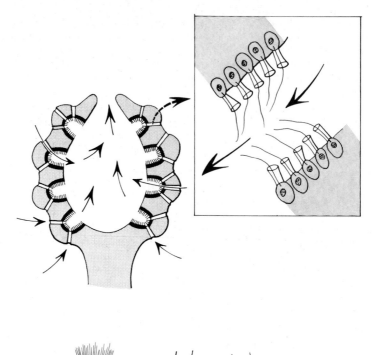

Fig. 24.4 *Circulation of Water Through a Sponge.* Flagellated cells line the canals within a sponge and cause a constant flow of water through the canals. (After Woodruff, 1941. *Foundations of Biology.* 6th ed. New York: The Macmillan Co.)

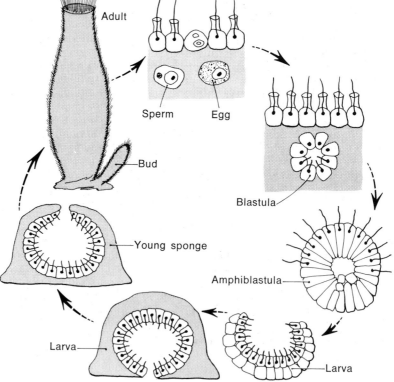

Adult

Sperm

Egg

Blastula

Amphiblastula

Bud

Young sponge

Larva

Larva

Fig. 24.5 *Life Cycle of a Sponge.* Sexual reproduction in sponges occurs when the flagellated sperm cell unites with an egg cell to form a zygote. The zygote undergoes several stages of development as it grows into an adult.

Jellyfish, Corals, and Sea Anemones—The Coelenterates, or Cnidaria

People who have been to the ocean have likely seen one or more species of **coelenterates.** Common members of the coelenterates include the *Hydra,* jellyfish, coral, and sea anemones (fig. 24.6).

All coelenterates have a single opening that leads into a saclike interior of the animal (fig. 24.7). Surrounding the opening are a series of **tentacles.** These tentacles possess specialized cells that can sting and paralyze small organisms—coelenterates are carnivorous animals. The paralyzed organisms are slowly moved into the animal by the tentacles. The coelenterates, as evidenced by the tentacles, exhibit some degree of specialization.

Fig. 24.6 Coelenterates. *(a)* Sea anemone. *(b)* Jellyfish. *(c)* Coral. *(d)* Hydra. (Courtesy of Carolina Biological Supply Company.)

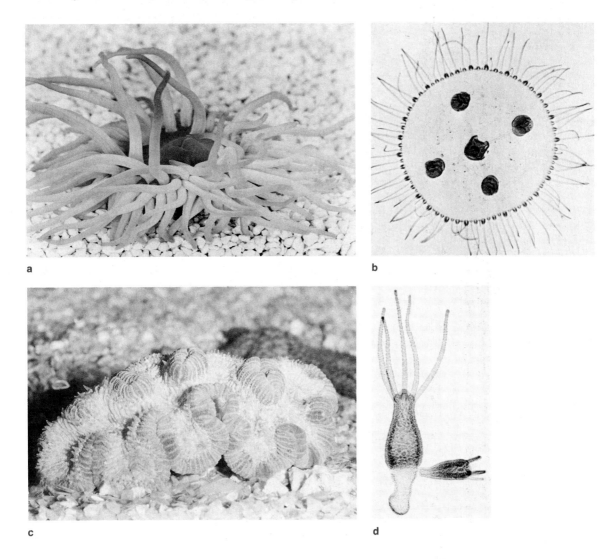

a

b

c

d

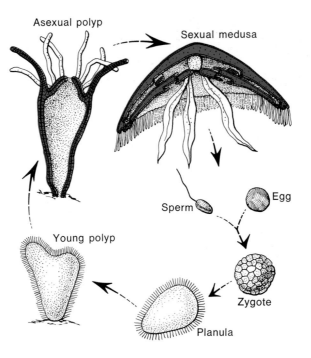

Fig. 24.7 *Life Cycle of a Jellyfish.* The polyp stage of a jellyfish reproduces asexually and these organisms develop into the medusa stage. The medusa reproduces sexually; the resulting zygote develops into a planula. The planula matures into the polyp.

Asexual polyp

Sexual medusa

Sperm

Egg

Young polyp

Zygote

Planula

A typical coelenterate has a free-swimming adult stage called the **medusa.** It will give rise by means of sexual reproduction to a **polyp** stage. This polyp stage is attached and reproduces by means of budding. Figure 24.7 illustrates the life cycle of a coelenterate.

Important Parasites—The Flatworms, or Platyhelminthes

There are approximately ten thousand species of **flatworms;** two-thirds of them are parasites. With such a variety, it is impossible to use one species to represent all the flatworms. There are three basic kinds of flatworms: the free-living flatworms (like planaria), tapeworms, and flukes (fig. 24.8).

The blood fluke is a common human parasite in much of Asia, Africa, and tropical America. The adult lives in the blood vessels of the intestines and bladder. Here it reproduces, and the fluke's eggs are passed out with the human solid waste material or urine. If the eggs are deposited in water, they will hatch into a free-swimming larva. The larva will enter the body of a snail, undergo development, and asexually reproduce within the snail. A stage that is produced by asexual reproduction will eventually leave the snail and swim about in the water. If this stage comes into contact with the skin of a human, it will drill through and enter a blood vessel. Here a sexually mature fluke will develop, and the life cycle will begin again (fig. 24.9). The blood fluke may cause diarrhea, abdominal pain, and anemia in the infected human.

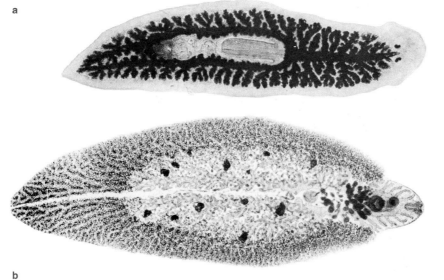

a

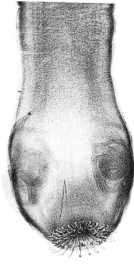

c

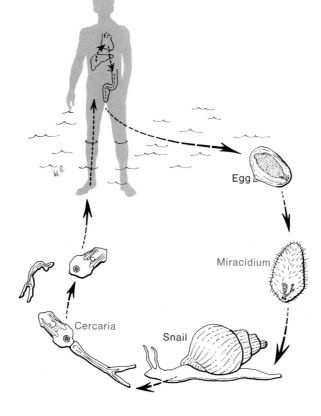

b

Fig. 24.8 *Flatworms.*
(a) Planaria. *(b)* Fluke.
(c) Tapeworm. (Courtesy of
Carolina Biological Supply
Company.)

Egg

Miracidium

Cercaria

Snail

**Fig. 24.9 *Life Cycle of the
Human Liver Flukes.*** The
fertilized liver fluke eggs
pass out of the human and
develop into the miracidium
stage. This stage enters a
snail for additional development, and the larva leaves
the snail in the cercaria
stage. This stage bores
through the skin of a human.
It then develops into a
mature organism.

Each species of fluke requires a particular type of snail for the development of its larva, and a particular type of animal for the development of its adult stage. If any stage in the life cycle of a fluke enters the wrong animal, development will not proceed and that stage of the fluke will die. "Swimmer's itch" is caused in humans when a larval stage of a duck blood fluke enters the body. The larva cannot mature within the human body, but it does live for a few days before dying. This temporary infection causes an itchy red rash.

Common but Poorly Understood—The Roundworms or Aschelminthes

Most people are not aware of the large number of **roundworms** present in the world; nor are they aware of the economic losses caused by roundworms. If you were to take a shovelful of rich soil and count the roundworms, there would be millions of them present. Each year in the United States, roundworms cause several billion dollars worth of damage to crops and livestock.

The roundworms are found throughout the world, inhabiting both soil and water environments. They may be found as free-living forms or as parasites. All species of vertebrates can be infected by some type of roundworm parasite. Figure 24.10 illustrates a roundworm parasite that infects humans. Other common roundworms are pinworms, *ascaris,* and Trichina (fig. 24.11).

Fig. 24.10 *Life Cycle of a Hookworm.* Fertilized hookworm eggs pass out of the human and develop into the larva. The larva bores through the skin of a human and develops into an adult.

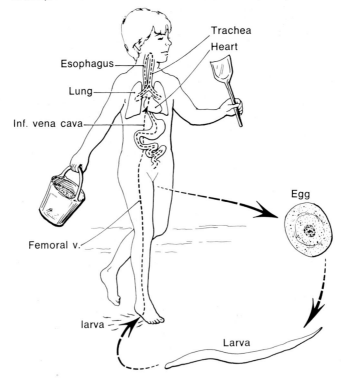

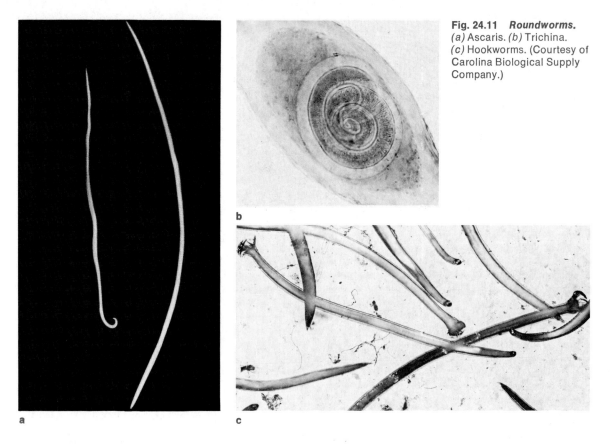

Fig. 24.11 *Roundworms.*
(a) Ascaris. *(b)* Trichina.
(c) Hookworms. (Courtesy of
Carolina Biological Supply
Company.)

a

b

c

Let's Go Fishing—The Annelid Worms

The segmented worms, **annelids,** are known to almost everyone as earthworms, leeches, and clam worms; but they hold special meaning for the
fisherman because the common earthworm is a well-known fish bait. Most
moist soils will support at least some species of earthworms. In saltwater
areas, the clam worm is commonly found in the sand and is also used for
fishing (fig. 24.12).

The members of this group of animals have evolved some fairly complex forms of specialization. There is a well-developed digestive system,
circulatory system, nervous system, muscular system, reproductive system,
and excretory system (fig. 24.13). Annelid worms play a very important
role in terrestrial ecosystems. Earthworms eat the soil as they burrow through
it. The organic foods found in the soil are digested by the worm, and the
undigestible materials are eliminated from the digestive system unchanged.
Earthworms also come up to the surface to feed on fallen leaves. These habits
have very beneficial effects on the soil. The soil is loosened and turned over,
and the organic material from dead plants and animals is mixed into it. All
of these activities improve soil quality and allow for better plant growth.

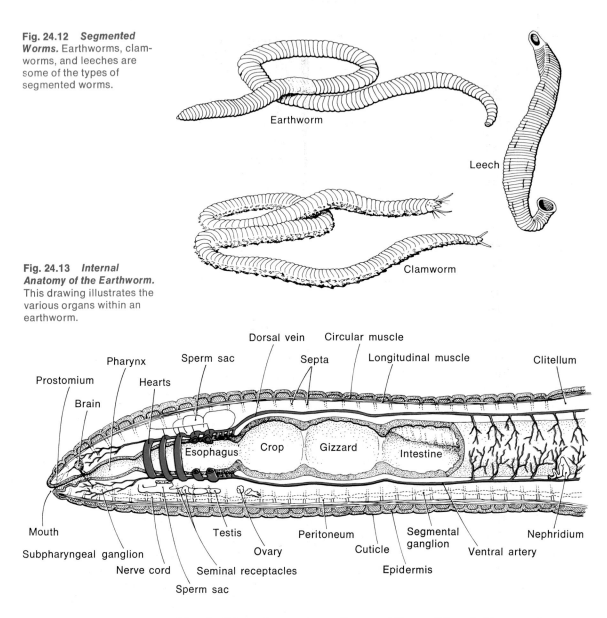

Fig. 24.12 *Segmented Worms.* Earthworms, clamworms, and leeches are some of the types of segmented worms.

Earthworm

Leech

Clamworm

Fig. 24.13 *Internal Anatomy of the Earthworm.* This drawing illustrates the various organs within an earthworm.

Dorsal vein
Circular muscle
Septa
Longitudinal muscle
Clitellum
Sperm sac
Pharynx
Hearts
Prostomium
Brain
Esophagus
Crop
Gizzard
Intestine
Mouth
Testis
Peritoneum
Segmental ganglion
Nephridium
Subpharyngeal ganglion
Ovary
Cuticle
Ventral artery
Nerve cord
Seminal receptacles
Epidermis
Sperm sac

Man's Most Important Competitor—The Arthropods

All **arthropods** have jointed legs and a hard **exoskeleton** on the outside of their body for protection. They have well-developed mouthparts and possess a highly developed nervous system (fig. 24.14). The diversity of animals in this group is greater than that of any other single phylum of animals. The arthropods are found in every type of habitat. They contain more species than are found in the remainder of the animal kingdom. Figure 24.15 shows examples of the five major classes of arthropods.

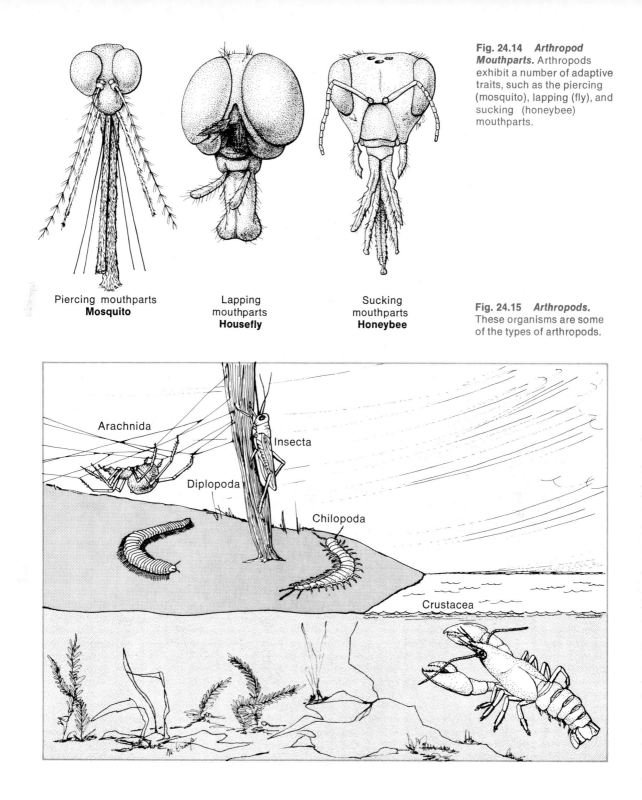

Fig. 24.14 *Arthropod Mouthparts.* Arthropods exhibit a number of adaptive traits, such as the piercing (mosquito), lapping (fly), and sucking (honeybee) mouthparts.

Piercing mouthparts
Mosquito

Lapping mouthparts
Housefly

Sucking mouthparts
Honeybee

Fig. 24.15 *Arthropods.* These organisms are some of the types of arthropods.

Arachnida

Insecta

Diplopoda

Chilopoda

Crustacea

Animals   419

Such common animals as crayfish, lobsters, barnacles, shrimp, and crabs are examples of **crustacea** (fig. 24.16). A number of animals in this class are of economic value to man as a source of food. The crustaceans have gills that serve as respiratory organs. There is great variation among the twenty-six thousand species of this class, and they range from free-swimming shrimp to fixed types, such as barnacles. Barnacles attach themselves to the hulls of saltwater ships and slow it down. Large amounts of money are spent annually in this battle against the barnacles.

The **insects** represent the largest single class within the animal kingdom. Some characteristics are common to all insects (fig. 24.17). They all have three body segments—head, thorax, and abdomen—and there are three pairs of legs attached to the thorax. A series of **tracheae** serve as a means of gas exchange. The insects are either male or female individuals. The young in some species develop as larva and after a period of time go into a **pupa** stage. The larva undergoes additional development in the pupa stage and emerges from the pupa as a sexually mature adult (fig. 24.18). The change from egg to larva to pupa to adult is called **complete metamorphosis.**

Many people confuse the insects with the **arachnids.** The arachnids include spiders, ticks, king crabs, and scorpions (fig. 24.19). This group of arthropods has four or five pairs of legs, which allows these animals to be easily distinguished from the insects, which possess only three pairs of legs.

Fig. 24.16 *Crustaceans.* Crustaceans are a major grouping of animals within the arthropods.

Shrimp

Crab

Barnacles   Lobster

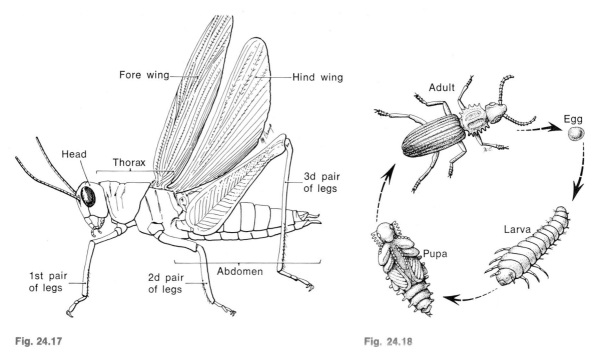

Fore wing — Hind wing

Head
Thorax
3d pair of legs

1st pair of legs
2d pair of legs
Abdomen

Fig. 24.17

Adult — Egg
Pupa — Larva

Fig. 24.18

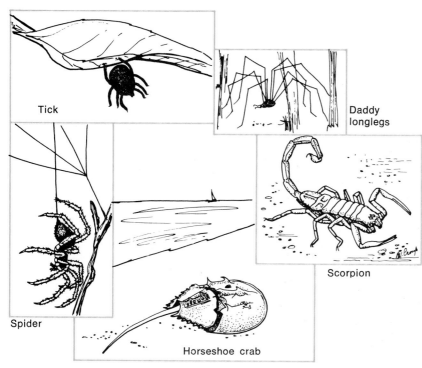

Tick

Daddy longlegs

Spider

Scorpion

Horseshoe crab

Fig. 24.19

Fig. 24.17 *Characteristics of the Insects.* All insects have three body segments with three pairs of legs attached to the thorax.

Fig. 24.18 *Life Cycle of an Insect.* Life cycles of some insects involve complete metamorphosis.

Fig. 24.19 *Arachnids.* These organisms are some of the types of arachnids. Arachnids are characterized by having four pairs of legs.

Cockles and Mussels Alive, Alive Oh! The Mollusks

The **mollusks** include many common species of animals, such as the oyster, clam, snail, octopus, and squid (fig. 24.20). All the members of this phylum have a soft body that houses the heart, digestive system, excretory system, nervous system, reproductive system, and other internal organs. A tissue called the **mantle** surrounds the body (fig. 24.21). In many species, this mantle contains specialized glands that secrete the material that will form a shell.

Another common group of mollusks are the **bivalves**—animals that have a two-part shell. Many of these species are valued as a food source for man. Most bivalves remain in one place and feed by circulating large amounts of water. As the water is circulated, the food is filtered out. Oysters, clams, and scallops are examples of the bivalves.

Cephalopods, mollusks with a distinct head, are the monsters of movies and television. The cephalopods include the octopus and squid, which in reality are very timid animals. These animals have a large head and a number of tentacles. The world's largest **invertebrate animals** (animals without a backbone) are members of this class. There are records of squid in excess of twenty meters in length and weighing nearly nine thousand kilograms.

Fig. 24.20 *Mollusks.* These organisms are some of the types of mollusks. Soft bodies are a characteristic of the mollusks.

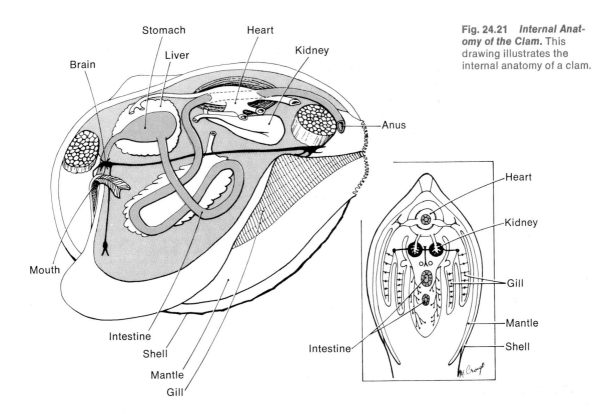

Fig. 24.21 *Internal Anatomy of the Clam.* This drawing illustrates the internal anatomy of a clam.

The Stars of the Animal Kingdom—The Echinoderms

Echinoderm means spiny skin, and a common characteristic of this phylum of animals is an **endoskeleton.** The skeleton inside the body has a number of spiny projections. The echinoderms are found only in saltwater habitats.

The starfish are typical representatives of these animals as are the serpent stars, sand dollars, sea urchins, sea cucumbers, and crinoids (fig. 24.22). Characteristics of these animals include digestive, reproductive, and nervous systems. The **water-vascular system** is a characteristic that is only found in the echinoderms (fig. 24.23). This system is a series of tubes that radiates throughout the animal. The water enters by means of an opening and travels through canals. The **tube feet** are located on the arms and are used like little suction cups. By controlling the water pressure in the water vascular system, the echinoderm can suck itself onto surfaces. By fixing and releasing these tube feet, it can move through its environment or capture food.

In the echinoderms, the sexes are separate and fertilization occurs outside the female's body. The eggs hatch into a larval form that must undergo metamorphosis to become an adult.

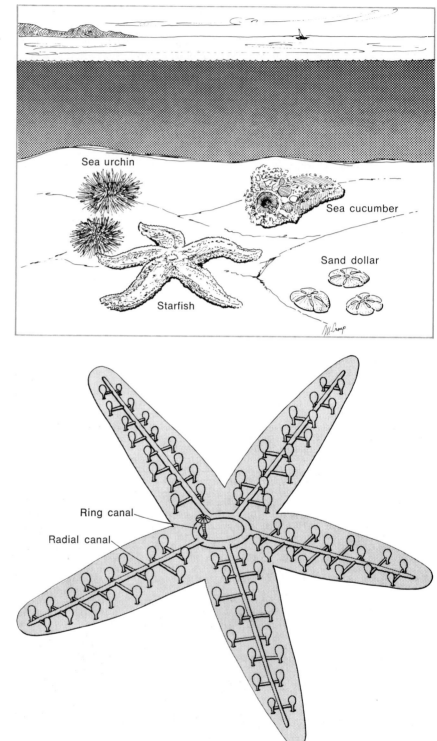

Fig. 24.22 *Echinoderms.*
These organisms are some of the types of echinoderms.

Sea urchin

Sea cucumber

Sand dollar

Starfish

Ring canal

Radial canal

Fig. 24.23 *Water Vascular System of a Starfish.* The water vascular system is a characteristic unique to the echinoderms.

The Top of the Line—The Chordates

The **chordates** are animals that at some time in their life have all three of the following characteristics: **gill slits, dorsal hollow nerve cord,** and **notochord.** Gill slits are openings that allow water to pass from the throat to the outside. In the aquatic chordates, these slits are a part of the respiratory system. They allow for the movement of water over the gills and the exchange of gases between the animal's blood and the water. The terrestrial chordates have gill slits early in their embryonic stage, but the slits do not carry over to the adult stage. In land animals a pair of gill slits has become modified into **eustachian tubes,** connecting the ear to the throat. In higher forms of animals the dorsal hollow nerve cord makes up the brain and spinal cord. The notochord is a stiff, rodlike structure along the back of the animal; it provides support for the animal. All of the animals presented in the remainder of this chapter are chordates.

The vertebrates are a group of chordates that includes most of the animals we see in our daily lives. In the **vertebrates,** the notochord is found in the developing embryo but is replaced by a series of vertebrae that collectively make up the **backbone.**

The Jawless Ones—Agnatha

The **agnatha** represent the most primitive form of living vertebrates. An example of these animals is the sea lamprey (fig. 24.24). These fishlike animals have no jawbones, but they do possess a **cartilaginous** skeleton. Cartilage is a dense type of supporting tissue that does not have the mineral deposits found in the harder supporting tissues known as bone. The fins of these animals are not in pairs. A large **caudal** (tail) **fin** is the main method of movement for these animals.

Fig. 24.24 Lamprey Feeding Upon a Host Fish. Lampreys are parasitic organisms. (Courtesy of Michigan Department of Natural Resources.)

The adult lamprey spawns in rivers, and the eggs hatch into a larval form. This stage of the lamprey is an organism that filters microscopic food particles out of the water. The larval stage will remain in the river for as long as seven years before changing into the adult form. The opening of the locks in the canals around Niagara Falls enabled oceangoing vessels and saltwater lamprey to enter the lakes. The parasitic lamprey adjusted to the freshwater environment. Since that time, millions of dollars have been spent in an attempt to control this introduced pest.

Watch Out for the Sharks—Chondrichthyes

Movies and television have given most of us an introduction to sharks. But it would not be proper to think that all sharks are the large man-eating variety; only seven of the forty species are known to have attacked man. The adults of some species may seldom grow longer than three feet. Other forms of sharks may grow over fifty feet long. Some large species of sharks feed on microscopic marine organisms. The sharks have a highly developed cartilaginous skeleton and paired fins. The sharks and rays are the principal members of this class (fig. 24.25).

Fig. 24.25 *Sharks and Rays.* These organisms are some of the types of cartilaginous fishes.

Labels in figure: Black bass, Salmon, Garfish, Perch, Sea horse, Catfish, Eel, Flounder

The Bony Fish—Osteichthyes

Whenever the term fish is used, it usually applies to the group of animals that make up the **bony fish** (fig. 24.26). Bony fish evolved in fresh water and later some forms adapted to a saltwater environment. The gill slits are covered by a protective organ called the **operculum.** The body is covered by overlapping scales. The fish produce a slimy mucus as a means of reducing friction and protecting their bodies from infection. Many a fisherman has let a fish slip through his fingers because of this mucus. Most of the bony fish have an **air bladder,** a sac that can be changed in size and regulates the density of the fish. This allows fish to remain at a given level without expending large amounts of energy to keep from sinking or floating. Sharks do not have an air bladder; they must swim constantly or they will sink.

By Land and Sea—The Amphibians

The **amphibians** were the first of the vertebrates to inhabit the terrestrial areas of the earth. The larval amphibians are almost fishlike in nature. They are freshwater organisms that possess external gills and a caudal fin for locomotion. Through a gradual series of changes, the gills disappear and lungs

Fig. 24.26   *Fishes.* These organisms are some of the types of fishes. They inhabit saltwater or freshwater environments. Some species can survive in either environment.

Fig. 24.27 *Life Cycle of a Frog.* Fertilized frog egg cells develop into the tadpole stage. This stage undergoes metamorphosis and develops into an adult frog.

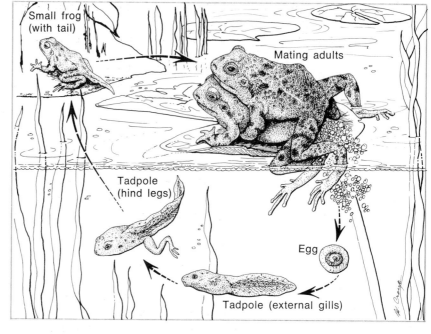

Small frog (with tail)

Mating adults

Tadpole (hind legs)

Egg

Tadpole (external gills)

Fig. 24.28 *Amphibians.* These organisms are some of the types of amphibians. *(a)* Salamander. *(b)* Frog. *(c)* Grass Frog. (Courtesy of Carolina Biological Supply Company.)

a

b

c

develop, and four appendages appear that develop into legs. Such changes enable the adult animal to partially adapt to life on land. However, the amphibians possess a method of reproduction that is not suitable for land. As a result, they are bound to the water during the reproductive period of their lives. Figure 24.27 illustrates the life cycle of a frog. Frogs, toads, and salamanders are types of amphibians, and they do not cause warts (fig. 24.28).

A Snake in the Grass

The **reptiles** were the first vertebrate animals to fully adapt to the terrestrial environment. This resulted from the evolution of the **amniotic egg** with a method of internal fertilization (fig. 24.29). The **amnion** is a membrane that encloses a fluid-filled area surrounding the developing embryo. In addition to the amnion, the egg contains an **allantois,** which is a storage area for waste material. Blood vessels in the allantois are used in the exchange of gases between the embryo's circulatory system and the atmosphere. A **yolk sac** is a membrane that develops from the young and surrounds the yolk of the egg. The **chorion** is a membrane that completely encloses the developing young and the other membranes. These membranes and a protective shell are part of the egg that can protect the embryo during its development. Internal fertilization freed reptiles from returning to water to reproduce.

Since the reptiles were the first vertebrates to occupy the land, they filled many niches. As a result there was a time called "The Golden Age of Reptiles" when reptiles were the dominant land species (fig. 24.30). A series of geological and evolutionary events caused the decline of the reptiles. Today the reptiles are fewer in numbers and only occupy a small number of niches. Snakes, lizards, turtles, alligators, and crocodiles are all that remain as representatives of this class (fig. 24.31).

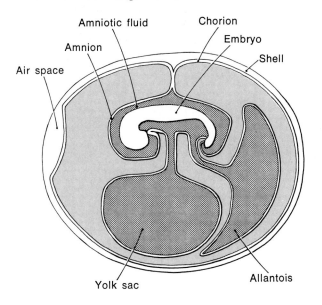

Fig. 24.29 Amniotic Egg. Amniotic eggs provide nutrients and protection to the developing embryo. This type of egg allows for embryonic development outside an aquatic medium.

Fig. 24.30 *Prehistoric Reptiles.* These organisms are some of the types of early reptiles. These representatives of the reptiles could not successfully compete for survival. They are, therefore, extinct. (Courtesy of Field Museum of Natural History. Artist, Charles R. Knight.)

Fig. 24.31 *Reptiles.* (a) Water moccasin. *(b)* Turtle. (Courtesy of Carolina Biological Supply Company.)

Come Fly With Me—Birds or Aves

The **birds** are a class of vertebrates that are capable of flying. A constant body temperature provides an internal environment that can produce the large amounts of energy required for flying. An efficient mechanism is required to supply an adequate amount of oxygenated blood to the muscles. A high metabolic rate is required for a rapid conversion of food into muscular energy. In birds the evolution of a highly developed circulatory system provides the means of moving large amounts of oxygen throughout the body. The development of feathers provides a light, efficient body insulation, and thin-walled bones reduce body weight. Many forms of beaks and feet have evolved as different species of birds specialized into specific niches (fig. 24.32). The amniotic egg and internal means of fertilization found in the reptiles is also the method of reproduction and development in the birds.

Fig. 24.32 *Adaptive Features of Some Birds.* The evolution of various types of beaks and feet have enabled the birds to adapt to many types of environments.

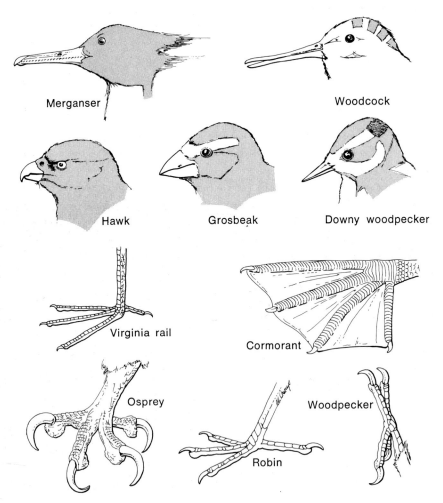

Merganser

Woodcock

Hawk

Grosbeak

Downy woodpecker

Virginia rail

Cormorant

Osprey

Robin

Woodpecker

The Cream of the Crop—The Mammals

In the evolution of animals, the degree of complexity continued to increase and reached its most advanced form in the mammals. All the mammals except for the **marsupials** and the egg-laying mammals (monotremes) have a **placenta.** This organ allows the female and the developing embryo to have a constant exchange of materials throughout the period of development. In addition to the placenta, the mammals also have fur that insulates the body, and **mammary glands** that produce milk for their young.

The mammals have a constant body temperature and a highly developed circulatory system that moves blood to all parts of the body. The brain of the mammals is more highly developed than in other types of animals. This results in a group of animals with a higher degree of intelligence. Typically, the mammals exhibit more care and protection of their young than do other types of animals.

There are three basic types of mammals. The egg-laying monotremes are the most primitive (fig. 24.33). These animals have fur and primitive mammary glands that lack nipples; and the young are hatched, not born.

The marsupials have fur and developed mammary glands, and give birth to their young. But all of the young are born prematurely and crawl into a pouch to complete their development. The opossum and kangaroo are examples of marsupials (fig. 24.34). The placental mammals are those that give birth to fully formed young. Mammals occupy a wide variety of niches and habitats. They are found in terrestrial, freshwater, and saltwater environments and have many adaptive mechanisms that enable them to live in such diverse areas (fig. 24.35).

Fig. 24.33 *Duckbill Platypus.* This unusual mammal is found in Australia and the surrounding islands. This egg-laying organism is a very primitive type of mammal. (Courtesy of Australian News and Information Bureau. Photograph by W. Pedersen.)

Fig. 24.34 *Marsupials.* The young of these animals are not fully developed at birth. They undergo further development within the pouch of the female. (Kangaroo photo courtesy of Australian Information Service; photo by W. Brindle. Opossum photo courtesy of Michigan Department of Natural Resources.)

Fig. 24.35 *Mammals.*
These organisms are some
of the types of mammals.
(Courtesy of Michigan
Department of Natural
Resources.)

Summary Animals are many-celled organisms that must eat food. They reproduce either sexually or asexually and show various degrees of structural complexity. Sponges represent a form of life only slightly above that of one-celled organisms. They filter seawater for nutrients. The coelenterates are more complex and have an attached polyp form and free-swimming medusa form. They use stinging cells to aid in the capture of food. Flatworms are mostly parasitic and have complex life cycles that involve more than one host. Roundworms are extremely common organisms, and some of these are also parasitic. The annelid worms are segmented and are much more complex than any of the previous organisms. The earthworms are valuable additions to the soil. Arthropods are extremely successful. They have an external skeleton, and have adapted to a great variety of niches. The mollusks are an important source of food for man and usually have a shell they use for protection. Echinoderms also have a protective skeleton, but it is found within the body. They have a unique water-vascular system that serves many purposes. The chordates include those animals with gill slits, dorsal hollow nerve cords, and notochords. Among this group are the fish, amphibians, reptiles, birds, and mammals. The fish are adapted to an aquatic existence while the reptiles, birds, and most mammals are air breathers. The amphibians show features of both.

Major Groups of Animals

Sponges (Phylum Porifera)

1. Attached to an object
2. Two cell layers
3. Body has many pores and canals
4. No movable appendages
5. Intercellular digestion
6. Aquatic organisms

Coelenterates (Phylum Coelenterata)

1. Digestive cavity
2. Two life stages: attached polyps and free-swimming medusae
3. Tentacles having stinging cells
4. Radial symmetry
5. Nerve net
6. Aquatic organisms

Flatworms (Phylum Platyhelminthes)

1. Flattened body
2. Bilateral symmetry
3. Three germ layers
4. Incomplete digestive system
5. Nervous system
6. Usually hermaphroditic

Roundworms (Phylum Aschelminthes)

1. Complete digestive tract
2. Unlined body cavity
3. Sexes usually separate
4. Unsegmented body
5. Cylindrical body with cuticle
6. Many forms are parasitic

Segmented Worms (Phylum Annelida)

1. Segmented body
2. Circular and longitudinal muscle layers
3. Closed circulatory system
4. Respiration by skin or gills
5. Organ systems present
6. Usually have a larval form

Arthropods (Phylum Arthropoda)

1. Jointed legs
2. Chitinous exoskeleton
3. Compound eyes
4. Three body regions: head, thorax, and abdomen
5. Fertilization usually internal
6. Striated muscle fibers

Mollusk (Phylum Mollusca)

1. Body has anterior head region, dorsal visceral hump, and ventral foot
2. Usually has an open circulatory system
3. Chambered heart
4. Sexes usually separate
5. Many forms have a shell
6. Bilateral symmetry

Echinoderms (Phylum Echinodermata)

1. Spiny-skinned
2. Radial symmetry, usually five-parted
3. Only found in saltwater environment
4. No head
5. Larval stages
6. Water-vascular system

Jawless Fishes (Class Agnatha)

1. Sucking mouth
2. Unpaired fins
3. Two-chambered heart
4. Poikilotherms
5. Single gonad, no duct

Cartilaginous Fishes (Class Chondrichthyes)

1. Cartilaginous skeleton
2. No swim bladder
3. Lateral line
4. No operculum
5. Paired fins
6. Internal fertilization

Bony Fishes (Class Osteichthyes)

1. Bony skeleton, scales present
2. Operculum present
3. Swim bladder usually present
4. Well-developed jaws with teeth
5. Two-chambered heart
6. Usually external fertilization

Amphibians (Class Amphibia)

1. Usually moist skin, no scales
2. Aquatic larvae and terrestrial adults
3. Usually two pairs of legs
4. Lungs present in adults
5. Three-chambered heart
6. Usually external fertilization

Reptiles (Class Reptilia)

1. Scales present
2. Internal fertilization
3. Amnionic eggs
4. Imperfectly formed four-chambered heart
5. Respiration by lungs
6. Poikilotherms

Birds (Class Aves)

1. Body covered with feathers
2. Forelimbs usually adapted for flight
3. Complete four-chambered heart
4. Beak present, no teeth
5. Amnionic eggs
6. Homotherms

Mammals (Class Mammalia)

1. Body covered with hair
2. Mammary glands present
3. Male copulatory organ, internal fertilization
4. Placenta present
5. Limbs with five digits
6. Complete four-chambered heart

If man became extinct as a result of a catastrophe, what changes would occur in the rest of the animal kingdom?

Questions

1. What are the major groupings of animals?
2. What is the importance of an amniotic egg?
3. List three characteristics of the chordates.
4. What is a larva?
5. How does sexual reproduction differ from asexual reproduction?
6. What is a tissue, organ, organ system?
7. How does a polyp stage differ from a medusa stage?
8. Give two examples of mollusks.
9. List three characteristics of each of the following: agnatha, sharks, bony fish, and amphibian.
10. List three similarities among reptiles, birds, and mammals.

Chapter Glossary

agnatha   The class of jawless vertebrates. Example: lamprey.

air bladder   A sac used to regulate the density of certain bony fish.

allantois   An embryonic membrane used in gas exchange and waste removal.

amnion   An embryonic membrane that contains liquid and surrounds the embryo.

amniotic egg   Any egg in reptiles, birds, and mammals that develops embryonic membranes.

amphibians   Vertebrates that must return to water to reproduce. Examples: frogs, toads, and salamanders.

annelids   Segmented worms. Examples: earthworms, leeches, and clam worms.

arachnids   A class of arthropods. Examples: spiders, scorpions, and king crabs.

arthropods   A phylum of animals that have an external skeleton and jointed appendages. Examples: insects, spiders, and crustaceans.

asexual reproduction   Any method of reproduction that does not involve the mixing of genetic material by fertilization.

aves   Class of chordates to which the birds belong.

backbone   The series of vertebrae found in vertebrates.

birds   Vertebrates that have wings, feathers, and a high metabolic rate. Examples: sparrows and chicken hawks.

bivalve   Mollusks that have two parts to their shell. Example: clams.

bony fish   A phylum of fish having a hardened skeleton composed of mineral deposits in the bones.

budding   A kind of asexual reproduction that is the result of an outgrowth of a new individual from the parent.

cartilaginous   A kind of tissue that serves as a skeleton in many animals, particularly in sharks.

caudal fin   A tail fin.

cephalopods   A group of mollusks that have a head and tentacles. Examples: squid and octopuses.

chondrichthyes   The class of chordates to which the sharks belong.

chordates   A phylum of animals that have a notochord, gill slits, and a dorsal hollow nerve cord. Examples: sharks, cats, frogs, and man.

chorion   An embryonic membrane that encloses the embryo and all of the other embryonic membranes.

coelenterate   A phylum of animals that have only one opening to a digestive sac and have stinging cells. Examples: jellyfish and coral.

complete metamorphosis   The life cycle of an insect, which includes an egg, larva, pupa, and an adult stage.

crustaceans   A class of animals that belong to the arthropod phylum. Examples: lobster, crayfish, and barnacles.

dorsal hollow nerve cord   The main part of the nervous system of the chordates.

echinoderm   A phylum of animals having an internal skeleton with spines. Examples: starfish, sea urchins, and sea cucumbers.

endoskeleton   A skeleton found within the skin of an animal.

eustachian tube   A tube that connects the throat to the ear; a modified gill slit.

exoskeleton   A skeleton that is found on the outside of an animal.

flagellated cells   Specialized cells found lining the canals of sponges that circulate the water through the sponge.

flatworms   A phylum of animals (platyhelminthes) with a flat appearance; many are parasites. Examples: tapeworms, blood flukes, and planaria.

gill slits   Openings that allow water to flow from the throat of chordates to the outside.

insects   A class of animals that belong to the arthropod phylum. Examples: grasshoppers, butterflies, and mosquitos.

invertebrate   Animals that lack a backbone.

larva   An incompletely developed animal that must change its form before it becomes an adult.

mammals   A class of animals that belong to the phylum chordates. Examples: kangaroos, humans, whales, and dogs.

mammary glands   Milk-producing glands of the female mammals.

mantle   A structure found in mollusk that produces the shell.

marsupial   Mammal with pouches in which the young develop after birth.

medusa   A stage in the life cycle of coelenterates that is free-swimming and umbrella-shaped. Example: the jellyfish.

mollusks   A phylum of animals with a mantle and usually a shell. Examples: squids, clams, and snails.

monotreme   A group of egg-laying mammals.

notochord   A rodlike structure along the back of chordates; used for support.

operculum   A protective cover over the gills of bony fish.

organs   Structures that consist of groups of tissues that work together to perform a particular function: Examples: heart, stomach, and brain.

organ systems   Groups of organs that work together to perform a particular function. Examples: digestive system, reproductive system, and circulatory system.

osteichthyes   A class of chordates to which the bony fish belong.

placenta   Organ for nourishing the developing mammal embryo.

polyp   A stage in the life cycle of coelenterates that is attached and is vase-shaped. Example: Hydra.

pupa   A developmental stage in the life cycle of some insects during which the larva changes into the adult form.

reptiles   A class of animals of the phylum chordates that have developed an amniotic egg and do not need to return to the water to reproduce. Examples: snakes, turtles, and dinosaurs.

roundworms   A phylum of animals (Aschelminthes) that are needle-shaped and are very common in soils; some are parasitic. Example: pinworms.

sponges   A phylum of animals (Porifera) that are very primitive and contain many canals; they filter water for food.

tentacles   Long flexible arms that can be used for obtaining food and defending the animal from harm.

tissue   A group of specialized cells that work together to perform a particular function. Examples: muscle, nerve, and blood.

tracheae   Breathing tubes in insects.

tube feet   Suction cuplike structures in echinoderms that are part of the water-vascular system.

vertebrates   Animals with backbones.

water-vascular system   A series of water-filled tubes that are found in the phylum of echinoderms and used for movement.

yolk sac   An embryonic sac containing stored food for the embryo.

Purpose   Now that you have been introduced to many of the principles of biology, you are ready to apply the knowledge you have gained. There are many problems in the modern world that have some basis in biology or some biology-related solutions.

One of these problems concerns the use of chemical methods to control pests. These controls may be essential to maintain our present standard of living. This chapter will give you an overview of the problem and some insight into the biological aspects of why it is a problem. In addition, you will be introduced to the nature of other solutions that may be more biologically sound.

Epilogue

25

What Is DDT?

DDT is an abbreviation for the chemical name of a **pesticide.** It stands for dichloro-diphenyl-trichloroethane. The structure of this arrangement of atoms is diagrammed in figure 25.1. DDT is one of the group of organic compounds called chlorinated hydrocarbons.

You will remember that an organic compound contains carbon, along with hydrogen, oxygen, and other elements. A chlorinated hydrocarbon is an organic compound containing carbon, hydrogen, and chlorine. This particular compound, DDT, was first produced in 1873, but wasn't used as an **insecticide** until 1944. It was discovered to have insect-killing properties by Dr. Paul Mueller; and for his discovery, he was awarded the Nobel Prize in Physiology and Medicine in 1948.

DDT was a very valuable tool used by the U.S. Armed Forces. During World War II, it was sprayed on clothing and dusted on the bodies of soldiers,

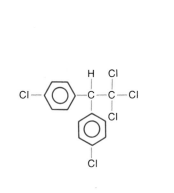

Chlorophenyl

Tri-chloro

Ethane

Fig. 25.1 *Structural Formula of DDT.* This diagram shows the arrangement of the atoms in a molecule of DDT.

refugees, and prisoners to kill body lice and other insects. Lice, besides being a nuisance, carry the bacteria that causes the disease known as typhus. When bitten by a louse, the person could contract the disease typhus fever. Body lice can be passed from one person to another by contact, or by wearing infested clothing. Thus, body lice are an important link in the spread of this disease. This use of DDT was so effective in the control of lice and typhus that peacetime uses were planned. Some people could see the end of pesky mosquitos and flies, as well as the elimination of many disease-carrying insects.

Even though DDT is often called a pesticide or insecticide, such terms are misleading, since they give the impression that only pests or insects will die from the chemical. A better term has been used in the past several years— **biocide.** This term means a killer of living things. It is a much more accurate term and implies that this killer poison has the ability to kill many forms of life.

There are a number of factors that determine how successful you will be in controlling a pest when using a biocide. First, you must choose a biocide that will cause the least amount of damage to the harmless or beneficial organisms in the community. Because many of the insects we consider to be pests are herbivores, their populations are controlled by insect carnivores. Generally, herbivores reproduce more rapidly than carnivores. Therefore, when a pesticide is used on a community and kills both the pest species and their predators, the herbivores will reproduce faster than carnivores, and the pest situation may become worse. This requires continued use of the biocide to keep things in check. Just this situation occurred in the citrus groves of California.

Enter Genetics

Even though there is much information on kinds and ways of using biocides, pests have not been eliminated. The insects have been one step ahead of the chemists, since nature equips a population with a variety of genes. Insect populations have genetic information that allows certain individuals to tolerate the chemical DDT. However, in most of the individual insects, the DDT interferes with the ability of a particular gene to make one of the hydrogen carriers that transfers H_2 in metabolic pathways. When this hydrogen carrier is not produced in sufficient quantities, a decrease in the respiration of food and the release of energy occurs, resulting in the death of the animal. However, certain individuals in the insect population have alleles that produce different enzymes. These enzymes allow a different biochemical pathway for hydrogen transfer—a pathway that is not influenced by DDT. Until DDT came on the scene, the individuals with this alternate pathway were no better off than the others. Once in the environment, however, the DDT acted as an agent selecting the normal individuals for death, and those with the alternate genetic pathway for survival.

Natural Selection

Only those few who survived were able to reproduce. Eventually, with the continued use of DDT as a selector, most insects in the population were those who had the ability to tolerate DDT. At this point we say that the species is **resistant** to DDT. The people who had foreseen the end of all insect pests had not reckoned with the genetic diversity of the gene pools of the insect. Rather than the end of pests, they saw the evolution of populations of insects tolerant of DDT.

Community Consequences

Another problem that has been overlooked deals with the community in which the insect lives. When DDT is applied to an area to get rid of the "pests," it is usually dissolved in an oil or a fatty compound. It is then sprayed over an area and falls on the plants that the insects use for food, or directly on the insect. Eventually, the insect takes the DDT into its body where it interferes with the normal metabolism of the organism. If small quantities are taken in, the insect will begin to digest and break down the DDT as if it were any other organic chemical compound. Since the DDT is soluble in fat or oil, the insect stores the DDT or its broken-down products in the fatty tissue of its body. Sometimes the insect manages to break down and store all the DDT, and therefore survives. If an area has been lightly sprayed with the biocide, some insects will die, some will tolerate the DDT, and some will survive because they will be able to store the DDT in their fat cells. As much as one part of DDT per one billion parts of insect tissue may be stored. This is like one drop of biocide in one hundred railroad boxcars. That's not very much DDT! If you were to spray an area with a small concentration of the chemical in order to kill an insect pest, the algae and protozoa of the area may accumulate up to two hundred and fifty times the concentration of DDT sprayed, since they also concentrate the biocide. The algae and protozoa are eaten by insects that are in turn eaten by frogs. If you measure the concentration of DDT in frogs, it may be two thousand times the concentration originally sprayed. Birds that feed on the frogs and fish in the area may accumulate as much as eighty thousand times the original amount. What was originally a very small concentration of biocide used to kill insects has now become so concentrated in certain carnivores and other organisms that they are also threatened. For example, birds generally cannot tolerate these high levels of DDT, and in several well-documented cases, many birds have died as a result of the biocide. DDT is known to interfere with eggshell production by limiting the amount of calcium deposited in the shell. These thin-shelled eggs are more easily broken. This problem is more common in carnivorous birds, since they are at the top of the food chain. One of the dangers of using a chemical as a biocide is that it tends to become concen-

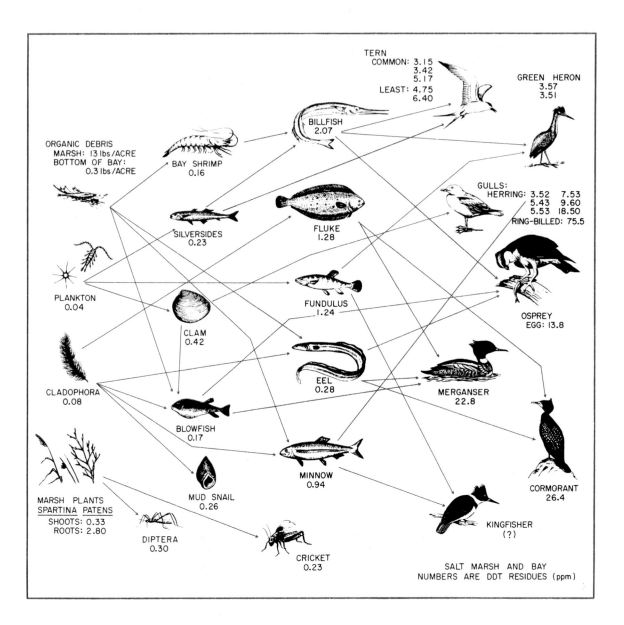

Fig. 25.2 *Biological Amplification of a Biocide.* Note how the concentration of the biocide increases as it passes through the food chain. (Courtesy of Brookhaven National Laboratory.)

trated in the higher trophic levels of an ecosystem. This situation is referred to as **biological amplification** (fig. 25.2). As a result of the buildup of pesticide in the food materials that man eats, many humans have up to thirty-five parts per billion DDT in their fat cells. A great deal has been written recently about the dangers of this quantity of DDT in the fat cells of humans. But the fact is we really do not know what the potential dangers are. It has been noted that nursing mothers need to be particularly conscious of the problem, since breast milk contains a great deal of fat and dissolved DDT. If the milk you bought in a store had as much DDT in it as some mother's milk, it would be illegal to sell!

What was originally used to kill insects has proven to have many more effects than expected. Instead of killing the pest, it selects for survival those insects that can tolerate it. Instead of harming only the insect pests, it accumulates in other forms of life and causes reduced reproductive ability in birds, and many health concerns in humans. All in all, DDT has not been the gift to mankind that we originally thought; so in the early 1970s, the future sale of DDT in the United States was prohibited.

Alternatives

You may very well ask at this point, "why, if DDT was so bad, did we use it for almost thirty years?" The answer is in part a lack of time and personnel to thoroughly research the problems. In addition, the answer is an economic one, since DDT was very effective for several years in controlling crop pests. The use of biocides increases farm crop yield significantly. A farmer cannot sell the crop if it is eaten by insects. If some farmers in an area are using biocides to help them get higher yields and more money, others will also have to use the same or similar control measures, or they will go bankrupt. There is a very strong agricultural lobby in Washington that opposed the banning of DDT. In a world where the human population is rapidly increasing and where life-styles are such that blemished fruits or vegetables are unsellable, it just makes good economic sense to increase the production of "perfect" agricultural goods in quantities sufficient to meet the market demands. So you, the customer, are in part the cause of the increasing use of chemical pest-control methods. You demand that the farmer produce perfect goods in ever-increasing quantities.

There are other methods whereby we can grow sufficient food without dangerous accumulations of chemical poisons. Much work is being done with **biological control.** This means introducing predators of the pests into the community and encouraging them to naturally control the pest population. However, hidden danger might arise when the number of predators reaches a critical level; they may become more of a problem than the original insect pests. Such a situation occurred when the mongoose was introduced into parts of South America for the purpose of controlling the snake populations.

When the snakes were under control, the mongoose became a problem in its own right because it began to prey on many other types of animals.

Another example of biological control occurred in California during the early 1900s. The scale insects on orange trees greatly reduced the health of the trees and reduced crop yields. The introduction of a species of ladybugs from Australia very shortly brought the pests under control. Years later when chemical pesticides were first used in the area, so many of the ladybugs were accidentally killed that the scale insects once again became a serious problem.

Certainly, one partial solution to the biocide problem would be to slow the growth of the human population. If we could stop the human population from increasing in size, we would not have to put so much time and energy into getting high crop yields to feed people. Of course, control of human population involves philosophical, political, moral, and ethical questions, as well as economic and agricultural ones.

Hopefully, the future will hold a combination of solutions: a slowing of the birthrate with greater attention given to the quality of life; discovery or synthesis of more specific pesticides to kill only specific organisms; and greater use of biological control mechanisms. Table 25.1 compares DDT, as we know it, and a perfect pesticide still to be produced.

Table 25.1 *Comparison of DDT with a Perfect Biocide*

DDT	Perfect pesticide
1. General, kills many different organisms in addition to the pest	1. Specific—kills only the species meant to kill
2. Persistent—retained in the environment for many years	2. Nonpersistent—would last for only a few days
3. Does not break down or breaks down to chemicals that are deadly	3. Breaks down to harmless materials
4. Cheap and easy to produce	4. Cheap and easy to produce
5. Not safe in high concentrations and harmful to man	5. Safe to store and use by man

It's Up to You

Today, much is said about the "good ole days" and it is fashionable to "put down" our ancestors for the mess the world is in. Is the elimination or near-elimination of certain species of animals a fair price to pay for a larger human population? Will the elimination of certain species alter the ecosystem, and thus influence man himself? Are humans playing the game of greed? Are we using nature's resources for survival, or is each of us greedily collecting all we can for ourselves? These questions require personal consideration by each of us. So, be concerned about the whole environment—the world. Study, learn, think, and decide what *you* are doing to the biosphere. Are *you* helping or hindering the system? It's *your* world; *you* decide.

biocide An assortment of organic chemicals that kill living things.	***Chapter Glossary***

biocide   An assortment of organic chemicals that kill living things.

biological amplification   Concentration of a chemical as it passes through the food chains of an ecosystem.

biological control   The use of predators, parasites, or other biological agents to keep a population of unwanted organisms in check.

insecticide   Those biocides specifically effective in killing insects.

pesticide   A chemical that kills "pests." Problematical term because it implies that the chemical can distinguish pests from nonpests.

resistant   An inherited ability to tolerate a particular substance or condition.

Glossary

accessory structures Structures that are parts of some flowers, but are not directly involved in gamete production.

acid A substance that gives up hydrogen ions (H^+) when dissolved in water. Acids also act as hydroxyl ion (OH^-) acceptors.

acid group A portion of an organic molecule that is composed of one carbon atom, two oxygen atoms, and one hydrogen atom arranged as

acquired characteristic A characteristic of an organism gained during its lifetime, which is not caused by its genes and therefore is not transmitted to the offspring. Example: cutting off the tail of a dog in a particular breed has to be done generation after generation.

activation energy The energy required to start a chemical reaction.

active site That part of the enzyme that reacts with the substrate.

active transport A method whereby a cell transfers materials through its membrane, and in the process expends energy.

adaptive radiation A rapid form of divergent evolution resulting in a great variety of related species.

adenine A double-ring nitrogenous base molecule found in DNA and RNA. It is the complementary base of thymine or uracil.

adenosine diphosphate (ADP) ADP plus phosphate and energy are used to make an ATP molecule.

adenosine triphosphate (ATP) An organic molecule that is able to store the energy needed for immediate use by the cell.

aerobic respiration Metabolic process requiring the use of free oxygen.

afterbirth Another name for the placenta, which is released from the uterus after the child is born.

age distribution The ratio of juvenile, sexually active, and postreproductive individuals within a population.

agnatha The class of jawless vertebrates. Example: lamprey.

air bladder A sac used to regulate the density of certain bony fish.

algae Plantlike protists that are green and can carry on photosynthesis.

allantois An embryonic membrane used in gas exchange and waste removal.

alleles Alternative forms of the genes for a particular characteristic (i.e., brown-eye genes and blue-eye genes are alternative alleles for eye color).

alternation of generations The cycling of a sporophyte generation and a gametophyte generation in plants.

amino acid A simple organic molecule that has an *acid group*

(—C—O—H) on one end and an *amino group*

on the other end—the building blocks of proteins.

amino group A portion of an organic molecule containing a nitrogen atom and two hydrogen atoms.

amnion An embryonic membrane that contains liquid and surrounds the embryo.

amniotic egg Any egg in reptiles, birds, and mammals that develops embryonic membranes.

amphibians Vertebrates that must return to water to reproduce. Examples: frogs, toads, and salamanders.

anaerobic respiration Metabolic process not requiring the use of free oxygen.

anaphase A stage in mitosis identified by the separation of chromatids (daughter chromosomes) and movement toward the poles.

angiosperms Plants that produce flowers and fruits.

Animalia Classified into this kingdom are multicellular heterotrophic organisms that require a source of organic material as food.

annelids Segmented worms. Examples: earthworms, leeches, and clam worms.

annual A plant that completes its life cycle in one year.

antheridia (antheridium, sing.) The structure in lower plants that produces sperm.

anticodon A sequence of three nitrogenous bases on a tRNA molecule, capable of hydrogen bonding with three complementary bases of a mRNA codon during translation of protein synthesis.

anus The opening of the digestive system through which undigested food is eliminated.

arachnids A class of arthropods. Examples: spiders, scorpions, and king crabs.

archegonium The structure in lower plants that produces eggs.

arthropods A phylum of animals that have an external skeleton and jointed appendages. Examples: insects, spiders, and crustaceans.

-ase A suffix that identifies a word as an enzyme.

asexual reproduction Any method of reproduction that does not involve the mixing of genetic material by fertilization; propagation of an organism without the union of sex cells.

astrology The study of the stars and planets and how they influence human events.

astronomy The scientific study of the structure and activities of the stars, planets, and other heavenly bodies.

atom The smallest particle of an element that still retains all the properties of the element.

atomic number The number that is assigned to an element and is determined by the number of protons in an atom of that element.

autotroph An organism that can manufacture its own food from simple inorganic molecules.

aves Class of chordates to which the birds belong.

backbone The series of vertebrae found in vertebrates.

bacteria Procaryotic single-celled organisms of the kingdom Monera. Generally, they do not contain photosynthetic pigments.

base A substance that gives up hydroxyl ions (OH^-) when dissolved in water. Bases also act as hydrogen ion (H^+) acceptors.

behavioral isolating mechanisms Genetically determined behavior that prevents interbreeding between species. Examples: courtship behavior and nesting behavior.

biochemical pathways Specific series of major chemical reactions.

biocide An assortment of organic chemicals that kill living things.

biogenesis A theory stating that a living thing can arise only from a living parent.

biological amplification Concentration of a chemical as it passes through the food chains of an ecosystem.

biological chemistry The study of the chemistry of living things.

biological control The use of predators, parasites, or other biological agents to keep a population of unwanted organisms in check.

biology The study of life.

biomass The total weight of a particular kind of organism in a given situation. It is used for comparison purposes when numbers of organisms or size of organisms would lead to confusion.

biome Large geographic areas that are composed of particular kinds of communities.

biosphere The area in, on, and around the earth that supports life.

birds Vertebrates that have wings, feathers, and a high metabolic rate. Examples: sparrows and chicken hawks.

bivalve Mollusks that have two parts to their shell. Example: clams.

bloom A rapid increase in the number of algae cells—a population explosion.

blue-green algae Chlorophyll containing monera that typically contain a blue-green pigment.

bony fish A phylum of fish having a hardened skeleton composed of mineral deposits in the bones.

breech birth A birth in which the head is not born first. Example: an arm or the feet may appear first.

breed A deme that differs significantly from others of the same species. Usually used to refer to man-made demes of animals.

budding A kind of asexual reproduction that is the result of an outgrowth of a new individual from the parent.

calorie The amount of heat necessary to raise the temperature of one gram of water one degree centigrade.

cambium A tissue in higher plants that produces new xylem and phloem.

capsule Part of the sporophyte generation of mosses that contains spores.

carbohydrate An organic molecule that contains carbon, hydrogen, and oxygen in the following ratio: CH_2O.

carbon dioxide conversion stage
Stage of photosynthesis that
removes carbon dioxide from the
atmosphere and uses it as a raw
material to make a simple
carbohydrate.

carnivore   Meat-eating animals.

carrying capacity   The optimum
numbers of individuals of a
species that can survive in an area
over an extended period of time.

cartilaginous   A kind of tissue that
serves as a skeleton in many
animals, particularly in sharks.

catalyst   A material that increases the
rate of a chemical reaction.

caudal fin   A tail fin.

cells   The general structure of all life.
Microscopic in size, and com-
posed of organized living material
called protoplasm. Named by
R. Hooke.

cell plate   The first indication of the
formation of a cell wall during
plant mitosis.

cellular respiration   Chemical breakdown of organic (food)
molecules with subsequent
release of energy.

centriole   A tubular organelle
located just outside the nucleus,
which functions in cell division.

centromere   A region of a chromosome where chromatids are
joined.

cephalopods   A group of mollusks
that have a head and tentacles.
Examples: squid and octopuses.

chemical bond   The attraction that
one atom, ion, or molecule has for
another atom, ion, or molecule.

chemical reaction   The interaction
between two or more chemicals,
whereby new bonds are formed
and energy is subsequently
exchanged.

chitin   A substance resistant to many
solvents and found in the cell
walls of fungi. It differs slightly

from material of the same name in
insect body walls.

chlorophyll   The green pigment associated with energy conversion.

chloroplast   Organelles in green plants
where the chlorophyll is located.
It is the site of food production—
photosynthesis.

cholesterol   A steroid molecule found
in the bile, which can be converted
to vitamin D by sunlight.

chondrichthyes   The class of chordates to which the sharks belong.

chordates   A phylum of animals that
have a notochord, gill slits, and a
dorsal hollow nerve cord.
Examples: sharks, cats, frogs,
and man.

chorion   An embryonic membrane
that encloses the embryo and all
of the other embryonic
membranes.

chromatid   One of a pair of duplicate
genetic strands. This pair makes
up the chromosome in the early
stages of mitosis.

chromatin material   The genetic
material composed of DNA and
protein; it is called a chromosome
when coiled.

chromosomal mutation   A change in
the gene arrangement in a cell,
as a result of breaks in the backbone of the DNA molecule.

chromosome   Coiled-up chromatin
material containing a package of
genetic information. The number
of chromosomes in the cells of a
species is consistent. The threadlike structure appearing in
mitosis that contains the genetic
instructions (DNA), controlling
the cell's characteristics.

cilia   Short, flexible hairlike filaments
that beat rhythmically and propel
the cell through the water or
bring food into the cell.

cleavage furrow   The indentation of a
cell membrane of an animal cell

that finally pinches the cytoplasm into two parts.

climax community A stable stage in succession, in which the numbers and kinds of organisms remain relatively unchanged.

clone A line of genetically identical organisms that are maintained by asexual reproduction.

codon A sequence of three nucleotides on a mRNA molecule that directs the placement of a particular amino acid during the process of protein synthesis.

coelenterate A phylum of animals that have only one opening to a digestive sac and have stinging cells. Examples: jellyfish and coral.

coenzyme A material that works with an enzyme in carrying out a reaction.

colon The large intestine. Water and salts are absorbed from the contents of the colon.

colony A cluster of independent cells produced by cell division.

commensalism The relationship between two kinds of organisms in which one benefits and the other is not affected.

community The interrelationships among various populations sharing a similar habitat.

compete Two or more organisms attempting to acquire some substance necessary for their survival. Examples: space, water, and oxygen.

competition The relationship between two species in which each population is adversely affected by the other.

complementary base The base that can form hydrogen bonds with the base of a specific nucleotide. Adenine is said to be complementary to thymine, since two hydrogen bonds can form between them in a DNA helix.

Guanine is complementary to cytosine, and cytosine is complementary to guanine.

complete metamorphosis The life cycle of an insect, which includes an egg, larva, pupa, and adult stage.

complete protein Protein molecules that provide all the essential amino acids.

compound A substance made up of atoms of two or more kinds of elements chemically bonded together.

condom A mechanical conception-control device used by men to cover the erect penis.

cone A reproductive structure of gymnosperms that produces pollen in males or eggs in females.

consumer Various plant-eating or meat-eating animals.

contractile vacuole A special water container in a cell. It accumulates and then expels excess water.

controlled experiment A comparison of two systems identical in all but one respect.

control mechanism The limiting factor or combination of factors that determines the population size in an area.

convergent evolution A pattern of evolution leading to similarities among different lines of evolution. Example: fish and dolphins both have similar body shapes though they are unrelated.

copulation The act of transferring sperm from the male into the female reproductive tract.

covalent bond The attraction between two atoms formed by the sharing of electrons.

crossing-over The exchange of a part of a chromatid from one homologous chromosome with an equivalent part of a chromatid from the other homologous chromosome.

crustaceans A class of animals that belong to the arthropod phylum. Examples: lobster, crayfish, and barnacles.

cytoplasm One of the two types of protoplasm; that portion of the cell excluding the nucleus.

cytosine A single-ring nitrogenous base molecule found in DNA and RNA, which is the complementary base of guanine.

daughter cells Those two cells that are the result of cell division.

daughter chromosome A separate chromatid, moving to one of the poles during anaphase.

daughter nuclei The two nuclei that are the result of mitosis.

death phase That portion of the growth curve indicating that there is a decrease in numbers of individuals in the population.

decomposer Bacteria or fungi that convert organic material into inorganic material.

dehydration synthesis A type of chemical reaction in which two molecules are combined, with the loss of a molecule of water.

deme A local, recognizable population that differs in gene frequencies from other local populations of the same species.

denature To change a protein in such a way that it can no longer function as an enzyme.

deoxyribonucleic acid (DNA) Molecule in the nucleus of a cell that functions as a blueprint for the synthesis of proteins. That chemical containing the hereditary information.

deoxyribose A five-carbon sugar component of deoxyribonucleic acid (DNA).

diaphragm A mechanical conception-control device used by women to cover the entrance to the uterus.

dicot An angiosperm that contains two seed leaves in its embryo.

differential reproduction Those organisms having better genetic information for a particular environment out-reproduce the organisms having less desirable information.

differentially permeable membrane A membrane that selectively allows some particles to pass through it and prevents others.

differentiation The process of development that results in cells with structures and functions that are different from other cells in the same body.

diffusion The net movement of a diffusing substance from an area of higher concentration to an area of lower concentration. This net movement is due to the relative probabilities of randomly moving particles.

diffusion gradient The difference in concentration of a substance in two areas.

digestive tract The series of tubes and structures that break down complex food molecules and absorb nutrients into the body.

dihybrid cross A genetic study in which two characteristics are followed from the parental generation to the offspring.

diploid Represented as 2N. This is the term given to a cell having both sets of chromosomes, one set from the maternal parent and one set from the paternal parent.

divergent evolution A pattern of evolution that slowly generates a greater variety of species from a common ancestor.

DNA duplication The process by which the genetic material (DNA) of the cell reproduces itself prior to its distribution to the next generation of cells.

dominant allele The gene that when present with its allele expresses itself and masks the effect of the other gene.

dorsal hollow nerve cord The main part of the nervous system of the chordates.

double bond The attraction between two atomic nuclei in which two pairs (4) of electrons are shared covalently. It is usually denoted by two lines between atoms. Example: $O{=}C{=}O$.

double helix Two regularly twisted strands of DNA that are parallel to each other.

Down's syndrome A genetic disease resulting from the presence of an extra chromosome. Symptoms include thickened eyelids, low level of intelligence, faulty speech; sometimes called mongolism.

duodenum The upper portion of the small intestine into which flows various digestive enzymes and materials from the stomach, liver, and pancreas.

echinoderm A phylum of animals having an internal skeleton with spines. Examples: starfish, sea urchins, and sea cucumbers.

ecology The study of an organism in relation to its environment.

ecosystem A system of interacting organisms; influenced by abiotic factors and requiring light as the initial source of energy.

egg cells The haploid sex cells produced by sexually mature females.

electron A negatively charged particle located some distance from the nucleus of an atom.

electron microscope A tool that uses electrons rather than light to expose the structure of small objects. It has a greater magnification capability than the light microscope.

electron transfer system (ETS) A series of chemical reactions involving hydrogen, which yield energy to produce ATPs.

element One of the basic materials of which all substances are composed.

embryo The early stage in the development of a sexually reproduced organism.

endoplasmic reticulum (ER) Continuation of the cell membrane. It forms canals throughout the cell.

endoskeleton A skeleton found within the skin of an animal.

end product The new molecules formed from the substrate.

energy The ability to do work. Different forms are interconvertible to other forms, such as light energy to chemical energy, or chemical energy to heat.

environment The total of all living and nonliving factors that influence an organism.

enzymatic competition Several different enzymes competing for the same substrate molecule.

enzyme A special kind of protein produced by living cells that are able to speed up the rate at which chemical reactions take place.

enzyme-substrate complex The physical union of an enzyme molecule with a substrate molecule.

equatorial view The view of a cell during metaphase that presents the chromosomes arranged in a line across the middle of the cell.

esophagus A tube that conducts food from the mouth to the stomach.

essential amino acids Those amino acids that are not made by the human body, but must be taken in as a part of the diet. Examples: lysine, tryptophan, and valine.

ethyl alcohol One of the end products of fermentation in plants and microorganisms.

eucaryotic A type of cell with a true nucleus separated from the rest of the protoplasm by a nuclear membrane.

eustachian tube A tube that connects the throat to the ear; a modified gill slit.

evolution The slow change in living things, so that they can cope with changes in their environment over many generations.

exoskeleton A skeleton that is found on the outside of an animal.

extinct Types of organisms that once existed but are no longer in evidence today.

extinction The nonsurvival of a particular species. Usually results from the inability of the species to cope with environmental change.

fat Large organic molecule that is composed of three fatty acids and a single glycerol molecule.

fatty acid A long carbon chain with an acid group ($-\overset{\overset{\text{O}}{||}}{\text{C}}-\text{O}-\text{H}$) at one end.

feces The name given to the undigested food material eliminated from the digestive tract through the anus.

fermentation An anaerobic process that converts pyruvic acid to alcohol, and carbon dioxide in plants or to lactic acid in animals.

fertilization The joining of haploid nuclei, usually from an egg cell and a sperm cell, resulting in a diploid cell called the zygote.

First Law of Thermodynamics Matter and energy cannot be created or destroyed, but can be converted into different forms.

flagella A few hairlike structures that are longer than cilia and project through the cell membrane. They function like oars for locomotion.

flagellated cells Specialized cells found lining the canals of sponges that circulate the water through the sponge.

flatworms A phylum of animals (platyhelminthes) with a flat appearance; many are parasites. Examples: tapeworms, blood flukes, and planaria.

flower A complex structure made from modified stems and leaves; it produces pollen in the males and eggs in the females.

fly ash Small particles that are released from industrial smoke stacks and settle out of the air onto houses, trees, cars, and other physical surfaces.

food chain The direct flow of food and energy from the producer through a given series of consumers.

food web The flow of food and energy between food chains.

fraternal twins Two offspring that are born at the same time, but are the result of the fertilization of two separate eggs.

fruit The structure in angiosperms that contains seeds.

fungi Protists that have cell walls and lack chlorophyll.

gallbladder A saclike structure that holds bile before it is released into the small intestine.

gallstones Crystals of cholesterol formed in the gallbladder.

gamete Haploid sex cell.

gametophyte generation The haploid generation in plant life cycles. They produce gametes.

gametogenesis Gamete generating; the meiotic cell division process resulting in the production of sex cells.

gas Of the three states of matter, the one that is highest in kinetic energy—molecules are moving very rapidly.

gene A unit of heredity located on a chromosome and composed of a sequence of DNA nucleotides.

gene flow The movement of genes within a population from place to place as a result of migration, and from generation to generation as a result of sexual reproduction.

gene frequency The percentage of sex cells that contain a particular allele.

gene pool All of the genes of all of the individuals of the same species.

genetic counselor A professional biologist with specific training in human genetics and gene frequencies of less desirable alleles.

genetic isolating mechanisms Characteristics determined by genes that prevent interbreeding between species.

genetic recombination The regrouping of parental genetic material at fertilization.

genetics The study of genes, how genes produce characteristics, and how the characteristics are inherited.

genotype The catalog of genes that an organism has, whether or not these genes are expressed.

genus A classification name given to groups of species that are very similar; together with the species name, it forms the scientific name.

geographic barrier Any physical factor that prevents the movement of a population.

geographic isolation A separation by barriers of members of the same gene pool into two or more groups.

germinate To begin to grow.

gill slits Openings that allow water to flow from the throat of chordates to the outside.

glycerol The three carbon molecules that combine with fatty acids to form fats.

glycolysis The anaerobic stage of carbohydrate respiration.

Golgi apparatus A specialized region of the ER that functions in secretion and/or packaging of these secretions.

grana Areas of concentrated chlorophyll within the chloroplast.

granules The miscellaneous stuff in a cell. Too small to have a well-defined structure.

growth curve The graphic expression of increasing or decreasing numbers of individuals in a population through time.

growth factor A nutrient that is needed by the body for proper functioning, but only in very small amounts. Examples: vitamins and minerals.

guanine A double-ring nitrogenous base molecule found in DNA and RNA, which is the complementary base of cytosine.

gymnosperms Plants that produce their seeds in cones.

habitat The natural place where an organism lives.

habitat preference A genetic isolating mechanism that controls the behavior of separate species and prevents these species from living in the same location.

haploid A single set of chromosomes —represented as N. This haploid number results from the reduction division of meiosis.

Hardy-Weinberg Law Populations of organisms will maintain their gene frequencies from generation to generation as long as mating is random, the population is large, mutation does not occur, and no migration occurs in or out of the population.

herbivore A plant-eating animal.

heterotroph An organism that cannot manufacture its own food, but requires complex organic molecules from living organisms or other sources.

heterozygous A condition when a diploid organism has two different allelic forms of a particular gene.

high-energy phosphate bond A type of bond found in ADP and ATP, which when broken yields more energy than regular covalent bonds.

homologous pair of chromosomes A pair of chromosomes in a diploid cell that contain similar pairs of genes throughout their length.

Homo sapiens The scientific name of man.

homozygous A condition when a diploid organism has the same allelic forms of a particular gene.

hormone Chemical substances—steroid molecules—released from glands in the body and have a regulating affect on other parts of the body.

host An organism that provides the necessities for a parasite—generally food, a place to live, etc.

hybrid The offspring that results from a mixture of the two parental genotypes.

hydrogen bond A weak bond formed by the attraction between a positively charged part of one molecule and a negatively charged part of another molecule.

hydrolysis A type of chemical reaction by which a large molecule is split into smaller molecules, with the addition of water.

hydroxyl ion A negatively charged group composed of one oxygen atom, one hydrogen atom, and one extra electron.

hypha The basic unit of structure of a fungus consisting of a branching filament. Some have many nuclei not separated by cross walls, while others have walls.

hypothesis A possible explanation of, or answer to, a problem or question. This guess should account for all facts observed and be a testable answer.

identical twins Two offspring that are born at the same time and are the result of the fertilization of one egg that has separated into two cells.

imperfect flowers Flowers containing either male or female reproductive structures, but not both.

independent assortment The term that relates to the fact that the segregation, or assortment, of one pair of chromosomes is not dependent upon the segregation, or assortment, of a second, third, etc., pair of chromosomes.

inhibitor A material or condition that decreases the effectiveness of an enzyme.

initiator codon A nonsense codon that indicates to the cell the beginning of a gene.

inorganic molecules Molecules that do not usually contain carbon atoms in chains.

insecticide Those biocides specifically effective in killing insects.

insects A class of animals that belong to the arthropod phylum. Examples: grasshoppers, butterflies, and mosquitos.

interphase The action stage in the growth of a cell. The between division stage. DNA duplication occurs during interphase.

intrauterine device (IUD) A mechanical conception-control device placed in the uterus to prevent embryo attachment.

invertebrate Animals that lack a backbone.

ion An atom with a charge; either negative ions have gained electrons or positive ions have lost electrons, such that the electron and proton number are not equal.

ionic bond The attraction between a positive ion and a negative ion.

isotopes Atoms of an element that have different atomic weights, due to varying numbers of neutrons.

kilocalorie One thousand times larger than the calorie, a measure of heat energy.

kinetic energy An ability to move. Electrons moving about the nucleus of an atom are exhibiting this energy of motion.

kingdom   The largest division used in the classification system of organisms.

Krebs' cycle   The breakdown of an acetyl group to carbon dioxide and hydrogen, with the formation of one ATP. Hydrogens are then carried to the electron transfer system for further energy release.

kwashiorkor   A protein deficiency disease.

labor   The contractions of the uterus that results in the birth of the young.

lack of dominance   The condition that exists when two unlike alleles are present and they both express themselves—neither is dominant.

lactase   An enzyme that is produced by the cells lining the small intestine and breaks the sugar lactose into simple sugars.

lactic acid   The end product of fermentation in animals.

lactose intolerance   A condition that results from the inability to digest lactose.

lag phase   That portion of the growth curve indicating that the increase in numbers is slow. It is usually the first phase of a growth curve.

larva   An incompletely developed animal that must change its form before it becomes an adult.

leaves   A specialized portion of higher plants that function primarily in photosynthesis.

legumes   Types of plants, members of the bean family, that can have a mutualistic association with nitrogen-fixing bacteria in their roots.

leukemia   A disease of the mitotic process of white blood cells. Its symptoms include an abnormally large number of white blood cells.

lichen   An association of an alga with a fungus, in which each benefit. A pioneer in plant succession.

life   (Has never been satisfactorily defined.)

life cycle   The series of stages in the life of any organism.

light energy conversion stage   Stage of photosynthesis that converts sunlight into electron energy with the subsequent production of $NADPH_2$, ATP, and atmospheric oxygen (O_2).

linkage group   Genes that are located on the same chromosome and tend to be inherited together.

lipid   A type of organic molecule that contains carbon, hydrogen, and oxygen; and usually does not dissolve in water.

liquid   Of the three states of matter, the one that has more kinetic energy than a solid, but less than a gas—molecules are moving over one another.

locus (loci, sing.)   The spot on a chromosome where an allele is located.

log phase   That portion of the growth curve indicating that the increase in numbers is very rapid.

lysosome   Special vacuole that contains strong enzymes.

macromolecule   Large organic molecule typical of living things. Examples: protein, DNA, RNA.

mammals   A class of animals that belong to the phylum chordates. Examples: kangaroos, humans, whales, and dogs.

mammary glands   Milk-producing glands of the female mammals.

mantle   A structure found in mollusk that produces the shell.

marsupial   Mammals with pouches in which the young develop after birth.

mass number   A number that identifies an isotope.

medusa   A stage in the life cycle of coelenterates that is free-swimming and umbrella-shaped. Example: the jellyfish.

meiosis   The specialized pair of cell divisions that reduce the chromosome number from diploid (2N) to haploid (N).

membrane   A very thin sheet of material; may be molecular in size or several cells thick.

Mendelian genetics   The pattern of inheriting characteristics that follows the laws formulated by Johann Gregor Mendel.

menses (period, menstrual flow)   The shedding of the lining of the uterus.

menstrual cycle   The continual building and then shedding of the lining of the uterus.

messenger RNA (mRNA)   A molecule composed of ribonucleotides. The sequence of nucleotides is determined by the sequence of nucleotides in a piece of DNA. This molecule functions as a copy of the gene and is used in the cytoplasm of the cell.

metabolic activity   Those processes such as photosynthesis, respiration, and protein synthesis that are part of normal cell activities.

metabolism   All of the series of complex chemical reactions within living things.

metaphase   A stage of mitosis marked by the arrival of the chromosomes at the equatorial plane.

microbe   Any single-celled organism; a common name used to refer to members of the kingdoms Monera and Protista.

microscope   A tool that is used to magnify objects. May use light and lenses or other forms of energy and photographic equipment.

minerals   Growth factors, usually inorganic salts. Examples: calcium, magnesium.

mitochondria   Membranous organelles that function in energy release from food. Their structure is a double membrane arranged into a rod-shaped organelle.

mitosis   The total process of cell division, which results in both the distribution of copies of the genetic information from the parent cell to the two daughter cells and cytoplasmic division.

molecule   A unit of matter composed of two or more atoms held together by chemical bonds.

mollusks   A phylum of animals with a mantle and usually a shell. Examples: squids, clams, and snails.

Monera   Classified into this kingdom of procaryotic organisms are one-celled organisms that do not possess a definite nucleus. Examples: bacteria and blue-green algae.

monocot   An angiosperm that contains one seed leaf in its embryo.

monohybrid cross   A genetic study in which a single characteristic is followed from the parental generation to the offspring.

monotreme   A group of egg-laying mammals.

morning sickness   One of the symptoms of pregnancy characterized by nausea, vomiting, and dizziness.

mosses   Lower plants that have a dominant gametophyte generation, no vascular tissue, swimming sperm, and spores.

mother cell   A cell that produces two daughter cells by the process of mitosis.

mouth   The opening to the digestive tract.

mucus   A slimy material produced in various parts of the digestive tract; aids in the movement of food through the system and protects the lining of the digestive tract from being digested by acids and enzymes.

multiple alleles   The concept that there are several different forms of genes for a particular characteristic.

mustard gas Used in the past as a chemical warfare material, it is known to cause chromosomal mutations. This nitrogen-containing compound is an example of a mutagenic agent.

mutagenic agent Anything that causes permanent changes in DNA.

mutation Any change in the genetic information.

mutualism The relationship between two kinds of organisms in which both benefit from the association.

mycelium The body of a fungus composed of hyphae.

NADP An electron acceptor and a hydrogen carrier.

natural selection Genetically differing organisms of a species reproduce at different rates. This tends to transmit to the next generation the more favorable genes in conjunction with a changing environment.

neutron A particle in the nucleus of an atom that does not have an electrical charge.

niche The functional role that an organism plays in its habitat. The life-style of an organism.

nitrogenous base A catogery of organic molecules found as components of the nucleic acids. There are five common types: thymine, guanine, cytosine, adenine, and uracil.

nondeciduous Refers to trees that do not lose their leaves all at once.

nondisjunction An abnormal meiotic division that results in sex cells having too many or too few chromosomes.

nonsense codon A three nucleotide sequence that is not translated. It can be used by the cell to indicate the beginning or end of a gene.

notochord A rodlike structure along the back of chordates; used for support.

nucleic acid Complex organic molecules made up of subunits called *nucleotides;* involved in storing and transferring information within the cell.

nucleolus A lump of RNA that is located in the nucleus and disappears during cell division. Its function is unknown.

nucleoplasm That portion of protoplasm in the nucleus.

nucleotide The basic subunit building block of the nucleic acids; each is composed of a five-carbon sugar, a phosphate, and a nitrogenous base.

nucleus The center of mass in an atom, containing protons and neutrons. The control center of a cell that contains DNA.

nutrient agar A nutrient medium used as a source of food for bacteria.

obese Extremely overweight.

observation The process of realizing that a problem or question exists and that there are several facts related to the problem, which one can perceive using sight, sound, etc.

offspring Descendants of a set of parents.

omnivore An animal whose diet includes both plants and other animals.

oögenesis The specific name given to the gametogenesis process that leads to the formation of eggs.

operculum A protective cover over the gills of bony fish.

optimum The best condition.

organelle Organized region in the protoplasm that has a specific structure and a specific function. Literally means 'little organs.'

organic compound Molecules containing carbon and (in the past) thought to be formed only by living organisms.

organic molecules   Molecules that contain carbon chains and are particularly common in living things.

organs   Structures that consist of groups of tissues that work together to perform a particular function. Examples: heart, stomach, and brain.

organ systems   Groups of organs that work together to perform a particular function. Examples: digestive system, reproductive system, and circulatory system.

osmosis   Diffusion of water through a differentially permeable membrane.

osteichthyes   A class of chordates to which the bony fish belong.

ovary   Female gonad (sex organ) responsible for the production of the haploid egg cells.

oviduct   The tube that carries the egg to the uterus, sometimes called the Fallopian tube.

ovulation   The release of an egg from the ovary.

oxidizing atmosphere   Containing oxygen (O_2), molecules.

parasitism   The relationship between two kinds of organisms in which one (the parasite) feeds on the other (the host) while living in or on the host.

partial protein   Protein molecules that do not provide all the essential amino acids.

penis   Male copulative organ—a portion of the male reproductive system that deposits sperm in the female reproductive tract.

pepsin   An enzyme that is produced by the cells lining the stomach and begins the breakdown of proteins.

peptic ulcer   A cavity formed in the wall of the digestive tract that is the result of the action of the enzyme pepsin.

perfect flowers   Flowers that contain both male and female reproductive structures.

perennial   A plant that requires many years to complete its life cycle.

peristalsis   Wavelike contraction of the muscles of the digestive tract, which moves the food through the tube.

pesticide   A chemical that kills "pests." Problematical term because it implies that the chemical can distinguish pests from nonpests.

petals   Modified leaves of angiosperms, a part of a flower.

PGAL   The simple sugar produced in the carbon dioxide conversion stage of photosynthesis.

pH   A number indicating the strength of acidity or basicity of a substance. The numeral 7 indicates neutrality; less than 7 is increasingly acid; and more than 7 is increasingly basic.

phenotype   The physical, chemical, and psychological expression of the genotypes possessed by an individual.

phloem   One kind of vascular tissue found in higher plants; transports food materials from the leaves to other parts of the plant.

phosphate   A group of atoms composed of phosphorus, oxygen, and hydrogen atoms. This group is part of the backbone of a nucleotide.

phospholipid   Special kind of lipid important as a part of cell membranes.

phosphorylate   To add a phosphate group (PO_4) to another molecule.

photosynthesis   Major chemical pathway that converts light energy into chemical-bond energy in the form of food.

phylum   A classification name given to groups of organisms in the same kingdom.

pistil The female reproductive structure in flowers.

placenta An organ made up of tissues from the embryo and the uterus of the mother that allows for the exchange of materials between the mother's bloodstream and the embryo's bloodstream; it also produces some hormones.

Plantae Classified into this kingdom are multicellular autotrophic organisms.

pleiotrophy The multiple effects that a pair of alleles may have in the phenotype of an organism.

point mutation A change in the DNA of a cell as a result of a loss or change in a nitrogenous base sequence.

polar body The smaller cell formed by an unequal meiotic division during oögenesis.

polar view The view of a cell during metaphase, which presents the chromosomes arranged roughly in a circular pattern.

pollen The male gametophyte in gymnosperms and angiosperms.

pollination The transferring of pollen in gymnosperms and angiosperms.

polygenic inheritance Concept that a number of different pairs of alleles may combine their efforts to determine a characteristic.

polyp A stage in the life cycle of coelenterates that is attached and vase-shaped. Example: Hydra.

polypeptide Chain of amino acids that is usually less than 100 amino acids long.

polyploidy The possession of three or more complete sets of chromosomes ($3N$, $4N$, etc.) by a cell.

population A group of individuals of the same species within a specified area who are able to reproduce with each other.

population explosion Occurs toward the end of the log phase of growth when numbers of individuals are increasing very, very rapidly.

predation The relationship between two kinds of organisms in which one (the predator) directly attacks and eats the other (the prey).

predator The organism that attacks and eats its prey.

pregnancy In mammals, the period of time during which the embryo is developing in the uterus of the mother.

prey organisms The organism that is attacked and eaten by its predator.

probability Chance that something will happen. Often expressed as a ratio in percent or fraction.

procaryotic Cell having nuclear materials that are not separated from the rest of the protoplasm; they do not have a nuclear membrane.

producer An organism that can convert completely inorganic material into organic material. Green plants are usually considered to be the producers.

product The material that results from a chemical charge. Products are usually on the right in a chemical equation.

prophase A stage at the beginning of mitosis in which the chromosomes become visible.

prostate A portion of the male reproductive system that produces a portion of the semen.

protein Chain of amino acids that is usually more than 100 amino acids long.

protein synthesis The process whereby the tRNA utilizes the mRNA as a guide to arrange the amino acids in their proper sequence.

Protista   Classified into this kingdom of eucaryotic organisms are one-celled organisms that possess a definite nucleus.

protobiont   First life.

proton   A positively charged particle in the nucleus of an atom.

protoplasm   A general term meaning 'living juice.' It is the term for the living contents of cells.

protozoa   Animallike protists that lack cell walls.

pupa   A developmental stage in the life cycle of some insects during which the larva changes into the adult form.

pyruvic acid   The three-carbon compounds formed from glycolysis.

race   Demes that differ significantly from others of the same species.

radiation sickness   Disease of the mitotic process that is linked to an overexposure of high energy radiation. This radiation interferes with the normal ability of a cell to divide.

radioactive   Applies to an atom having an unstable nucleus that flies apart. An isotope that is likely to break apart like this is said to be a *radioactive isotope*.

range   Geographic distribution of a species.

reactant   The material(s) that engage in chemical changes. Reactants are usually on the left side of a chemical equation.

recessive allele   The gene that when present with another allele does not express itself, and is masked by the effect of the other allele.

rectum   The final portion of the digestive tract in which undigested food is stored before being eliminated through the anus.

recycling   The reprocessing of a material so it can be reused many times.

reducing atmosphere   Containing molecular hydrogen (H_2) or other molecules bound to hydrogen. Example: nitrogen with hydrogen—ammonia (NH_3).

rennin   A digestive enzyme that is found in the stomach and curdles milk.

reproduction   The ability to produce more organisms like oneself.

reproductive capacity   The potential number of offspring that a population can produce.

reptiles   A class of animals of the phylum chordates that have developed an amniotic egg and do not need to return to the water to reproduce. Examples: snakes, turtles, and dinosaurs.

resistant   An inherited ability to tolerate a particular substance or condition.

ribonucleic acid (RNA)   A molecule that is similar to DNA and functions in the decoding of the hereditary information, as it is used in the cell.

ribose   A five-carbon sugar component of ribonucleic acid (RNA).

ribosome   Small glob made of protein and RNA, located throughout the cytoplasm wherever protein is being constructed.

roots   Specialized structures for the absorption of water in higher plants.

root hairs   Tiny outgrowths of roots that improve the ability of plants to absorb water.

roundworms   A phylum of animals (Aschelminthes) that are needle-shaped and are very common in soils; some are parasitic. Example: pinworms.

saliva   A digestive juice produced by the salivary glands, which aids in the digestion of starches and also moistens the food.

saturated fat   Fat that is composed of fatty acids that do not contain double bonds between any of the carbons.

science A study or collection of knowledge in an orderly fashion.

scientific method A logical approach to problem solving, using observation, questioning, and experimentation.

scientific name The one name of an organism that is internationally recognized. It consists of the genus, written first and capitalized, followed by the species, usually written in lowercase. It is printed in italics, or underlined.

scrotum A sac that contains the testes.

seasonal isolation A genetic isolating mechanism that prevents inter-breeding of species because gametes are produced at different times of the year.

seasonal reproductive patterns Most plants and animals reproduce at specific times of the year; their sexual behavior and ability to reproduce is restricted to a particular time of the year.

Second Law of Thermodynamics The concept of the change of one form of energy to another with an associated loss of usable energy. This loss is in the form of heat.

seed A specialized structure that is produced by gymnosperms and angiosperms and contains the embryo sporophyte.

seed coat A protective layer around seeds.

seed leaves Embryonic leaves in seeds.

segregation Separation of homol-ogous chromosomes during anaphase I.

selecting agent A factor in the environment that chooses certain members of a population to reproduce better and/or faster than other members.

semen The fluid, produced by the seminal vesicle, prostate, and bulbo-urethral glands of a male, that carries sperm.

seminal vesicle A part of the male reproductive system that produces a portion of the semen.

sepals Accessory structures of flowers.

sex cells The haploid cells, either sperm cells or egg cells, produced by sexually mature organisms.

sex-linked A gene located on the chromosome that determines the sex of the offspring.

sex ratio The relative number of male and female members in a population.

sexual intercourse The mating of male and female; the action of depositing sperm in the reproduc-tive tract of the female.

sexual reproduction Propagation of organisms that involves the union of gametes from two parents.

sickle-cell anemia A disease of an individual caused by a point mutation. This misinformation produces sickle-shaped red blood cells.

simple sugar The simplest unit of a carbohydrate.

small intestine The portion of the digestive tract in which most of the digestion occurs.

solid Of the three states of matter, the one that is lowest in kinetic energy—molecules are vibrating in place.

speciation Those processes that result in the production of a new species.

species A population of organisms that can naturally interbreed to produce fertile offspring.

specificity A property that only one enzyme can physically fit with a particular substrate.

sperm cells The haploid sex cells pro-duced by sexually mature males.

spermatogenesis The specific name given to the gametogenesis process that leads to the formation of sperm.

sphincter muscle   A circular muscle that when contracted closes the digestive tube.

spindle fibers   A series of fibers that are formed between the poles of a cell. Centromere of each chromosome attaches at the midpoint of a spindle fiber.

sponges   A phylum of animals (Porifera) that are very primitive and contain many canals; they filter water for food.

spontaneous generation   The theory of the origin of life, stating that living things arise from nonliving material.

spontaneous mutation   A change in DNA caused by an unidentified environmental source.

spores   Haploid structures produced by sporophytes.

sporophyte   The diploid generation in the life cycle of plants that produces spores.

stamen   The male reproductive structure of a flower.

stationary growth phase   That portion of the growth curve indicating that the number of births is equal to the number of deaths; therefore, the number of individuals in the population is static.

stem   The upright portion of a higher plant.

steroid   Complex lipid molecule, characterized by ringlike arrangements of atoms.

stomach   The portion of the digestive tract that begins the digestion of proteins.

stroma   Membranous region of the chloroplast that is not associated with chlorophyll.

structural formula   Shows the arrangement and bonding of the various atoms within a molecule.

structural gene   A sequence of DNA nucleotides that specifies the structure of a particular protein (enzyme).

structural protein   A protein that forms part of the framework of cells and holds the various parts of a cell together.

subphylum   A classification name given to groups of organisms in the same phylum.

subspecies   A separate population that exhibits genetic traits different from the main population. Local demes that differ from others of the same species.

substrate   The material that the enzyme combines with in the reaction. The materials are changed into the end products.

succession   The orderly process of change in the populations of a community over a period of time.

symbiosis   Any of a number of close relationships between two species of organisms, which may or may not be beneficial to the various kinds of organisms.

symbiotic nitrogen-fixing bacteria   Organisms mutualistically associated with the roots of legumes, which change atmospheric nitrogen into a form of nitrogen that the plant can use.

synapsis   The physical closeness of the two members of a pair of homologous chromosomes as they come together and line up on the equatorial plane.

telophase   The last phase of mitosis, characterized by the division of the cytoplasm and the reorganization of the daughter nuclei.

template   A model from which a new structure can be made; this term has special reference to DNA as a model for both DNA duplication and synthesis of RNA.

tentacles   Long flexible arms that can be used for obtaining food and defending the animal from harm.

terminator codon A nonsense codon that indicates to the cell the end of a gene.

testes Male gonad (sex organ) responsible for the production of the haploid sperm cells.

testosterone The male sex hormone produced in the testes that controls the secondary sex characteristics.

Theory of Natural Selection Genetically differing organisms of a species reproduce at different rates. This tends to transmit to the next generation the more favorable genes in conjunction with a changing environment.

thymine A single-ring nitrogenous base molecule found only in DNA, and not in RNA. It is the complement of adenine.

thyroid gland A structure located in the neck of humans, responsible for producing chemical control molecules such as thyroxin. Malfunction of this gland results in slowed or accelerated metabolic activity.

thyroxin The chemical produced by the thyroid gland. Its function is the control of the metabolic rate.

tissue A group of specialized cells that work together to perform a particular function. Examples: muscle, nerve, and blood.

tracheae Breathing tubes in insects.

transcription The first of two stages in protein synthesis; it involves the formation of mRNA from a template of a structural gene in the DNA.

transfer RNA (tRNA) A molecule composed of ribonucleic acid. One end of the tRNA serves as the attachment point to mRNA, while the other end is the attachment point for a particular amino acid. The tRNA molecules function as amino acid carriers in the process of translation.

translation The second of the two stages in protein synthesis; it involves the pairing of mRNA codons with tRNA anticodons and results in alignment of the proper amino acids as determined by a structural gene.

trophic level Stages of energy flow through an ecosystem.

tube feet Suction cuplike structures in echinoderms that are part of the water-vascular system.

Turner's syndrome A genetic disease resulting from the lack of one of the chromosomes. Symptoms include lowered intelligence, thick neck, sterility, and usually shortness.

turnover number The number of molecules of substrate that one molecule of enzyme can react with in a given unit of time.

ulcer An open sore.

ultrastructure The cellular structures not visible using a light microscope.

umbilical cord The cord that contains the blood vessels that lead materials between the placenta and the embryo.

unsaturated fat Fat that is composed of fatty acid that contains double bonds between some of the carbons.

uracil A single-ring nitrogenous base molecule found only in RNA and not in DNA. It is the complement of adenine.

vacuole A membranous container inside a cell. Specialized vacuoles may be termed food vacuole, water vacuole, etc.

variety A deme that differs significantly from others of the same species. Usually used to refer to man-made demes of plants.

vascular tissue Specialized tissue that transports fluids in higher plants.

vas deferens   The portion of the sperm duct that is cut and tied during a vasectomy.

vertebrates   Animals with backbones.

villi   A microscopic fingerlike projection from the lining of the small intestine, which increases the surface area of the digestive tract.

virus   A nucleic acid-protein particle that shows some characteristics of life only when found inside a living cell.

viscous   A measure of degree of runniness. Example: molasses is more viscous in winter than in summer.

vitamin deficiency disease   Poor health caused by the lack of a certain vitamin in the diet. Example: kwashiorkor.

vitamins   Growth factors needed in the diet in small amounts.

vomiting   Forceful ejection of food from the stomach through the mouth.

water-vascular system   A series of water-filled tubes that are found in the phylum of echinoderms and used for movement.

wood   The xylem of gymnosperms and angiosperms.

x-radiation   A high-energy beam capable of causing mutations in DNA.

xylem   A kind of vascular tissue that transports water from the roots to other parts of the plant.

yolk sac   An embryonic sac containing stored food for the embryo.

zygote   The diploid cell that results from the union of an egg cell and a sperm cell.

References

Alexopoulos, C. 1962. *Introductory mycology*. New York: John Wiley & Sons.

Arey, L. B. 1965. *Developmental anatomy*. 7th ed. Philadelphia: W. B. Saunders.

Barnes, R. D. 1968. *Invertebrate zoology*. 2d ed. Philadelphia: W. B. Saunders.

Best, C. H., and Taylor, N. B. 1958. *The living body*. New York: Henry Holt.

Bird, R. D. 1930. "Biotic communities of the Aspen parkland of central Canada." *Ecology,* vol. 11, no. 2.

Bold, H. C. 1967. *Morphology of plants*. New York: Harper and Row.

Bordwell, F. G. 1963. *Organic chemistry*. New York: Macmillan.

Carson, R. 1962. *Silent spring*. Greenwich: Fawcett Publications.

Cheng, T. C. 1964. *The biology of animal parasites*. Philadelphia: W. B. Saunders.

Cole, H. H. 1966. *Introduction to livestock production*. San Francisco: W. H. Freeman.

Committee on Resources and Man, Preston Cloud, Chairman. 1969. *Resource and man*. San Francisco: W. H. Freeman.

Cronquist, A. 1973. *Basic botany*. New York: Harper and Row.

Darwin, C. 1859. *The origin of species*. Garden City, N.Y.: Dolphin Books, Doubleday and Company.

Darwin, C., edited by Leonard Engel. 1962. *The voyage of the beagle*. Garden City, N.Y.: Doubleday.

Dasmann, R. F. 1968. *Environmental conservation*. 2d ed. New York: John Wiley & Sons.

DeBell, B. E. 1970. *The environmental handbook*. New York: Ballantine Books.

DeKruif, P. 1926. *Microbe hunters*. New York: Harcourt.

Ehrlich, P. R. 1968. *The population bomb*. New York: Ballantine Books.

Ehrlich, P. R., and Ehrlich, A. H. 1972. *Population, resources, environment*. 2d ed. San Francisco: W. H. Freeman.

Ehrlich, P. R.; Ehrlich, A. H.; and Holdren, J. P. 1973. *Human ecology: problems and solutions*. San Francisco: W. H. Freeman.

Goss, C. M. 1959. *Gray's anatomy*. 27th ed. Philadelphia: Lea & Febiger.

Guyton, A. C. 1969. *Function of the human body*. 3d ed. Philadelphia: W. B. Saunders.

Hardin, G. 1969. *Population, evolution, and birth control.* San Francisco: W. H. Freeman.

Karlson, P. 1963. *Introduction to modern biochemistry.* New York: Academic Press.

Lerner, I. M. 1968. *Heredity, evolution and society.* San Francisco: W. H. Freeman.

Levine, R. P. 1968. *Genetics.* 2d ed. New York: Holt, Rinehart & Winston.

Lorenz, K. Z. 1952. *King Solomon's ring.* New York: Thomas Y. Crowell.

Luria, S. E. 1973. *Life: the unfinished experiment.* New York: Scribner.

Marquand, J. 1968. *Life: it's nature, origins, and distribution.* New York: W. W. Norton.

Mayer, E. 1963. *Animal species and evolution.* Cambridge, Mass.: Belknap Press.

Merrell, D. 1962. *Evolution and genetics.* New York: Holt, Rinehart & Winston.

Muller, W. H. 1974. *Botany, a functional approach.* New York: Macmillan.

Odum, E. P. 1953. *Fundamentals of ecology.* Philadelphia: W. B. Saunders.

Rabinowitch, E., and Govindjee. 1969. *Photosynthesis.* New York: John Wiley & Sons.

Rosebury, T. 1969. *Life on man.* New York: Viking Press.

Rudd, R. L. 1964. *Pesticides and the living landscape.* Madison: University of Wisconsin Press.

Schaller, G. B. 1972. *The Serengeti lion.* Chicago: University of Chicago Press.

Shklovskii, I. S., and Sagan, C. 1966. *Intelligent life in the universe.* San Francisco: Holden-Day.

Simpson, G. G. 1964. *The meaning of evolution.* New Haven, Conn.: Yale University Press.

Smith, R. L. 1966. *Ecology and field biology.* New York: Harper and Row.

Stern, C. 1973. *Principles of human genetics.* San Francisco: W. H. Freeman.

Storer, T. I., and Usinger, R. L. 1972. *General zoology.* 5th ed. New York: McGraw-Hill.

Taylor, G. R. 1963. *The science of life.* New York: McGraw-Hill.

Von Frisch, K. 1950. *Bees: their visions, chemical senses, and language.* Ithaca, N.Y.: Cornell University Press.

Wagner, R. H. 1969. *Environment and man.* 2d ed. New York: W. W. Norton.

Watson, J. D. 1965. *Molecular biology of the genes.* 2d ed. New York: W. A. Benjamin.

Weisz, P. B. 1968. *Elements of zoology.* New York: McGraw-Hill.

White, A.; Handler, P.; and Smith, E. L. 1959. *Principles of biochemistry.* New York: McGraw-Hill.

Villee, C. A.; Walker, W. F.; and Smith, F. E. 1968. *General zoology.* 3d ed. Philadelphia: W. B. Saunders.

Index